Thank you Fran!
02/14/17

Steel Standing

The Mystery. The Journey. The Miracle.

This is a gift. A true story.
Medical Mystery!

Enjoy!

2012

www.steelstadingbook.com

Steel Standing, LLC

Library of Congress Cataloging-in-Publications Data

Davis, Christa C.
Steel Standing
The Mystery. The Journey. The Miracle.
Christa Carmell Davis
ISBN 978-0-9852149-0-6
1.) Health 2.) Spirituality
Library of Congress Control Number 2012933814

Cover Design, Layout Design, Interior Graphics, and Photos
by: Christa C. Davis, Steel Standing, LLC

Author Photo by: Patti Ford Photography

Project Management by:
Barbara M. Lee, Red Horseshoe Books

Printed in the United States of America

Steel Standing

The Mystery. The Journey. The Miracle.

True Story Written by Daughter
Christa Carmell Davis

The Mystery. The Journey. The Miracle.

Steel Standing Contents

STEEL STANDING

The Mystery. The Journey. The Miracle.

INTRODUCTION

BY KENNETH C. SANDS, M.D.

As an Orthopaedic surgeon specializing in total joint replacements, I have been blessed to help thousands of patients. Every patient's experience is different as they move down the road of recovery. A large part of my practice deals with revision surgeries. These cases are usually more complex and their outcomes are not as predictable. One of my most memorable experiences started the day I met with Patricia Harton, her husband Tom, and daughter Christa.

Patricia Harton presented to my office initially because of pain in her left total knee replacement. What started out as a routine revision total knee surgery developed into a journey that effected everyone's life involved with Ms. Harton. During my time with them, I witnessed a daughter's dying devotion to her mother, and a family deeply rooted in faith. I also saw an amazing personal transformation and inner strength in Patricia as she went through this process step by step.

Their journey brings to light issues associated with metal allergies, doctor/patient relationships and faith. Particularly during this time in Orthopaedics, the issue of metal allergies and the affect of metal on the human body are being thoroughly investigated. Currently, allergic reactions to metal implants are considered extremely rare. However, as more cases like Patricia's come to light, we are learning daily some of the signs and symptoms of metal allergies.

I am honored to have been a part of this amazing and at times sobering true story of a patient's struggle with metal toxicity, the medical field, and her undying faith in God.

Kenneth C. Sands, M.D.
Orthopaedic Surgeon
Adult Joint Reconstruction

The Mystery. The Journey. The Miracle.

METAL MENTALITY

BY VERA STEJSKAL, PH.D.

The effect of heavy and transition metals on human health has been the focus of my life for the past 20 years. It wasn't always my passion. I started my career as an immunologist at Astra, a pharmaceutical company in Sweden.

One of my initial assignments was to develop an objective diagnostic test to screen for drug allergy among workers in Astra's factories. The test I created was based on the well-known technology of lymphocyte transformation testing (LTT), which I modified until it was accurate and reproducible.

In 1990, a colleague of mine, a dermatologist, expressed a wish to try the test on patients who claimed that their symptoms were caused by their dental metal restorations. Since metals like mercury are very toxic, perhaps a blood test would be better suited for this kind of testing than adding metals to the skin through patch testing.

Soon the test, by now named M.E.L.I.S.A., an acronym for Memory Lymphocyte Immuno Stimulation Assay, showed that indeed, some individuals reacted to metals present in their dental crowns and fillings. This immune reactivity was the reason for not only well-known local symptoms like skin and mucosal symptoms, but also less recognized systemic symptoms like extreme fatigue, joint pain and mental fog ("flu-like" symptoms). The symptoms normally disappeared when the source of exposure was removed.

While the majority of people tolerate metals, we know that there are those that suffer from certain metal exposure, mainly that arising from dental restorations, orthopedic implants, jewelry, cosmetics, environmental and occupational exposure.

Sadly, in medicine, the toxicological viewpoint is predominant: that it is the levels of metals that cause illness – which is opposite to the immunologic viewpoint, which recognizes that if somebody's immune system is hypersensitive, it does not matter how small the exposure is, it can still be enough to cause health problems.

I salute Ms. Davis for bringing the "metal mentality" into light and educating others. Metals enable us to create incredible tools that can help the human body but we need to make sure that those that are sensitive are offered metal-free alternatives. I hope this book will stimulate discussion and lead to more research into the field of metal-related illnesses.

Vera Stejskal, Ph.D.
University of Stockholm and
MELISA® Medica Foundation
Sweden

The Mystery. The Journey. The Miracle.

TESTIMONIALS

Steel Standing shares the journey of a mother and her daughter dealing with life threatening issues while coming to grips with God's powerful revelations through scientific solutions. The reality; it could be anyone's story!

This is a personal story of an allergic reaction internally to metal implants. Her daughter's prayerful research is an enjoyable read as she depicts her own desperate plea for God's answers while seeking medical solutions. Allergies can be a minor irritant but can become a life threatening toxin in a heartbeat.

I believe the reader will glean from a multitude of messages intertwined with some easily understood medical education and terminology which are well resourced. The daughter as the author, shares a realistic insight into her mother's incredible journey. Even though the adversity is life threatening, the family sought God in their struggles and praises Him in their triumphs! He provided ways most would find completely miraculous!

Having worked as a practitioner for many years, the grasp of science and a Higher Power are evident as stated in this true story. It is inspiring, demonstrating hope and faith are very much attainable! You will come to understand why they are Steel Standing.

William R. Brannon, O.D.

Having witnessed this story unfolding and developing from its earliest moments, it is truly an amazing account! Perhaps the most impressive aspect is the commitment of this daughter to her mother's recovery despite enormous odds, necessitating the virtual invention of a whole line of medical reasoning and inquiry.

Richard T. Hull, Ph.D.

Executive Director

Text and Academic Authors Association

The Mystery. The Journey. The Miracle.

SOUL DEDICATIONS

My Heavenly Father:
My deepest love to You for making the impossible, possible... for
answering heartfelt prayers. For teaching me more in the last five years
than I could ever fathom - understanding faith is the key,
and forgiveness is not an option.

+

My incredible mother and dear friend, Patricia: Thank you for being
an example of "steel" faith in Jesus Christ - for teaching our family the
example of prayerful perseverance; an ongoing lesson!

+

William Thomas Harton: Your tremendous love, and encouragement
gave all of us a constant sign of hope in dismal times when we needed
our earthly Poppa. You are loved, beyond words!

+

To my brother and my sister-in-law: Thank you for your endearing
support. Your presence behind the scenes of this rare journey illustrated
our family's love for one another is unconditional and infinite.

+

To the next generation of children in this family: Wee; Long Ears; Tippy
Toes; Tiger; and Bama Boy -May you come to know the power of prayer
as the generations before us believed in God, the Father; Jesus Christ,
His Son; and the Holy Spirit. They believed and hoped that your lives
would continue our family's faith in the Impossible.

+

Tremendous appreciation to Steel Standing's incredible contributors -
Their proofing skills are "As good as it gets!"
Patricia Davis Harton, Denise M. Martin, William R. Brannon, O.D.,
Linda Nelson, and Brenda Brewer Hoyt.

+

Soul Dedications

To every caregiver: No matter your beliefs, thank you for dedicating your time and life so others may live.

+

For those who have great faith and need encouragement:
Keep believing!

+ + +

"... All things are possible to those who believe."

Mark 9:23

The Mystery. The Journey. The Miracle.

Moving Forward

By Christa C. Davis

Steel Standing is a true story based on my Mother's healthy body gradually deteriorating before my eyes. Always sharing a very close bond in our mother-daughter relationship, it would be our closeness that made me more aware of the slightest differences in her physical abilities and activities.

Watching her body succumb to various degrees of weakness on a daily basis was only made possible after I did the unthinkable. I resigned at the height on my career as a communications specialist at an up and coming nuclear energy organization, slated to expand as one of the first in the United States to receive Presidential support.

My main work site was located six hours from my hometown where Mother had lived her entire life. When I resigned, I not only walked away from my career hopes, I left behind everything that had once been important in my life. It was no longer what I believed I was supposed to be doing. There was something deeper that moved me. I couldn't deny my gut wrenching directive, which led me home.

My change of residence evolved primarily in becoming Mother's caregiver. Returning home shifted into a surreal and unique journey as Mother silently battled to sustain her health, and eventually her life.

As I became Mother's full time caregiver, I soon discovered this assignment was the hardest yet the most rewarding job of any I had ever faced, including key leadership positions in reputable organizations. The journey also opened up new avenues in communications I never could have fathomed. So my career never stopped, it simply made a transition.

After many years eagerly learning diverse key communication venues in marketing, advertising, publication, public relations and graphic design, the one area I had sufficient experience but neglected to apply in my daily life was communicating through prayer to God. Now, I was eagerly persevering to seek Him. Through His guidance, as I placed my faith and complete trust in Him, I was led on a path not yet seen but deeply sensed.

Soon, I would come to understand our mother-daughter relationship was paralleled in so many ways throughout our new journey, side by side.

As my Mother's health slowly but steadily declined, I sincerely prayed from my heart for God to please heal her. There are many wonderful people in the world. My Mother was one of the few, always uniquely standing out from the crowd. Radiant yet humble, energized yet quietly invigorating; she is extraordinary.

As a Christian family, we always strived to keep a realistic and spiritual balance in our lives seeking God's direction and Divine intervention, especially in times such as Mother's circumstances. We are also keenly aware and depend on the innovative technological advances in medical science. Spending over half of my professional career marketing health care, working directly in clinical and non-clinical environments; I have tremendous respect on every level from top to bottom in the medical industry of helping others.

During this journey, we witnessed God healing my Mother in miraculous ways, most directly through physician care. I do believe the same God which inspired the Bible to be written through others, is also the same God who heals through others with innovative medical resources available.

Science is science. Facts are facts. Whether you believe God created all things or not, the scientific facts shared throughout this true story were revealed to me as I sincerely prayed for answers, directions and guidance. Therefore, it is evidenced by my faith in God, as the only way so much indisputable medical discovery could have been divulged to me from the most unlikely sources, incidents and timing.

As I sought God's direction, instinctively I was led to do the research efforts providing scientific findings and case studies, which linked the medical mystery to what appears to be a medical breakthrough. I shared the scientific facts with seasoned medical practitioners. Some disavowed any possibility of a metal implant linking to muscle weakness, even though I had documented support from prominent medical researchers. Others seemed skeptical simply because there had never been a case reported in the United States to make the medical connection. The battle was overwhelming to prove the theory, as was Mother's battle to survive. Often, it was not any easy process in trying to get a physician's attention, but God provided the way.

Steel Standing begins as a descriptive chronological recollection of the struggles we faced which escalates into the discovery of how metal allergies developed in Mother's body tissues, due to the specific types of metals in her hip and knee replacements. The allergic reaction to certain types of metals ignited poisonous ions which created toxicity. Medical documentation is provided with highly credible references.

In time, I would understand why I was prompted to do the unthinkable. My journey in coming home was to do exactly what I did. In taking care of Mother, I was in a position to be her shadow while she experienced unusual physical health encounters. This gave me tremendous insight, more than medical records or documentation could explain, predict or reveal.

Being present during the majority of her physicians' visits, numerous tests procedures, countless lab visits, hospitalizations, and rehabilitation sessions, made it possible to apply my experiences from my career and college education to share her story.

My assignment since returning home involved many tasks. This was not a clear edict until mid-February 2010. In God's perfect timing, this task was revealed.

In writing her story, I believe it will inspire others by her courage, faith, and willingness to keep fighting for life.

Prior to Mother's journey, when I heard the term "healing," I thought of "flesh wounds." I learned there is a much deeper meaning. The healing process goes beyond flesh, or surface wounds, as an opening slowly forms into a scar.

Words can be just as sharp as a surgeon's scalpel. My Mother experienced both types of invasions from which she had to heal. Healing is about caring for another's soul as well as their physical being.

When I finally sat down to pen Mother's health experiences, emotional ties ran deep. Her story is certainly not the world's worst medical mystery; however, the battle was difficult and prolonged.

When it comes to an individual's health… no amount of money, or societal, marital, or family status, religious denomination, or from what part of this world may you hail… your health can change with your next breath.

Only God knows when your first breath began, and when your last one is drawn. He dispenses each. What happens between the beginning and ending breaths can be remarkable, based on our choices in life.

> *"The Lord knows the thoughts of man,*
> *that they are a mere breath."*
> *Psalm 94:11*

Life can be short. Breathe deeply, exhale gratefully, live healthy, and know who is the "Keeper" of your soul.

Christa

The Mystery. The Journey. The Miracle.

Chapter 1

PrePrayer Yourself

Vividly recalling the moment as if it were yesterday, I remember sensing Mother needing me to be physically at her side. At the time, six hours of driving was between us. A new client recently signed with my small marketing business. There was a heavy agenda of details and deadlines needing my attention. So, I didn't have a clue how I could physically be with her. Yet, the sensing was so strong, I felt it would be regrettable if I didn't go.

As mother and daughter, we have always been close, sharing whatever ventured in and out of our lives. Whatever the measurement of time or space between our geographical locations, there was never any distance in our hearts. Mother is deeply entrenched in my life; therefore it's no wonder why I would feel so incredibly compelled to share the incremental details of her amazing medical mystery.

My Mother is a friend to all, and any one she meets. Her name is Patricia. Anything else was simply unacceptable. Should the idea arise to call her "Pat" or "Patty," don't dare think about shortening "Patricia!" There was nothing doing by cutting her formal name to an average "nick name." Many years later, her best buds at work and church, began to acknowledge her as "Trish." Her character and integrity were identical to how she felt about her name. Her father, Edgar, named his only beloved child "Patricia," because he wanted her to grow up to be a lady. She accomplished his goal as it was her goal as well; a lady with a heart as a servant for God.

Tough and determined; yet gentle and humble, her personality was as large as the room she entered. She was never one seeking the center of attention; instead the attention always seemed to center around Mother. Caring, warm, genuine, with a heart for others… are just a few of the many distinguishing traits I witnessed in her interaction with her family and friends, never meeting a stranger.

Her rare and implausible sense of humor can make anyone laugh in the most trying times in a person's life. As a healthy and vibrant individual, the only physical ailments Mother ever experienced were occasional migraine headaches, depending on the stressful state of our immediate family, or an infrequent kidney stone/infection. Those are the only health issues I can recall, since my early childhood.

It took a tremendous amount of formidable forces to bring Mother's jovial spirit down. Regardless of how she felt physically, Mother was always a dependable and responsible person. She retired in 2002 after working full time at our local power company, spending dual amounts of time as church pianist for over 50 plus years of service. Whatever troubles she lived through, happiness was her mask. Mother makes the best out of every day, with a smile in her heart equivocally expressed on her face and in her attitude.

She came from a long line of independent women where females were known for their leadership roles founded in their perseverance which exerted their devout faith in God. She simply lives as an example of those gone before us, radiating the same strengths with her internal loveliness excelling beyond her physical beauty.

So, when I "sensed" or had a "gut feeling" or "knowing"… whatever resonates with one's "honing in" process…I just "knew" I had to be with her, not fully understanding why.

The "knowing" would ultimately lead me to a well populated town in Alabama. Mother and my stepfather - affectionately referred to as "Poppa" or "Poppa Tom" - were staying with his grandson Zachary[1], which was about two hours from our hometown in Centre where my folks resided. This trip had been planned for quite some time when they were asked to stay for several days while Poppa's youngest son, Ryan[2] and his wife, Ashley[3] traveled across country on a business trip.

For Mother and Poppa, this trip was going to be more like a vacation "get-away" with the special added bonus of spending quality time with Zachary. Ryan and Ashley's house was centrally located in one of the prime residential areas of the city making driving routes easy to maneuver, which provided a direct access to Zachary's school. One of Mother and Poppa's biggest draws to visit, was the delectable eating spots and a newly renovated shopping mall with a host of stores easily captivating an entire day.

When the long awaited and highly anticipated trip arrived for Mother and Poppa, it would be a very rare morning for both. Mother woke up with a migraine; oddly, Poppa woke up not feeling well, either. This was highly unusual, especially for both to be sick much less on the same day! However, just as I would have imagined, Mother and Poppa put on their best faces and headed on their way. Once they arrived, Mother called me to share they were doing okay, but I knew "okay" was far from being "truly all right."

Over the next couple of days, Mother and I talked more frequently than usual. Later, I learned neither felt any improvement from whatever was ailing them from the very start of this trip. I knew they were not able to give Zachary their very best attention, which was their heartfelt desire. In their effort to entertain an eight-year-old, while keeping his school schedule and extra-curricular activities on track, they felt their best intentions to have quality time with him had diminished during the course of the week due to their lack of extra "get up and go."

As an only child, Zachary is a terrific kid, easily entertained with computer games and studious reading. For a young boy, his manners were impeccable, as he is always extremely helpful. So, I really wasn't too concerned about Zachary missing out on anything special, since he was self-sufficient. My concerns were focused on Mother and Poppa feeling poorly.

During this transition of my single-again life, I resided in the southwest area of Atlanta, Georgia, starting my entrepreneurial dream of marketing and advertising. I believed it was time to start my own creative themes, living near a large town with a multitude of business opportunities. Contemplating a trip to their visiting Alabama city was a minimum of six hours - that's if the traffic on the Atlanta interstate was not horrific.

My newest client, a major residential and commercial real estate agency in Metro Atlanta, was a huge business break with commitments, deadlines and a large volume of creative work. My career is my professional passion. I've always been extremely fortunate to love what I do for a living! Additionally, one of the most awesome benefits of self-employment is the ability to work on your time schedule, which can also be a tremendous disadvantage, if you don't find a balance between work and life.

The biggest drag for my entrepreneurial situation was being tied down to a CPU desktop computer! Six weeks earlier, I ordered a customized laptop primarily for business presentations to hopefully garner a wider client base. My business investment plan was simple; own a laptop and work virtually from everywhere at anytime. My dream was to head to the beach with laptop in tow at some point in the near future. Where Mother and Poppa were staying did not fit into my dream escapade, although it was located in a picturesque area of Alabama.

Continuing to check with my folks periodically, I quickly discerned neither were getting any better. It was a difficult position as my strong gut feeling became stronger. It appeared my hands were tied. My work projects had concrete deadlines for reviews, via internet conferences, etc. The long drive would take the majority of a day to travel, cutting into my productivity schedule.

Mother and Poppa were not the type of people to send up a flare or call anyone for help, unless it was a dire emergency. Although, it was not mentioned in our frequent talks, I sensed they were trying to make the best of their circumstances without admitting a need for assistance.

Not assured of what to do, I prayed for the unusual set of circumstances. Prayer was becoming an essential step in my walk as a Christian. Previously, I just never went to great lengths as a believer to close the gap in my learning distance. But now, I believed I needed direction as my gut feeling was increasingly questioning, "What am I to do?"

Mother's strong faith was passed through the generations before her, as she also taught both of her children; my only sibling, a younger brother and me, to have faith in God. We were educated to give our problems to God, as well as our joy. As He knows all, God works things out for the best, which He did and does. My prayers weren't always answered like I thought they should be, yet in time the answers always turned out better than I could have imagined. The next step for me at this point, was to pray specifically in how I could help Mother and Poppa with His divine intervention.

While sitting at my desk after I had prayed, I clearly recall receiving an email from the computer vendor. It stated my new customized laptop would be shipped in four to six weeks. I felt my hands were tied but knew I had done everything I could, even with a strong uneasy feeling, which continued to linger.

The next morning, I was totally surprised when a large truck appeared in my driveway. Before the courier had time to ring my door bell, I met him carrying a rather large box. Completely stunned, I saw the return address was from the computer vendor. My new laptop had arrived by express special delivery! I was in awe of God's answer to my prayer request as I praised Him while I opened the box knowing this had to be a miracle of God. There was no doubt! I was headed to help my folks!

After hours of downloading my software programs and necessary files, I decided to leave early the next morning, Thursday, March 1, 2006.

About midway through my trip, which was hassle free from traffic, I called Mother on my cell phone to cheerfully report I was in route to help them. Mother began to cry, which was a rarity. I could hear my tender hearted Poppa in the background weeping as he began blowing his nose while Mother repeated my news to him.

With my new laptop, I had everything I needed to go, work, and assist my folks. This was indeed confirmation of where I was supposed to be during this time. Considering their ages… late 60s and early 70s… both were in exceptional health. With two different sets of symptoms, a virus or bug had already been dismissed. I kept thinking how strange it was for both of them to not feel well. This didn't make sense to me. I could not understand why I felt I had to go and help them.

When I arrived in the outskirts of town, I called to let them know I was only a short distance away. As I turned into the driveway, I was surprised to be met with a gracious welcome. I immediately noticed Poppa's pale face and his weak eyes. Once I entered the house, their gratitude was expressed in their compassionate hugs. No matter how tired I was from traveling almost six hours in a semi-rushed nonstop drive, the thrill of seeing my family alleviated any exhaustion.

Poppa shared the latest news. Mother, due to relentless nausea associated with a migraine, had to be taken to a local hospital ER. It was after midnight before they returned to the house. Again, it was confirmation for me to make the trip.

Shortly after arriving, a decision was made to go out for dinner. The idea of a change of scenery lightened the downtrodden couple's spirits. Mother, Poppa, Zachary, and I loaded in the SUV in search of a restaurant to please everyone, with quite diverse appetites.

The outing was successful. We all enjoyed a good meal. Once we returned to the house, everyone headed to bed - I headed towards my laptop! Even though I was a little worn from the day's travels, the evening dinner had reenergized me. I decided to work. Staying ahead of my deadlines would allow me to enjoy the next couple of days with less pressure.

Without realizing how quickly time had passed, I checked my watch; it was 4:00 a.m.! Prying myself from the chair, I stretched and yawned as I stood up after sitting for so long. There was a keen sense of accomplishment in getting a lot of work completed. The laptop had already met my need for mobility as a wise investment. I knew I made the right decision, and I was in the right place!

What was to come in the next few short hours would unquestionably confirm the "gut feeling" I believed God had given me. I was preprayered!

+ + +

Chapter 2
SHE'S HIP

After arriving in town, I felt assured I was exactly where I needed to be and relieved to be under the same roof. Once we all had a good meal, I was able to accomplish a great deal of work to stay ahead of my work deadlines. Suddenly a good dose of fatigue hit my body like a ton of bricks!

My energy was quickly evaporating, as I headed over to the couch in the recreational den, where I had set up my temporary work space. Before my head hit the pillow, I was zapped, falling sound asleep in my clothes and shoes. It seemed like I had just dozed off when I felt a nudge on my shoulder. I was in such a deep sleep, I barely remember hearing Poppa call my name. I tried to remember where I was, while attempting to wake up.

Once I was able to open my eyes, it appeared as if Poppa was standing in his skivvies and T-shirt! He was never one to parade around the house without having on pants and a shirt, or a robe. While rubbing my eyes, I became somewhat cognitive - but for the life of me, I could not comprehend what he was saying. My slow response was obviously due to post-exhaustion. I remembered trying to focus on my watch, when I realized I had only slept for a mere two hours.

The vision of Poppa was easier to grasp than attempting to translate what he saying. Immediately various thoughts began to ignite … "Is Zach late for school? Was I supposed to take him and forgot?"

Still in a state of slumber, neither question was even close to being adequately correct when I finally understood Poppa's frantic repeat,

"Get up! Get up! It's your Mother! She's fallen!"

That got my attention!

My brain kicked into alert mode as if someone had yelled "earthquake!" I jumped to my feet still dressed in yesterday's attire, as I hurriedly followed him through the house with no idea where she fell. Poppa led on through the kitchen/dining area, where three descending steps were adjacent to the opening of a sun room. Mother was face up on the tiled floor almost in a slumped position with both legs lying flat, side by side. The upper portion of her back, neck, and head were supported by the arm of a love-seat. It looked as though she had just slid down and sat on the floor. Both of her legs were slightly sprawled.

Clem, Zach's wonderful house dog, was devotedly standing next to Mother. Our family has always had an inside house dog, so it wasn't surprising with Mother's animal charisma for Clem to cling to her for his needs. He adored her from the first moment they met and enjoyed when she visited. They had a very special bond.

Clem was not an ordinary dog. He was incredibly smart and extremely well-trained. Seeing Mother with Clem in the sun room at that time of morning, appeared as if she were going down the steps to let him out the back door, which opened to a fenced-in backyard. He was a pretty smart dog. Perhaps, Clem was going to let Mother out!

As she lay on the cold tile floor in a sleeveless long nightgown, my immediate concern was where she had been hurt. Although she was not moving, my first thought was her left knee.

The previous summer of 2005, Mother was trying to scare a "Tom cat" away from our barn. The cat ran under the bush-hog. She had the bright idea that if she jumped on the back of it, a loud noise would frighten the cat away. When landing on both feet, her left knee bent in reverse like a Flamingo bird's. Mother said afterwards that it was "not my smartest idea." I thought at the time, "Ya think?"

Her little adventures of playing "protective momma" to her other barn cats had left her with a bad injury continually getting worse with any increased knee movements. She had already sought medical attention through a local orthopaedic surgeon near Centre, for a laparoscopic procedure. It appeared to have botched things far worse. Mother's suffering became burdensome to her active lifestyle.

Given her past knee injury, as I saw Mother lying on the sun room floor, I wondered if she had re-injured her knee when she fell down the steps. Yet, I sensed it was far more serious as her face quickly became washed out. I began to talk with her. She was barely coherent as I tried to carefully assess her injuries. It was evident she was not going to be getting up on her own. I asked where she was hurting. She didn't respond clearly, nor did she flinch. Her long nightgown was draped over her legs blocking any visible damage or bruising.

I continued to ask "where" she was hurting. Mother mumbled, but I just couldn't decipher what she was trying to say. Then I noticed a large puddle of urine on the floor between her and Clem, as he remained faithfully by his friend. The look on Clem's face was sadness. If only he could've talked, we would have had all the details!

I asked, "Mother did you, or Clem, wet the floor?" Mother quietly murmured "My hip… broke my hip." I thought "Her hip? How's that possible? She is not old enough to have a broken hip." In my immediate assumption, she was not "old enough" to have a broken hip! Wrong! Anyone can break any bone at any age.

My next idea was to check her legs. As I barely touched her right heal, she hollered out in dire pain. Mother was not one to yell or shout, not even when my little brother and I got into trouble. This was definitely serious and very sobering.

During this entire time, while closely examining Mother's situation, I yelled for Poppa to call 911. I grabbed my cell phone, which was still in the side pocket of my cargo pants. The thought occurred to call Jean, a friend and retired nurse. She answered on the first ring, which was unusual since she was not an early riser.

My college education is a non-clinical health degree, which included extensive emergency preparedness courses. But, I honestly could not think what to do! Jean was such a comfort as I explained the situation. She calmly gave me directions, step-by-step. Her years of skilled nursing were obvious, with the added bonus that she had previously lived in the same town where we were located. Jean knew the area and the nearest major trauma center. She was the perfect person for God to place in my thoughts to call during this emergency.

While Poppa was talking to the 911 dispatcher on the nearby

kitchen phone, I noticed how clever he was to flip over a magazine by the telephone to use the mailing label to give an accurate physical address. At best, it was difficult for either of us to grasp what had occurred to Mother that frightful morning. Her color was becoming more of a pasty gray, as I feared she was about to pass out. Jean continued to stay on the cell phone with me, reassuring everything was going to be fine.

The way Mother landed from the fall was a miracle. She was propped only two inches from a wooden decorative ornament at the end of the love-seat. If she had hit her head, or her neck on the ornament, the fall could have potentially injured her worse than a leg - paralyzing her, or could have possibly been fatal. It was obvious Mother was in severe pain as she laid on the floor, barely conscious, occasionally moaning. Yet, I knew the way she fell, God's protection kept Mother from being injured far worse.

You may be thinking, "Why didn't God just keep the fall from happening at all?" That I can't answer. What I have learned: There is a purpose for everything, even if we don't understand at the time. If this "accident" had never happened, we would not have had the opportunity to discover and share her valet testimony of faith in God, nor the invaluable health information revealed in *Steel Standing*. As I reflect on that March morning, in recounting her story to share with others, incredible revelations have arisen since her fall!

As Poppa continued to share the details of Mother's situation with the 911 dispatcher, Jean instructed me to cover Mother with a blanket… something I knew, but couldn't think clearly enough to do. She reminded me that Mother was probably going into shock, if in fact she did break her hip. Then Jean told me to relay to Poppa, that if Mother did indeed have a broken hip, 911 should be alerted to send enough EMS staff to assist lifting her. Excellent medical advice!

Being awakened abruptly, learning one parent was down as the other one appeared to be a prime candidate for a heart attack, while he was doing a jittery nervous prance trying to talk calmly with the 911 operator - the last thing we needed that morning was an ambulance with bunk beds for two! Seeing Mother on the floor in her condition was enough to make anyone's heart faint.

Within three minutes after Poppa hung up the phone with 911, an ambulance and a fire truck arrived at the house. After a quick assessment of the scene, the sun room doorway was the best and closest exit, however, it was a smaller than average door width. It was not wide enough for a gurney or a body board to keep a patient horizontal in a stable flat position.

A different tactic was required to lift Mother off the floor. Quickly, the EMS crew decided to use a folded bed sheet. This idea was compromising and offered no support to her body. But was the only way to get her out of the house, swiftly. If Mother, more than likely had a broken hip, this transition of placing her body onto the sheet would be even more painful! The EMS crew carefully rolled and turned her into position as the sheet was placed under the length of her body. She began high-pitched cries of pain. Lifting her up was another horrendous feat, as Mother continued to yell. She was definitely aroused from her almost unconscious state screaming in sheer agony!

The advice Jean passed on for more EMS helpers to lift Mother was brilliant. It took four men to pick Mother up while trying to maneuver her less than petite body through the small doorway opening and onto a gurney. Her stature is 5'6, wearing a size 14 in ladies clothing. She was physically fit and big boned! It was difficult for the men to pick her up while trying to be extremely careful to keep her hip and leg as immobile as possible.

Once she was carried through the smaller than average sun room door, she was placed on a gurney. The EMS team immediately headed from the backyard around the side of the house to the ambulance located at the front driveway. Mother's screams continued, as the pain seemed unbearable even for a person of high tolerance. I held her right hand trying to reassure she was going to be okay. She was a strong lady. She had played the piano for hours almost every day since the age of four. Mother had a very muscular grip. At one point, she clenched my hand so incredibly tight, I thought she was going to break it!

Everyone was moving as rapidly, and as carefully, as possible. Each of the men held securely to the four corners of the gurney, trying their best to stabilize the rough ride on a bumpy brick path. Tears came streaming down my face. I felt so badly for Mother knowing she was in such tremendous pain. She was not to the point of tears; but was clearly in absolute misery. Jean had reminded me earlier in our conversation, once Mother was loaded in the ambulance she would arrive at the medical center almost immediately. It was only ten minutes by car. In an emergency vehicle, it would definitely be quicker.

As the EMS crew and I continued to make our way towards the ambulance, Mother held to my hand, never letting go. I was at her right side as we hurried. The only passage way from the sun room to the front of the house was a narrow brick pathway, which didn't allow room for a side runner next to the gurney. So, I waded through a dense row of thick prickly briar bushes landscaped between the side of the house and the path. At one point, some briars ripped my right pants leg just below my knee, as I barely remembered the pain. I was determined not to let go of Mother's hand until she was safely lifted into the back of the ambulance.

Mother again screamed even louder during the lifting process as the EMS crew placed her into the ambulance. Every movement was sheer torture for her. Once loaded, she looked back as if she expected me to climb in to go with her. I told her and the EMS crew that Poppa and I would meet at the hospital. Thank goodness, I began "thinking." It crossed my mind that Mother would need her ID and insurance cards. Perhaps the thorny briars triggered my thought processing.

Poppa proceeded to get Zachary dressed and ready for school. Somewhere in the middle of this panicked-stricken morning, Poppa and I actually exchanged quick ideas for Zachary's agenda. As I headed to the hospital, Poppa carried Zach to school. He would then meet us at the ER.

On my way to the hospital, I called my younger brother Jack[4], who works for a medical center near our hometown. Jack actually answered his cell phone on the second ring, which was another miracle early that morning, due to his busy schedule. I shared the news. He said he was walking out the door. Then I called one of my best friends, Kate[5], who lived nearby. Without knowing it, she was off work that day. She said she'd meet us at the hospital.

By the time I arrived and found a place to park, the ER physician had already x-rayed Mother's right hip and had notified the "on call" orthopaedic surgeon, in case she needed surgery. Within just a few minutes, the ER physician brought the x-ray to show me where Mother's hip had a clean break in the neck of her femur, which connects to the head or ball, located next to her pelvis. It was difficult at best to fathom the reality that Mother had a broken hip.

The physician surmised the same occurrence that Mother may have fallen, as I explained where she was found. Apparently she over-stepped, missing one of the shallow-depth steps, which most likely caused her to go mid-air. When she landed on her hip, the bone was unable to absorb the fall without fracturing as soon as she hit the tiled floor, previously a concrete patio converted into a sun room.

While she was laying on the hospital gurney in the ER, I.V. meds were already being administered to keep her sedated until she would be taken to surgery. She said she was still experiencing some pain, but mostly Mother was in and out of a drowsy sleep, as her body lay perfectly still.

Everything happened so quickly. My head was spinning about the time Poppa arrived. After carrying Zachary to school, Poppa called Ryan and Ashley on the way to the hospital. They called some of their friends in town to make arrangements for Zachary to stay after school, and said they would be returning home on the first flight the next day.

As bad as things appeared, everything was starting to come together and settle down. Poppa and I were so glad Mother was in a city with a designated trauma center and the latest technology with an abundance of specialty physicians. I knew she was in good hands. Things could have been far worse for her situation, if she had been in a rural area.

The ER physician reported to us, that it would be approximately three hours before Mother's surgery. When the nurses came to ask questions concerning Mother's medications, allergies, prior health problems, health history and other pertinent information, I mentioned her previous knee injury. During the fall, everything was so focused on her hip; the possibility of re-injuring her left knee had not even crossed my mind until that point.

To this day, Mother reminds me, what she believes was totally unnecessary pain she endured being moved again for additional x-rays - all because I mentioned her previous knee injury for precautionary measures. Fortunately, there was no damage to her knee, but I thought it was best for it to be checked. She may never agree with my decision, but she still trusts my judgment in taking care of her... so far.

While nurses and techs were frequently coming and going from Mother's ER unit, I noticed Poppa sat quietly in a corner chair slightly slumped, looking exasperated and exhausted. What a frantic morning! He seemed to be trying to absorb what occurred, as it felt more like a dream than reality. His thoughts seemed to be written all over his face: "What was ahead for her after surgery and recovery? How would she adapt since she was so active?" I could just imagine the heartfelt emotion he was experiencing for her painful situation and their future. They were about to celebrate their fifth year of marriage.

Mother married Tom Harton in May 2001. He is a wonderful stepfather and a loving husband. As the character of "Forrest Gump" stated so eloquently while representing a fictitious life in "Green Bow," Alabama... "We go together like Peas and Carrots..." Well, that would be "Trish and Tom," except their home is in "Centre," Alabama.

Poppa is more than terrific to all of us, not just to the lady he loves and married. They have very similar personalities, which keeps both of them laughing, when crying could be the only other option. Poppa is so encouraging to her, and never once giving her any reason to be concerned in any situation. He is the type of man my Mother deserves to be loved by.

While standing in the small ER unit leaning against a wall, my clouded thoughts carried me off on a daydream excursion while the time passed. I couldn't help but think how devastating this was for all of us, but primarily for Mother. She was an energetic lady who made a room light up by walking into it. It was a shock for Mother to be injured with a break in her hip.

As kids, my brother and I played outside more than inside. Mother took the time to teach us how to throw and catch a softball, - how to bat. Back in the day of rolling yards on Halloween, when it was considered an innocent "treat," Mother had one heck of a trick throw with a special unique grip for holding the toilet paper roll. Her spin left a long flowing paper trail waving, as if it were attached to a high flying kite. Yep, my Mother was always "hip!" That's a good 1970's term from my generation.

During our childhood days, our home was filled with neighborhood kids. Mother always made our friends feel especially welcomed, cooking special things for mid-afternoon snacks, whenever she could find the time. She was "one of the kids." She was one of us! "How would a broken hip affect her?" That would pose questions and answers in ways I could not comprehend, while propped in the ER that day trying to come to grips that this incident was indeed a reality.

During my earlier jaunt, while holding Mother's hand as I went through the prickly briar shrubs before she was loaded in the ambulance, I had ripped my pants leaving an open gap. There was enough blood showing through the torn fabric and on my knee that it caught the attention of an ER tech who gave me a bandage and ointment. Having worked closely with clinical care departments in hospital settings, I knew the JCAHO (Joint Commission on Accreditation of Hospital Organizations) policies and procedures had strict standards setting specific guidelines for medical facilities and blood-borne pathogen awareness. However, I didn't realize at the time I had a cut on my right leg or any blood stains. Mother teases me to this day that my cut was just a "scratch," as she refers to it. But it was deep enough to leave a "memory" scar.

Within a short amount of time, Jack made his way into the ER. He traveled from the distance in almost half the time of the average drive. Kate arrived just moments after Jack. She was the sister we never had. Kate bonded with our family when we met over 25 years ago. She's a few years older than me, and the responsible one who could think in times of emergencies with a clear head. Mother was her "other" mom.

Kate asked the nurse the name of the orthopaedic surgeon that would be taking Mother's case. It was Dr. I. M. Doubter.[6] She called one of her friends to learn more about his professional background. We learned from a reliable source he was considered one of the best specialists in his field, with an outstanding reputation for hip replacements.

Soon my sister-in-law, Bridget[7], arrived. She was not one to drive with a heavy foot like her in-laws. We were a close-knit family - always ready and willing to help one another. It was reassuring to have everyone able to stop what they were doing to come to Mother's side. God made it possible for all of us to nestle around our "Momma Bird."

Once our family was gathered, it seemed time passed quickly. Soon, Mother was carried for surgery prep from the ER. Shortly thereafter, the family was called back to the private area where Mother was ready for surgery while laying in a hospital-type bed. It gave us an opportunity to meet Dr. Doubter and ask questions.

Mother was not yet in la-la land, however somewhat alert enough to understand what was occurring. Dr. Doubter stood on one side of Mother's hospital bed explaining where her hip was broken, as he displayed her x-rays so we could all see the damage needing immediate repairs. He shared what type of implant device he believed would work best for her complete recovery. It was a relief to meet with the orthopaedic surgeon that would be operating on Mother, since we had never met him.

As the techs wheeled Mother to surgery, we exited to the waiting room like a herd of lost sheep. Once again, I was ready to collapse. The Heavenly Father did an excellent job of keeping me going through my adrenaline rush earlier, but I was beginning to slow down from the hectic morning, as my body and mind were exhausted.

It was approximately 2:00 p.m.

Everyone sat within earshot of one another, discussing the details of how things happened, and particularly how odd it was for me to be in town when she fell. I knew I was where I was supposed to be!

We began to speculate the coming hours, days, and weeks for Mother's recovery. An occasional comment would catch my isolated thinking, reeling me back into the reality of the day, the moment, and the entire scope of things.

During the waiting time, which I think can be the most grueling test of a person's patience; I began to calm down from the "hurry-hurry-rush-rush-frantic-panic" morning and all before our first sip of java!

Although, I appeared to be sitting in a daze, I was still somewhat attentive, giving thanks to God for those who helped to get us to this point and everyone's safe arrivals.

My wandering mind could not help but query the "whys" of everything that had transpired in the past 24 hours. One of my biggest reliefs, besides Poppa, Jack, Bridget, and Kate being there, was that I would normally have been six hours or longer away, where I resided on the outskirts of Metro Atlanta. But I wasn't. I was right where I sensed God led me. I had never been so glad that I followed my "gut feeling." The timing of it all, was nothing short of amazing!

As I reflected on the before, during, and what was going to happen after Mother's recovery process, I knew God had made the impossible possible, so I would be near to help. I had no idea how much assistance would be required, but I was ready to do whatever it would take for Mother to get back on her feet again.

I continued to sit silently, praying for Mother's hip surgery to go smoothly. From time to time, I remembered the others chatting which was a reminder that I was not alone, nor were any of us in this eye-opening event. We were a family of strong faith anticipating an excellent outcome by the grace of God. My weary body was becoming more fatigued, yet my mind could not rest. My brain was still processing, as I relived the series of events, which seemed like days instead of mere hours.

Not knowing what Mother was going to be facing through her recovery, rehabilitation therapy, and adjusting to life with a new hip - I don't think any of us in our wildest dreams ever anticipated Mother of all people, would ever need a hip replacement due to a fall which caused a break in a vibrant healthy body!

Approximately four hours had passed. Dr. Doubter had our crew called to a private family room where he met with us to deliver the highly anticipated excellent news about Mother's surgery. She made it through the operation without any complications. He assured us everything looked great, and believed she would have a good prognosis with a full recovery. Dr. Doubter also shared that Mother had good solid bones, which helps a patient rebound quickly.

Two hours later, we were notified Mother was being released from post-operative (Post-Op) care to her designated hospital room. As I arrived and entered, I thought "This will become 'home' for the next few days."

I seemed to be the perfect candidate to stay with Mother since I could work from my laptop without losing income, while assisting her. One of the new amenities the medical center offered was Internet access.

This arrangement would free up my brother and sister-in-law. They had school-aged children with busy extra-curricular activities in addition to busy full-time jobs. It would also help Poppa with his business, which he continued to dabble with after his retirement. We were indeed blessed during these troubling circumstances. Everything was so much better than it could have been.

Becoming a part-time caregiver was not a completely new experience. Mother and I teamed up in 2002 to take care of my maternal Grandmother in the last few weeks of her life. Now, I would again be teamed up with Mother, as her caregiver through the recovery process.

However, I would not begin to comprehend the adjustments Mother would incur learning to walk again, sitting properly, getting in and out of a car or bed, bathing and showering, learning to dress, in addition to her forming new sleeping habits with a partial hip replacement. Until she could turn or roll-over on her side, she would have to learn to sleep flat on her back for several days, which quickly became extremely uncomfortable to the point of painful.

Since this occurrence, we have come to believe that accidents happen for a reason. For us, the reason became evident as I continue to share Mother's journey. I realized how "hip" my Mother is, and has, always been. The set of unpleasant circumstances gave me the added privilege to really get to know my Mother much better as an individual.

What she did for me many years ago, was a far cry for anything I could do for her, as she demonstrated throughout my life before I was a child she could hold or see. In the summer of 1958, Mother chose to have an experimental surgery. There was a high probability, she could be paralyzed at the age of 20.

Her obstetrician happily announced Patricia was pregnant with her first child. However, he also had to explain that her womb was upside down AND attached to her spine. Mother chose the surgery. The fetus (me) was expected to have been a miscarriage during the process. She walked away from surgery with success as God has immensely blessed "both of us" with His protection.

> *"For You formed my inward parts; You wove me in my mother's womb. I will give thanks to You, for I am fearfully and wonderfully made; wonderful are your works, And my soul knows it very well."*
> *Psalm 139:13-14*

Mother was going to walk away from this unique journey, birthing an incredible story to educate many others with similar issues. Maybe the details or events are different, but the healing process is very similar in most cases, for each of us - emotionally and physically.

Her faith and courage continued to be phenomenal as she began an entirely new walk in her life, stemming from this fall to rise up to become a more Christ-like example. Ultimately she would grow to be stronger in every sense as a human - emotionally, physically and spiritually.

Yep, my Mother's hip!

+ + +

Chapter 3

WALK THIS WAY

Soon, we became settled in the hospital room after Mother's emergency surgery. I did feel a little like a hobo living out of my duffle bag. Maybe if I clicked my heels together and repeated "I want to go home, I want to go home," the transition of events would send us back to our very own "Kansas" in our very own world, as we knew it before Mother's fall. But that was not to be. God had a different agenda.

Alas, reality sets in.

I learned to eat hospital food and enjoy it! Reality refocused my perspective on the many current blessings; Mother having wonderful health insurance while being treated in one of the top medical facilities in the state of Alabama, and in the southern region of the United States. This experience placed a new outlook in my view, learning to appreciate the quality of life in general, especially the little things taken for granted.

This inconvenient "break" in our daily ritual of living, happened for reasons I believed would be revealed. However, it was still March 2, 2006. I was trying to grasp the idea of our family dependence on Mother. She was clearly our hub. Now our family caregiver; the watchful parent and close friend to her grown children, was lying in a hospital bed flat on her back after her a hip replacement surgery. It was difficult to imagine our hub being temporarily out of commission!

Pillows were carefully positioned around Mother's right hip and leg with a drainage tube and catheter as evidence of her vulnerable state. When Mother was able to get up and out of the bed, an I.V. pump attached to her left arm would become a temporary appendage with her every move. The lingering aroma of new bandages and the sight of the yellow prepping stains from surgery were still painted on her leg, was a shocking reminder to start adapting my mindset in becoming more compassionate about her needs and confinement. She was an independent lady. Being strapped to a bed was not the ideal situation for anyone, but it was less than tolerable for Mother. Although, she never complained, I knew it had to be terribly difficult for her to adjust. She never doubted her situation, but instead prayed to God for His comfort. Mother was, and will always, remain an inspiration to me!

One of my first defense lessons was while learning to sleep on a chair, which makes into a bed. It was actually a façade called a "bed." Rest for me would be limited. I fought and wrestled with every move of a chair-bed gadget, all night to finally stay put in a sleeping position, without the bed making a chair again! That was how I got my exercise.

Work for me was interrupted a great deal in taking care of Mother's needs, but that is what I was there to do. It seemed she needed something just about the time I became somewhat comfortable, in what I believed was one of the most uncomfortable chairs known to mankind. Why are these chairs always located in hospital rooms when people need "comfort" during a difficult time? Having worked in hospitals, I heard many complaints when working in public relations about the furnishings, which are far from functional or comfortable. Previously, I had sympathy for family members; now I had empathy!

At least I could move freely and independently. Mother was not used to being "tied" down. She was a mobile "up and going" type A person, always doing for others. Mother needed a tremendous amount of care, as she was forced to adapt. It had to be unfathomable when she awoke from surgery, possibly in a bit of a shock - remembering and realizing she would not be able to just get up. She was never one to cry. I probably cried more than she did, particularly when she was in surgery, wondering and waiting. Believing and hoping.

Mother was a much better patient than I could ever be. Her needs included an endless amount of adjusting her bed covers, rearranging her pillows as she was often back-bound to the bed for hours on end. I also learned quickly to follow up at the nurses' station when Mother's pain escalated, indicating time for her next med dosage. Often times, the nurses became too busy with the demands of other patients overloading a nurses' human capabilities. Another tall order for me was encouraging Mother to eat the bland food compared to her own wonderful seasoned cooking. She had always been an extremely picky eater.

In 1969, I was in the fourth grade when our family traveled to San Juan, Puerto Rico, to visit our cousins and see the island. The dad of the family, Taylor[8], is Mother's first cousin. He was a plant manager for an international manufacturer. His first wife for many years and the mother of his children was named Faith[9]. It was a tremendous loss to our family when she passed on several years ago. But, Faith made her mark on life. Everyone was enriched with fond memories having known her. She was an amazing person always bringing fun to our family gatherings. She kept us entertained, especially the kids, during our visit to their Puerto Rican home.

Jack, my little brother, was three years old at the time of our trip. He was not as picky of an eater as Mother had always been. He had no idea the colored fluffy puffed round shaped hamster food was not cereal, as he consumed the entire box thinking it was snack food.

As I tried new ways to get Mother to eat, I recalled our San Juan adventure and wondered if a box of hamster food would have been more appealing!

As far as Mother's appetite on that trip, I have no idea how many grill cheese sandwiches she ordered for her meal when we dined out. With a vast array of seafood, fresh fruit, and so many other specialty items on most any of the San Juan restaurant menus, she religiously ordered a grilled cheese sandwich and a Coca-Cola°.

My task in trying to persuade Mother to eat her hospital meals, especially when liver and cabbage was delivered, was a no win situation. Quite honestly, I would be the same, if not worse! Our roles were reversed for this mother-daughter team, which meant I had to think as such. That's when I learned quickly why Jell-O° is such an important hospital side dish!

Her first rehabilitation therapy session began within 24 hours after her major surgery. This was my first experience with a joint replacement patient as a family member. I was shocked when the orthopaedic medical orders included Mother getting out of bed to walk and move her new hip so soon. Recalling the pain after she fell, I expected this experience to also be excruciating. I wanted to escape and leave the room, but I knew she would be depending on the "cheer leading support" while the physical therapists taught her new ways to become mobile, sit, stand, bend, and learn to use the toilet with handrail assistance. It was a new way of life, at best!

Mother was always a very private person when it came to using the bathroom. She quickly became dependent for me to speak on her behalf to shield what she felt was an invasion of privacy. This was probably one of the most difficult challenges and lessons in her new life: humility.

Upon her return home in the weeks ahead, handrails would need to added to all of Mother and Poppa's bathrooms, along with high-rise toilets. Those are the kind of toilets where a very young child can swing their feet while sitting, or least that was what I did at my Great-Grandmother's house when I was a youngster on her high-rise flusher.

It was a new world for Mother and for me, as I watched and learned. Seeing new health care techniques once again piqued my interest, as it did when I was in college. For my internship semester, I chose to work with geriatrics in nursing home facilities. I was relearning health-caring details 20 years later. Trust me, when I tell you that it prepared my caring skills for Mother, more than I could have imagined! Since my profession once included medical marketing and communications, Mother was confident the college education she had invested, would become handy on a very personal level. Why is it Mothers always know best? Most mothers, anyway!

Even with her keen sense of humor, it was difficult for Mother to adapt to new ways of accomplishing things, except perhaps, brushing her teeth. Taking showers and baths had to be reevaluated while learning a new level of awareness and caution around slippery floor surfaces. With every move of her body, she now had to rethink and retrain her brain with the utmost attention given to carefully rising, stepping, moving, twisting, and/or turning.

Over the next two days, as I adjusted my work schedule to meet set deadlines, Mother was up and walking. Her walker became her new best friend. She soon became free to roam when her I.V. meds were finally detached. Due to limited energy, her short "try out" runs were back and forth across her somewhat mid-sized hospital room. In no time, the physical therapists had Mother walking the halls. Her old personality was starting to return. Slowly, she began cracking jokes, which always provided contagious laughter. It was her way of turning tears into chuckles.

We quickly learned why bright neon-yellow tennis balls are used as covers on the two straight back legs of a walker with stabilized wheels on the front. Without the cushy durable surface which tennis balls provide, a certain noise alarms everyone… even the hard of hearing… within 100 feet. "Hey, here comes a 'walker talker'!" Sneaking up on anyone with a walker is not an option. Even the "rolling" wheels, which are affixed to roll straight, can wake the deepest sleep for hospital roommates a.k.a. "me" when Mother needed to get up in the middle of the night to go to the bathroom. Let's just say… she didn't have to call my name! She just had to grab her walker, which created the most irritating noise, doubling as an alarm and wake-up call. Needless to say, I quickly went out and bought a can of tennis balls, puncturing two to snuggly fit on Mother's walker with a spare in case of a blow out!

Mother really was an exceptional patient as she is an exceptional parent and friend. Occasionally, her wit showed up when I least expected her funnies to come tumbling out. I would find myself bent double laughing! The levity kept us going as we were reminded "laughter is the best medicine."

The morning Mother was transported to the rehab unit for inpatient therapy just across the way from the hospital, the nurse rolled Mother in a wheelchair while I rolled a cart full of flower arrangements, clothing, and her new best friend, "Walker" with its tennis attire attached.

When we arrived, we were expecting to enter a private room. We had not been told she would have a roommate. To give a better visual of this arrangement, we made two steps into the room with just enough space for the wheelchair, not the overloaded cart, and stopped. There was the bed. A large curtain, was the room divider, as it was pulled about three-fourths of the way. It was opened just enough to say hello to the other patient if you stood near the end of the bed.

At best Mother's nerves were a bit on edge. Her entire world from a physical, emotional, and spiritual sense was like putting "play dough" in a microwave for a few seconds. Her abilities and adaptability were completely different. She wasn't nearly as flexible, being able to use her body as she had before the fall. Her thinking process as to how to face life from this point was a bit jarred, also. Most likely, she was still recovering from a long mild shock of a major life-changing event. It could have been worse. It could have been better. Either way, it was how it was to be.

The lovable, adorable person whose humor was one of her strong suits - well let's just say that "suit" must have been sent to the cleaners! Not lovable. Not adorable. Her sense of humor withdrew like a turtle crawling back into its shell. Given the circumstances, it was understandable. I prayed she would be better than before, in ways we could not imagine. This stage of her first real transition was not going well... at all! Hence the turtle syndrome proceeded with caution.

Mother's bed assignment was right next to the large handicap sized door entrance to the room. The bathroom, which had another large handicap sized door, took up a considerable amount of "swing" space in this "petite" rehab suite. It was located between the patients' beds aligned at the end of the pulled curtain divider.

My thoughts began accessing the situation in an instant. Immediately, I knew this arrangement was not going to work. Mother didn't have to say one word. It had nothing to do with the TV being on the wall above the bathroom door. It wasn't anything personal about Mother having a roommate although the patient had a very disturbing cough with a deep croup-like rattling sound, which could unease the calmest of nerves. I truly felt sorry for the other patient's health situation, which was unknown to us due to HIPAA[73] (Health Insurance Portability and Accountability Act of 1996) regulations. The fact Mother's bed was right next to the main door of the room, which also happened to be across the hall from a very loud gathering place, was not helpful.

Mother is a very, very private person when it comes to private matters of her body, and its private functions and outcomes in the bathroom. She never seemed the type who could have adjusted to the Armed Forces, or any place where community showers and bathrooms were standard accommodations.

Given the circumstances, before she uttered a sound, I saw her starting to look at me. I knew that look before her head was turned for me to see her eyes! It was not the rare occasional look of "You're in trouble!" ... which is all it ever took to get my attention to behave.

No… this was more like a frightened child's stare silently screaming… "Please do NOT leave me like this!" I knew prior to Mother being transferred to the Rehab facility, I would not be able to stay with her, as I had been doing in the hospital. Besides... where would I sleep? There wasn't enough room for a "chair-bed gadget" much less a straight-up guest chair!

I immediately leaned over and whispered for her not to panic, as I sensed she was getting upset trying to cope with a less than ideal situation. The return of humor I recently witnessed just vanished. Right now - nothing was funny.

I quietly prayed in my thoughts asking the Father to please help me, help her! I could only imagine if God wondered why we couldn't just cope and stop asking for help so often. But we knew He would answer our prayers, no matter what I might have wondered about God's idea of our coping.

It was also time to practice my public relations skills from the days when I worked in a medical facility. Understanding the basic structure of how healthcare systems work, I thought maybe I should check with the patient care coordinator. While walking down the hall, I continued praying in my thoughts asking God to please open up a private room if possible or let there be a short waiting list.

Often times, we all must learn to adjust to various situations. Given the circumstances, it would be a miracle if she didn't have to share a small room and a small bathroom ... what you might say "out in the open" for everyone to be alerted with every little move. Or big move, on a good functioning day!

The first place I went was the nurses' desk. I asked for the patient care coordinator. Turns out she was standing right in front of me! I explained the situation as professionally as possible. She understood without me having to explain in detail. Without delay, she picked up a clipboard with a list for inpatient registrations. A room was currently available with no waiting. That was a prayer answered quickly!

By the time I returned to Mother's room, she seemed to be in much better spirits. Her humor was once again revived as she struggled to find her own personal comfort zone. I think she sensed God had provided for her in a time of panic, which might not be a large obstacle to others - but after all, the Good Lord knew His daughter, and what she could and could not tolerate.

Within an hour, we were notified Mother would be transferred to a private room. Her assigned nurses were already sad to see Mother leaving their care, where she would be moved to another wing of the facility. That's how quickly my Mother, the personable, loving and witty "never meets a stranger" naturally draws people to her. I was so glad to see her withdrawal and panic had been alleviated!

To our surprise, Mother was moved to one of the largest rooms I have ever seen in a hospital, or rehab facility. We had plenty of room for everything, plus there was a love-seat. However, it was against inpatient rehab rules for me to stay overnight with her. The only way she would relearn how to live independently was through the skills and training of several specialty therapists, without family assistance during her stay.

Quite honestly, I was actually relieved I would not be staying with her. My work deadlines were close to lagging and I needed a place where I could focus. The visiting hours allowed me to be with her from 5:00 p.m. – 11:00 p.m. through the week, then all day on Saturdays and Sundays. It turned out to be the best arrangement, although at first I felt odd leaving her alone to adjust by herself.

In meeting with the physical therapist, we learned Mother's need for proper clothing consisted of sports attire and work-out shoes while doing her exercises and recuperating. Mother was a lady who liked to dress like a lady, meaning she wanted her clothes to fit.

My major in college was health requiring several activity participation classes in recreation and physical education. The majority of my wardrobe was casual clothing, which included khakis, sweat pants, roomy T-shirts and tennis shoes. This was not how Mother preferred to dress, so it was yet another adjustment for her to make. It was also another expense neither of us had taken into consideration. Fortunately, Mother had a retail department store charge card that I could use at the nearby mall. It was time to shop "my way" to buy clothes for which I was accustomed to, but for Mother's needs.

Off to the mall I headed, finding several things for her to wear while taking into consideration her right thigh's eight inch incision, plus mobility and comfort. Wearing long gowns for sleeping as she was accustomed, was not going to be suitable for quite some time.

That was yet another adjustment for Mother as she had to learn to sleep in shorter gowns versus longer gowns so they would not become twisted, as she was taught a new way to lay down and sleep in a bed.

First, she had to sit, then slowly lift both of her legs, keeping them together (help was required for the first six weeks), while twisting her body to keep her hip immobile. Only after being able to do more of this new way to lay down, could she begin to sleep on her side with a pillow between her knees, which was taught by the therapist. The requirement for a pillow between her knees was to distribute her weight evenly to accommodate her healing hip bone and newly inserted metal implant so it would heal properly.

Additionally, this new sleep technique also kept her from creating a forceful motion on her newly inserted hip replacement from popping out of socket before it was completely healed. When I witnessed her new sleeping challenges, I never again took for granted the ability to able to roll-over on my side, or any other way I wanted to toss and turn, to sleep.

Tennis shoes were the only sports clothing items Mother had ever worn besides an occasional pair of blue jeans. But tennis shoes were not an option for Mother until she could learn to correctly bend-over or prop her foot on a stool to tie her shoes. Bending her hip past a 90 degree angle was not an option, nor could she prop her knee. She had to learn to put on and pull up her socks with something resembling a long shoehorn.

At first, her mobility and stability was limited. With a healing hip replacement, comprised of metal implants in her thigh attached to her pelvis, she had no flexibility in the beginning. Therefore, if she ever fell, getting her up would be extremely difficult and painful for her to experience. Not to mention acquiring the use of a forklift! And quite possibly requiring surgery again if the hip replacement popped out of socket.

Because of her challenge of not being able to bend over very far, my only option to purchase were "slip on" shoes. There was no doubt in my mind that she would detest the ones I had selected, but there was little choice.

As soon as I pulled the shoes out of the box, the look on her face said it all! However, she did understand the design was for her own safety in relearning to walk with emphasis to keep her right foot and toe from dragging as she took each step. She worked on retraining her upper right leg muscles by lifting her right foot with various exercises. This was not an easy task as her muscles had been severely shifted and stretched after the incision to prepare her femur and pelvis to insert the metal replacement or implant.

Before the hip replacement, Mother was a "high heels" lady. Shoes made the outfit. She was always a respectable woman who loved to dress in nice clothes. But she had a serious matching fetish, which was passed down to both of her children. Mother was not necessarily into top dollar clothing; but she always bought quality clothes for ladies who had attractive physical features. She never dressed like a slouch, even at home whether working or playing with us outdoors. However, now the "relaxed loose" clothing was a requirement. The former days of dressing in high heels were a faint possibility at best!

Her new world kept changing/evolving almost daily, if not hourly.

She continued to be a good sport (no pun intended). When I presented her new line of clothing, I had to listen to a lot of flack. I kept in mind that Mother was having to adapt, she was still in pain quite a bit. She needed someone to listen to her vents, which were really not complaints, as much as talking through her new mode of living. It was a compromise she had not planned; which no one does when things happen.

However, after one therapy session on an exercise mat, she quickly realized "loose and comfortable" clothing was an important part of her rehabilitation and recovery process. When she admitted I was right, I couldn't help but grin from ear to ear. But, I kept my "I told you so" comments silenced. Now was not the time to pour salt into her emotional wounds, which were possibly deeper than her physical ones.

After we had some pep talks and prayer times, Mother was good to go. Poppa was the best support of all. He convinced her that she looked good no matter what she wore! Her new specialized clothing line, "loose as a goose" worked until she got better. Her goal was to return to her preferred fashion style. To my surprise, she continued enjoying her sweatpants.

Mother would call me during her lunch breaks to share what she learned, or how difficult her inpatient therapy sessions were going, as she relearned to walk, sit, and bend properly. It was better for me not to see her struggles. Since her fall, I was overly protective of her every move, just as she had been with me when I was a toddler taking my first steps.

During Mother's inpatient rehab, I needed a temporary home. From the moment Kate approached me in the ER, the first thing she said after asking about Mother, was to offer her townhouse for our family's use. What a wonderful gesture and huge relief! It was completely furnished with all the utilities connected, and available. It was conveniently located only a few miles from the medical facilities. Talk about your needs being met and exceeded! God was provided for us with blessings through others.

Kate and her husband built a new house in the outskirts of town and decided to keep the townhouse. I was ever so grateful to be able to temporarily live in a place that I was familiar with, on my occasional trips through the years to visit her. It was a perfect place to relax, work, and literally "felt at home." While I had use of the townhouse, Poppa stayed with Ryan and Ashley, which gave him time to enjoy being with Zachary. During the week, Poppa returned to their Centre home to oversee his business.

My first day in the townhouse, I sat on the bedroom floor in a bewildered state of mind. Kate dropped by after work to check on me. Beyond exhausted, I looked up when I heard the front door open and the most welcoming sound of Kate's voice as she called out "Chritter." (A nickname she coined for me long ago due to my love for animals.) I explained how everything seemed to be moving like a fast-paced merry-go-round. She knew I was worn out.

The most wonderful part of our sisterhood and close friendship was that we often spoke without saying a word. She wandered over and sat down then gave me a big ole sisterly hug. My emotions suddenly let go. It was the first time I had allowed myself to really cry since Mother's fall. Kate was so supportive and nurturing. Just when I needed her compassion and care, she was there to provide comfort which felt like it came from God. After we talked, my emotions finally settled down. The shock was beginning to wear off. It was good to be able to share what was spinning around in my mind with someone whom I considered family.

I knew Mother was going to be fine, but the accident was so "out of the blue." Psychologically, I had to release my sorrow and grief for Mother, as she was adapting to a new way of life. Thanking God became a daily prayer as I learned to unwind and share my concerns with Him. I was grateful Mother was alive! I knew things could have been so much worse but it was still a life-altering experience for her, and for our family. In spite of it all, we were incredibly blessed!

Lots of changes were occurring in almost every facet of Mother's life. Remarkably, she learned to cope and move forward as she walked onto a new "Centre" stage for "Trish." She turned her world around making the best of the situation, she even adapted new eating habits.

In the dining hall of the rehab center was a piano. Her talent was instrumental in keeping her soul inspired - as well as many other souls, as they listened to her unique musical gift. With her God-given abilities as a pianist playing for all types of events throughout her life, she lit up the dining area each day for the other patients as they would gather around to listen to their favorite songs.

It had always been the way Mother expressed her feelings… like an intimate conversation with God as the notes seemed to resonate directly from the depths of her soul. It was a greatly needed emotional healing for her emotions. Mother began to feel a little more comfortable with the way life was going. Once again, her natural fun loving personality helped other people's worlds seem better, if only for a brief time.

Mother was so thankful for the quality of life she was again offered, adjusting to a new permanent way of living. Her physical strength was increasing, but her faith surpassed any limitations she may have had as she grew in her relationship with God. It seemed both of us had learned to depend on God to guide our steps. We were both learning to walk in new ways, emotionally, physically, and spiritually.

She quickly succeeded in learning to walk again in a very short amount of time. As I watched, I tried to imagine what it was like looking through her eyes, walking in her shoes. I developed a new appreciation for life from a completely different perspective.

Within the next six weeks Mother recovered in record time. Soon she graduated to a citizen "Jane" cane, no longer needing her best bud "Walker," adorned

with two bright yellow tennis balls with bald bottoms! Tennis balls and her racquet... she was game for anything with her "Walker," which was anything but silent when used! I was elated to learn a cane did not require a tennis ball! Imagine Mother feeling energized enough to make it pogo stick! She was returning strong and steady. Anything could have been possible with Trish!

The physical therapists asked the family members to meet for a consultation. Poppa, Jack and I attended the session and were given detailed instructions how to help Mother, and protect her new hip replacement.

Her healing had been progressing remarkably fast. She worked hard every day, driven with self-discipline. She became well known throughout the facility spending time visiting other patients, mostly those less fortunate with their injuries. It is Mother's way of showing Christ through her actions. She could talk the talk, and walk the walk.

A new dermatology problem arose when we learned Mother was allergic to latex tape. The rehab nurse changed the dressing over her incision. The first two times, the topical layer of her skin pulled off creating painful abrasive sores. The "ever so tough and highly tolerant" patient was in tears. Again, this was not something I was accustomed to seeing. Tears always seemed to be a last resort for Mother.

After the second time the tape ripped her skin, it was pretty evident Mother must be allergic to latex products. Previously throughout the years, she had other surgical procedures, but never experienced this type of skin reaction before, which appeared to be primarily from the tape.

The nurses gave me specific instructions for the proper way to cleanse her wound when changing her bandages, once she was discharged to outpatient rehab therapy. Until the skin abrasions healed, tubal antibiotic ointment was used regularly. Hand washing was required all the time for everything in caring for her, or using the gloves the facility provided. Mother's incision didn't heal as quickly as she physiologically recovered in her exercises.

An office visit to Dr. Doubter was required for Mother to be released from inpatient therapy to outpatient therapy. Upon entering the exam room, he asked "Where's your walker or your cane?" She replied, "I don't need anything." His face said it all! He was completely and pleasantly surprised that a 68 year old woman bounced back so quickly, as were the rest of her family and friends. I think she even surprised herself!

Once again, Mother progressed quicker than the average patient. When it was time for her to join me at the townhouse, small things became important. Again, it would most likely be insignificant to anyone who has never experienced a traumatic fall, or sustained a major injury.

For example, there was one single small step onto the front porch landing. This made it easier for Mother to enter through the front door of the townhouse. Also, the floor plan included two bedrooms and two bathrooms. One bedroom and bath was on the main floor. The other was located upstairs. Another convenience was that the outpatient rehab therapy clinic she chose, was less than two miles from our "home away from home."

Through it all, I was able to keep my small business going with my laptop. God provided for our every need. Things I previously never gave a second thought, were now seen as huge blessings. Once again, we learned to appreciate the simple things in life. Her fall was only the beginning of things to come for Mother, and for our family. Soon she would begin to consider having a total left knee replacement to relieve the continued pain since her hip - and her life - were becoming stable.

She was on a new journey learning to walk in a new way, having no idea of new uncertainties about to cross her path. Her new "walk this way" was just beginning. The future would prove to be quite the opposite of what we were anticipating.

+ + +

Chapter 4
HERE'S THE LATEST "KNEE-TAILS"

New stability would need to be provided in every aspect of Mother's life when she returned home to Centre. Doorways, stairs, and rugs on the floor - to name a few of the many possible obstacles we inspected for potential hazards. Besides entering and exiting the house, the bathrooms were prime areas that needed evaluation for safety. Virtually every step Mother made, would now have to be safety first!

She quickly recaptured her ability to drive, which helped her to feel independent, again. If the community and town folks had not learned about her unexpected hip mishap, no one would have suspected anything by the way Mother walked. Her gait was as natural as if she had never had a hip replacement.

One of the multitude of facts I learned about hip replacements, is that the length of the patient's leg can change if the surgeon does not perform an accurate measurement in surgery. It had never occurred to me when I saw a man or woman wobbling a bit when they walked, perhaps they may have had a possible hip or knee surgery affecting the span of their legs. Mother's legs were exactly the same length with no wobble in her walk, as she carried her body with a strong steady stride. How fortunate we were to be blessed with an excellent orthopaedic surgeon "on call" the day of her fall.

My life also started a new direction from my previous 10 weeks pace. Once I returned to my home in Georgia, many changes began both inwardly and outwardly. Being Mother's caregiver opened my eyes to the realization of how fragile the human body is, and the chances we often take… for granted. Not everyone who tumbles or falls is able to get up and walk away from a bad spill. Already safety conscious in most everything around me, I became more alert and invariably more considerate. If someone in public needed assistance with a door being opened, I extended a courtesy to strangers I wouldn't have previously thought to offer. A keen awareness was sparked in my actions, as I watched Mother's struggles, so I would be more careful.

Since Mother and I always shared a special bond, a real team spirit throughout the years, I was reminded how God always made it possible for us to be together – side by side – during our lives' tribulations and triumphs. From childhood to adulthood, we had not only formed a trusting friendship; we had developed a sisterhood.

The lingering thought from my gut feeling to go to her side when I sensed she needed me, never left as I became more in tune with the wondrous and mysterious ways God works. It was as if I simply "knew" it was the right thing to do, even if it didn't make any sense to anyone else. Never before have I been so glad I made the decision to go to Alabama in March 2006. I thanked God for ALL the blessings, which included being able to operate my business, as well as provide an income while caring for a parent. Incredible!

After returning to my Georgia home, one of the projects I had worked on during Mother's hip trip, was completed successfully. Nevertheless, my business was not thriving, but I was surviving. I began spending a considerable amount of time applying for jobs in my specialty area of communications, which included public, community, and media relations; marketing, advertising, and mid-level graphic design work.

My health degree was useful in helping Mother as a caregiver in addition to my professional experience in clinical and non-clinical settings, but I was also blessed with the innate ability of creativity utilizing my God-given talents through various forms of communications. This was truly my professional calling. It was as natural for me as it was for Mother to play the piano. Two different types of keyboards used to create a unique soundness in their element for others to sense; both were vibrant formats for ears, eyes and the imagination.

As I applied for jobs in many types of industries, one particular was a communications specialist at a nuclear plant with a reputable power company. However, to my dismay I received a rejection letter within two weeks. It was disappointing news, as I knew I was well qualified, but I shrugged it off shredding the letter, never thinking about it again. Advancing in corporate communications was a goal I had set to achieve many years ago with my successful climb up the proverbial career ladder.

Two weeks after receiving the rejection letter, an unexpected call from the power company caught me off guard! An administrative assistant asked if I was still interested in the communications specialist position, for which I had applied. Of course, without any hesitation, I immediately said "Yes ma'am!" It was like a dream come true. As a matter of fact, two more interviews came within the next 48 hours; one in north Georgia and the other was in Fairbanks, Alaska!

While I was seeking jobs, Mother was seeking surgical advice about her left knee needing a replacement. As her hip seemed to become stronger, the pain in her knee was becoming almost unbearable. She met with Dr. Doubter and the surgery was set for July 12, 2006, only four months after her hip replacement. As it turned out, my interview with the power company was scheduled on the same day, several hours away.

There was never a question about me going to the interview. Mother and I knew this was a golden opportunity. I knew she would be in great hands since she decided to use the same orthopaedic surgeon; in addition, family and close friends would be nearby. Based on the x-rays and Dr. Doubter's assessment of her knee's poor range of motion, Mother was diagnosed with a degenerative bone disease. The severe pain was due to bone-on-bone friction with every step and movement she made.

She had received great care with her hip replacement, in addition to our family getting to know the surgeon, and had become familiar with the hospital and rehab facilities. I believed she had made a good decision to have her knee replacement surgery performed in the same town.

Kate graciously offered for us to use the townhouse, again. This time I was able to "plan" ahead to join Mother after my interview, so I could assist during her recovery process. I was already broken-in like a good horse. No sense in training another poor soul to learn her wants and needs before she uttered a sound.

Mother and I had prepared in advance for the big day on July 12. My interview was in the morning, as was her surgery. My trip this time around was approximately eight hours away. After a very well received interview, I drove from Georgia to Alabama to assume the role as Mother's designated caregiver.

Once again, I was adjusting to sleeping on a chair façade resembling a bed for the next several days. This time, I came equipped bringing my own sleeping bag and pillow. I can sleep just about anywhere as long as I have my own pillow.

With my laptop and some minor work projects to keep my income afloat, I managed to stay busy in between assisting Mother with her needs. Visitors were gracious to drive from Centre along with the family members, as they waited patiently on the news of her surgery. As soon as I was in cell phone range, I called to learn of any updates. Finally, I received a call that Mother was doing fine.

After I arrived at the hospital, Poppa shared with me what he witnessed that occurred soon after she was brought to her hospital room from recovery. My sister-in-law, Bridget, and my step-brother's wife, Ashley, were waiting with Poppa in Mother's room. He said she was still "pretty much" out of it, as he described. He shared that Mother had briefly stopped breathing within approximately 30 minutes or less since being transported from recovery.

Poppa said Bridget was standing next to the bed, and immediately shook Mother trying to get her to breathe again. From what I understood from Poppa, it was a scary moment: touch and go for a few seconds regarding Mother's alertness to wake up. To this day, we have no idea what happened, but Poppa said it was very concerning. She never had another problem after that episode. But Bridget and Ashley were alarmed and proceeded to do what was necessary to make sure Mother had attentive care from the nurses, afterwards.

It was tag team time. Soon after I arrived, Bridget, Ashley, and Poppa left, as it was getting late in the day. The nursing staff continued to keep a close watch on Mother for the next 24 hours. However, it was only in the first few hours as the anesthesia began dwindling, Mother immediately began complaining about an unusual pain in her newly replaced left knee.

She felt it was not related to surgical recovery pain like she had with her hip. Her description for this new pain was completely different. She had a slight fever, as she continued to share how her pain was increasing.

Later that evening, Dr. Doubter made his rounds to check on Mother's condition. Although she was still somewhat groggy from the anesthesia, I remember her trying to be specific in explaining to him the unusual sensation in her knee. She reiterated that it was a "different" pain that was not related to her surgery incision. He recorded the problem in his medical notes, but said she needed to give her knee time to heal. It was as if Dr. Doubter heard what she said, but was skeptical of her complaint since the replacement surgery had been in less than 36 hours.

With the slight fever and the different pain, things did not start out as well with her healing process as it did with her hip replacement. It took three days before she could be helped out of the bed to begin therapy. It was extremely difficult for her to bend her knee.

As therapists worked with Mother, she continued to have severe pain when moving or exercising her knee, which was placed on a powered exercise knee-flexing machine to stretch and rebuild stamina in her leg muscles. She had more difficulty in bending her knee during these daily sessions. Over time, the flexing machine began to help her knee bending and moving, even though the pain persisted.

Determined to walk as quickly as she did with her new hip, Mother persevered. She said if she succeeded in recovering from a hip replacement in six weeks, she was not going to let a knee replacement keep her down.

In Mother's medical case, there was an advantage with her hip replacement being on her right side and the knee replacement being on her left. That was a blessing in working to recover and gain strength with her two surgeries being only a few months apart.

Within four days, she was released from the hospital. This time inpatient rehab therapy was not offered. We could only assume it was a different type of replacement so the recovery process was different for her hip procedure. Since Kate had generously offered her townhouse again, Mother decided to use the same outpatient rehab group in town to be near Dr. Doubter, should anything develop or worsen.

She had a very difficult time using her knee to get in and out of the car, sitting and rising, or most any movement involving her left knee. Being released from the hospital after just four days to begin therapy at an outpatient clinic seemed a fast route for recovery. But again, Mother put her best foot forward and was determined to follow all of Dr. Doubter's therapy instructions.

Over the next four weeks, Mother proceeded to do everything as directed by her physical therapists. It was all too familiar, adding a sense of comfort, by having an established rapport with the same professionals in the same town, and staying at the same townhouse.

During the weeks of therapy sessions, Mother was required to do more "at home" therapeutic exercises than she did with her hip recovery. She continued to have persistent pain as she tried to explain to the therapists how her odd ache did not seem to be related to her knee surgery or building her muscles.

During her outpatient rehab sessions, I was invited to observe Mother during the workouts for both her hip and knee. It gave me an opportunity to learn her exercise routines so I could assist Mother on the days that she wasn't assigned rehab therapy, but still needed to keep a rigid schedule of exercises.

There was never a doubt in my mind that Mother knew there was a significant difference from the surgery pain, which she said was also associated with an unusual relentless throbbing. She was very in-tune with her own body, aches and all. Another major sign that caught my attention was that her incision was not healing correctly, which reminded me of how slow her hip incision healed.

This time, Mother experienced some infection, but it was not due to latex tape as with her hip. I made extra efforts to ensure her medical records were well documented to reflect an allergy to latex products. Seeing somebody in so much pain leaves a lasting impression, especially with unnecessary skin abrasions from bandages designed to protect the healing process.

To our surprise, there was only one exam scheduled with Dr. Doubter after Mother's first two weeks of therapy. She had to use a cane for assistance to walk. As I accompanied her to the exam room, I recall how very sincere and explicit Mother was expressing her concerns to Dr. Doubter about the persistent pain she felt in her knee. The same pain she voiced with him on "day one," as noted in her hospital medical records.

He continued to tell her the pain was normal, as her knee needed additional time to adjust from the replacement and the recovery process. When Dr. Doubter asked Mother to describe her pain, she said, "It is a persistent ache with varying degrees of pain." His reply spoke volumes through his lack of verbal or facial expressions, which we interpreted as if he had very little concern.

Dr. Doubter was repetitious in his limited responses that her replacement simply needed time to heal properly. He told Mother if the pain continued, to return for another exam and x-ray within a few weeks. Since Dr. Doubter did a superb job with her hip replacement, Mother continued to accept his medical advice.

While Mother was completing her last week of outpatient rehab therapy, I was offered the career ladder corporate job with the power company as a communications specialist. It was an answered prayer as I would be closer to attaining my professional goal to gain experience in corporate communications. It seemed as if I were following in my Mother's professional footsteps. She had retired from a power company. I obtained my informal education about energy, power, and safety from listening to Mother about her work environment for most of my youth, college, and adult life.

During my interview, this vital information was useful in answering various job skill questions from a panel of five employees who conducted the interview process. Reflecting on the questions asked; most were not inquiries about communications, but about power and energy. What I informally learned from Mother's work environment, contributed greatly to the success of the interview.

It was time for me to return to my Georgia home to make arrangements for my household to be packed and moved to a new area. There were only three more days in Mother's scheduled outpatient therapy appointments, so Poppa took over primary duties as her caregiver.

Upon completing her outpatient therapy sessions, Mother and Poppa returned home to Centre. Immediately she began experiencing additional pain in trying to climb steps, get in and out of her car… basically any action requiring her to bend her knee. As I have repeatedly shared, Mother is not one to complain.

She called Dr. Doubter's office and made an appointment within two weeks after being released from outpatient therapy. When she met with Dr. Doubter, her chief complaint was persistent pain in her left knee. She had a slight fever, which fluctuated in addition to her incision not healing as fast as expected.

After their discussion, Dr. Doubter scheduled an additional four weeks of outpatient therapy three times a week. He also instructed her to apply more tubal antibiotic medication on the small incision knee wounds where the metal alloy staples were placed. For her pain, he prescribed one 30 day dose of Mobic. Arrangements were made for Mother to have outpatient rehab therapy at a local medical facility near their farmhouse.

Mother and I both found ourselves adjusting to new lives in different settings. Each of our situations appeared to be getting worse when we were in circumstances that should have proved to be more beneficial.

When Mother was going through her traumatic hip replacement in March 2006, I was experiencing a more in depth change in my prayer life. I began digging deeper into my relationship with God. I prayed for Him to show me how to become the unique person he designed me to be, even if it meant that I was to leave the corporate position I had eagerly wanted for many years. It was a captivating process, but it was painful as well.

For years my priorities were all about living each day "expecting" tomorrow to happen, and not focusing on the current day. There was no real joy or peace embedded within my soul; yet I was perceived by many as a fun loving person - a lot like my Mother, but not nearly in the same class act!

Within months of my new "dream" job, I was praying every day, many times a day, asking God to rescue me from what seemed like a hell on earth. I had asked God to open my spiritual eyes. This was something I have never prayed about before in my life. And I indeed saw the world in a new way!

My priorities began vastly changing. My career boiled down to a "Catch 22" scenario; darned if you do and darned if you don't! My ideal "dream" job was making life miserable. As much as I loved communications on a professional level, this was the first time I began to realize I was right in the middle of what appeared to be a misfit job situation. Oddly, it didn't start out this way until I prayed wanting more of God in my life.

In reflection, I understood my work situation rejuvenated my faith in God as I became more dependent on Him than at any other time in my life. During my daily commutes to work, I listened to contemporary Christian music artists in addition to Mother's recorded piano music. Every day, I repeated my prayer for God to use me for His benefit.

All the while, something deeper within sensed I needed to return home to Centre. It was not to escape or hide from the harsh reality of the working world I was experiencing, but there seemed to be more as to "why" God was allowing this work situation to be anything but a dream job. "But what else was I to do?" I repeatedly asked as the question lingered in my thoughts from time to time.

Meanwhile, back at the farm in "Sweet Home Alabama," Mother was still routinely traveling every four to six weeks for her knee to be examined by Dr. Doubter. After completing her second continuous rehab therapy of eight additional weeks, she saw little or no significant improvement. The pain in her knee persisted and worsened.

Regularly, Dr. Doubter ordered x-rays of her knee replacement. During the follow-up exams, he repeatedly had the same dialogue: "There is nothing wrong based on my exam and the x-rays." In his dictation, the medical records revealed her consistent complaints about her knee pain.

For a short duration, he continued to give her pain medication, which she had never been one to take a lot of medicine. Over time, Mother was experiencing as much pain as she had prior to her knee replacement. Others, who had been through the same procedure, assured Mother that their replacements caused them very few problems. Her hip continued to do extremely well, so she had a difficult time trying to cope with a knee replacement that just didn't feel right ever since she woke up from the surgery.

Mother continued to follow-up with Dr. Doubter on a regular basis. During each visit he repeated the same comment after every exam and x-rays: "It's just something you are going to have to learn to live with." This went on for six months. During those six months, I also experienced unexpected and unlikely "pain" in my new job. It appeared we were both going through two different types of trials without any positive results. Mother's challenges were primarily physical and mine were primarily emotional. Two different ranges of motion were waxing and waning with constant feelings of your knees buckling under you due to pressure.

In addition to Mother's severe knee pain, another health issue surfaced. Kidney stones began on a greater and more frequent basis. She had rare occasional kidney infections throughout her life. However, nausea, fever and intense pain in the mid-quadrant of her back persisted. If her urologist was not available, the only option was for Mother to go to an ER for medical attention.

In November 2006 Mother visited an ER near her home. A standard kidney x-ray exam was completed to check for any stones lodged in the renal area causing her symptoms. This x-ray revealed something significant requiring further attention, by another specialist.

Suddenly, Mother's health details were past her "knee-tails" which were no longer the main priority. An entirely new and astonishing health issue was surfacing.

+ + +

Chapter 5

TAKING THE NEXT STEPS

It would be a birthday I would never forget; one that would have a lasting effect on my world. It was Monday, January 16, 2007; the day Mother shared her recent diagnosis of Lymphoma. She drove from our hometown in Centre to meet me where I was attending a corporate business meeting. Mother shared the details, as I sat across from her in a fast food eatery. I slowly tried to absorb the incredibly shocking news.

The ER visit in November 2006 was nine months after her hip replacement and five months after her knee replacement surgeries. Mother shared more medical information that she neglected to tell me since I was consumed with my own problems at work.

She became deathly sick, suffering from severe mid-back pain along with a fever and chills. Highly aware of her body's aches and pains, Mother already knew she was experiencing a probable kidney stone and/or kidney infection. Both renal problems had occurred on an infrequent basis throughout her life, which resulted in her being more conscious when a certain pain radiated in the kidney area of her back. This particular health issue was more frequent compared to her previous medical history of kidney occurrences.

After registering at the ER, she was placed in an examination room and her vital signs were checked. The ER physician noted her symptoms, ordering lab work and x-rays. The x-rays showed multiple stones in both kidneys. However, the radiologist also discovered a small nodule in the mid to lower lobe of Mother's right lung. He met with Mother and Poppa directing a prompt follow-up within two weeks with her primary care physician and urologist. In the interim, she was prescribed pain medication.

Within 48 hours, her urologist examined Mother and arranged Lithotripsy; a process that pulverizes kidney stones with a laser but Mother was told by her physician, this procedure does not harm the kidneys. Once the stones are crushed, then the particles are voided like tiny bits of sand through the bladder.

As soon as Mother recovered from the kidney stone procedure, she made an appointment to see her primary care physician, Dr. James[10.] After reviewing the x-ray in question, he recommended that Mother should wait a few weeks and then complete a comparison x-ray.

In December, Mother returned to have a new x-ray of her lungs. The results revealed a significant increase in the nodule as previously viewed by the radiologist. Mother was immediately referred to a pulmonologist. Based on the x-ray, it appeared Mother had a form of metastatic cancer or an equivalent health concern, due to the rapid growth and increase in size in such a brief amount of time.

She was advised to have a CAT scan or CT scan, with contrast dye intravenously injected. The CT scan provides a clearer, more detailed image than an x-ray. The contrast dye shows more definition in both lungs, particularly emphasizing the suspicious nodule or any other unusual observations.

Prior to September when Mother had another kidney stone episode, a large kidney stone had been removed in June 2006. This procedure was within three months of her hip replacement.

My previous experience working in the medical arena required doing extensive research when challenged to write medical focused copy for physicians to use as promotional materials. As Mother continued to share more information, my mind was trying to recall the specifics about Lymphoma. It was vaguely a familiar area to me. I remembered it was a respiratory disease caused by fatal cancerous cells. Of course, my obvious question was "How is this possible?" It was exactly the same thought I had when Mother broke her hip.

Nothing was making any sense. Mother had just been through hip and knee replacement surgeries with extensive recovery rehab therapy sessions with her less than best knee replacement. Now she was facing a new diagnosis of Lymphoma? I always try to make sense out of things, especially when it really doesn't seem to make any sense at all.

My move to a new town for my "dream job" made it a seven hour drive to Mother and Poppa's home. It was not often I was able to return for visits, especially with new job demands. When I did, it was more of a quick overnight stay at Mother's house so I could spend what little quality time I had with them when in route to business meetings. Between those quick pit stops, and my hectic traveling schedule throughout the southern region, I didn't have the opportunity to visit as often as I liked.

So, my birthday was the first opportunity Mother was able to sit down and talk to me about her new diagnosis. When I asked why she didn't tell me sooner in a phone call about the possibility of Lymphoma, she said, "Sharing this issue over the phone was not how I wanted you to learn about my report." Since December, this was the first occasion for us to meet face-to-face.

In 2007 my birthday landed on a federal holiday. Our communications division was required to work with the opportunity to take another day off later in the month. We were on a tight project deadline. Two major events were on my docket that day: a team meeting with my manager; and my first six-month evaluation.

The Monday team meeting was scheduled for 9:00 a.m. This required me to travel on a Sunday. When Mother offered to meet me in town where the meeting was scheduled, it seemed like a great idea since her drive was only two hours away. She knew I was going through an unexpectedly trying time at work. At the same time, Mother was going through a rough time with her knee replacement - still experiencing great pain with each step - in addition to renal problems infiltrating both her kidneys. She wasn't feeling the best in the world, but you would never have guessed it by her spirit and her smile!

Having Mother with me on my birthday made the time together extremely special. She made the trip late Sunday afternoon, arriving at the hotel within an hour after my arrival. After my corporate team meeting on Monday morning, I was scheduled to travel for an emergency preparedness exercise about four hours south.

However, Monday proved to be a longer day at corporate headquarters than I had anticipated. My evaluation was delayed for two hours due to my manager's unforeseen work emergencies. It was late afternoon before I was able to meet up with Mother and share my good evaluation report.

Mother planned for us to dine at a nice restaurant to celebrate my birthday, as she was going to share her overwhelming health report. It was getting late as rain began moving in at a steady rate. The best alternative was a decent fast food place before parting ways. I thought I had a long tiring day, but I felt numb after learning of Mother's news. I could not imagine how long her days seemed since learning about her prognosis.

As we were sitting in the fast food restaurant, I became more baffled and perplexed with the detailed news. I tried to recall if any family member had ever been diagnosed with that type of cancer on Mother's side of the family.

For generations, we were all so blessed with excellent health. However, the same predominant thought continued to trouble me, "How could it be possible for Mother to be diagnosed with Lymphoma?" She never smoked. My parents were divorced, but neither had ever smoked. Her parents never smoked. Mother was never one to be around others who smoked. Later, I learned many things could cause Lymphoma. I was just thinking of what seemed to be obvious reasons, which was simply my first reaction to this shocking news.

We sat at the fast food table for the longest time with the longest faces. Occasional deep sighs interrupted the motions of eating. It was as if we were in our own little impenetrable bubble of solitude while the hustle and bustle of the world continued. In that instance, it was if no one else existed on the planet. As my eyes glazed over with information overload, a sinking feeling started to creep into my gut. I began to recap the previous year's health mishaps in my thoughts, "A bone breaking accident followed by degenerative knee restoration. Kidney stones being removed on an almost monthly basis. How do we repair this issue?" I was exasperated and wept quietly, not able to take my eyes off of Mother. I just wanted to comfort her and give her my full attention, thinking it could be one of the last few times together, as quickly as Lymphoma can penetrate the body.

Needless to say, Mother was at a complete loss in trying to understand her latest health concern. This was my Mother, the one woman I adored and depended on for whatever life brought my way. I was petrified, but I knew we both needed to depend on our faith in God to remain strong. Never one prone to "catching" germs, or rarely ever having the flu, she was certainly not one to "lie around" and be sick.

Mother was always a poster child for determination and living a healthy life. She was the witty one who always made others laugh. But this day did not have any laughter. In fact, I don't recall even one laugh. Mother is famous for her one-liner "country-isms" and her down to earth humor. There was nothing pretentious about Patricia. Instead caring gentle smiles were exchanged as our endearing glances were as vital as our verbal conversation.

Only three years into retirement, she spent most of her time as a caregiver for her mother, before my maternal Grandmother, passed away August 2002.

Life is not about fair, but all of this certainly did not seem fair to be my Mother's fate. So many people from our hometown died from many forms of cancer. Alabama has the sixth highest cancer mortality rate in the country.[11]

I continued thinking through my laundry list of obvious cancer causing culprits besides smoking. Then I thought perhaps it was from her work environment. "Was that a possibility?" My new organization was emphatic when it came to safety issues in the entire organization, top to bottom. I wondered if Mother experienced the same training and safety components when she worked for a power company.

Among her coworkers, there were insurmountable cases of all types of cancer-related deaths. Soon after many had retired, it seemed inevitable that some form of cancer would creep into their long awaited retirement, right when it was time to enjoy life. So, it was a valid assumption to ask Mother, "Could you possibly be a victim from any environmental hazards?"

For several years, my medical marketing experiences included working in worker's compensation/occupational health as I had to learn OSHA standards. The entire scope of possible clues began kindling my thought processes as my questions rolled one after another, hoping to link something to how she could have acquired Lymphoma.

As we continued to sit in a somber state of mind across from one another, the late afternoon quickly became early evening. It was a cold wintry drizzling day as night was fast approaching. Mother and I both had long drives ahead of us, especially if the weather became worse. The doors to the fast food restaurant swung open as a brisk wind was a stark reminder of the cold temperatures as bone chilling as our conversation.

Mother began reminiscing about delivering me on a wintry day very much like this one in January 1959. As much as I would have loved to be able to focus on my birth date and the events which transpired, my entire thought processes were completely zoomed into Mother and her new health challenge. My birthday was the last thing on my mind. Instead I thought about her next birthday, exactly one week to the day of mine. "Would it be her last?"... I wondered, as a deep sadness had me almost spellbound by her unexpected news.

As our late Monday evening discussion slowed down, we soon found ourselves sitting silently. There was nothing more to be said without additional information. Continued dialogue seemed futile.

As we got up to head to our cars, we reached to hug one another. As she held me tightly, I could sense an unfamiliar fear in her. The unknown was obviously overwhelming to Mother as I sensed adversity trying to replace her faith with fearful woes!

As highly optimistic as she had always been, Mother was struggling. Dreading to part ways. I became almost motionless, centering my attention on Mother. Rarely did she reveal her true concerns. However, she began expressing her fears, sharing in greater detail.

In my heart of hearts, there is only one Patricia; and none other like my Mother. She is the epitome of unconditional love, which comes from the God, we strongly believe in. It is a rare occurrence for me to be Mother's listener. She is always the one who listens and encourages others.

As she continued to share her vulnerability, despair lingered in her voice. Tears again flowed down her face. She wiped them away as quickly as they appeared. She was not one to easily display her emotions, especially in public. "Goodbye" was not a word I wanted to voice at that time. But we had to both go our separate ways, so we again shared a loving hug.

On my long work commutes I repeatedly listened to one particular Amy Grant Music[©12] more than any other Christian music artists. She wrote the lyrics as the chorus states: "Lay down your burden, I will carry you, I will carry you my child, my child. I will carry you.[©12] " The lyrics reiterate the same message I receive when reading the Scriptures from Matthew 11:28-30[13]. Another song providing great insight described how to share your burdens with God… by giving Him your details.

I wanted Mother to hear those lyrics and listen with her heart for reassurance that God was with her in every step of this journey. But more importantly, I wanted to share how I had learned to pray "specifically" about concerns, situation, fears, etc.

It occurred to me at the last minute before we parted ways, that maybe she would want to listen to the lyrics while we sat in my car. After the songs concluded, we sat in silence. Then I turned to Mother and said, "I really have been learning more about how to communicate with God through prayer, Mother. By sharing every detail with Him, by giving God all our burdens, we can get through anything."

She smiled as tears formed, and agreed. The daunting news was discouraging after having been through so much in such a short time, but I knew God was Greater. We knew if we earnestly believed with great faith, that God would provide a way.

Not knowing what was to come; Mother said, "If this is the way God chooses to take me, then I can understand. I can cope with it, with His help."

She began crying long and hard as I reached over to hold her, not able to understand how genuinely frightened this could possibly be for her. I had never walked in her shoes. One cannot fully comprehend the toil and strain another person goes through, or the choices they make in life, even if you experience something similar… everything is unique to each person in this life.

I prayed silently to the Father, asking for courage for each of us. I sensed a gush of strength and courage began to abound within me. Somehow through it all, I knew God was in the midst of one of the most difficult times in our lives. As the surge ran through my emotionally weary body, it seemed as if everything was beginning to make a little more sense. A strong thought came to mind… "Pray with an undeniable faith." I felt confident! No matter what Mother was facing, she was going to be alright.

During the previous two years, I had returned back to my basic beliefs in God seeking His guidance. I gained more knowledge and became more committed in my personal relationship with Him. My faith was primarily fed on a renewed desire to pray intimately to the Father. My professional track record had proved my abilities as a successful seasoned communication specialist in almost every imaginable way in the natural, yet prayer was one form of communication I had not adequately achieved until this season of spiritual growth in my life. I hungered for quiet prayerful times.

Learning to express what was in my heart and wanting to share my thoughts, longings and desires with My Lord, was a new awakening! Praying specifically about details made my days less burdened.

This new insightfulness while praying alone, proved to bring peace in my life as many barriers appeared before me. I reverently shared with God the things that hindered me from being a better person. This was an integral part of my newfound prayer life. It was changing me, as I was learning to see things in a different light, becoming more patient and more aware of other's needs around me.

Reaching deeper within was personally healing. I realized how things are not always about me. Praying for others to be emotionally and physically healed was always something I believed in, but never particularly in great detail. I was raised to pray for the sick but never prayed for God to heal anyone specifically.

I learned to truly communicate with the Father versus memorized verses or habit-forming prayers, repetitively phrased. And it all began when I asked God to teach me how to better communicate with Him. This was a brand new way of expressing my soul and I was learning to speak earnestly from my heart.

Prayer became the only way I could find any peace and relief from life's stresses. I sincerely and solemnly began praying for God to please rescue me from my highly coveted corporate job. The irony: I prayed for the Lord to open up this job for me!

No matter how much I prayed for God to "fix" things at work, ultimately, it seemed things were becoming worse instead of better. It was one way He could show me that there is more to life than a career. He gave me a wonderful job opportunity, but it was coming to a close as I could strongly sense I was needed at home to be supportive of Mother's needs.

There we were, sitting in my car instead of sitting in her home around the kitchen table where we shared most of our talks. My highly coveted job was taking over my life and stealing the natural joy in living. I was going and doing - never stopping. Fast pace. Fast schedule. Great fatigue. Mother's recently discovered illness was teaching me that I needed to slow down.

Since my first day at my new corporate job, there didn't appear to be anything I did that showed promise in the organization. How ironic it would be for my new corporate power company career to find closure; not in retirement as Mother's, but in contemplating resignation. One thing I learned over the past few months through Mother's challenges, was that life is short. We should capture our happiness and enjoy it to the fullest!

When Mother and I parted ways that sad January 16 night, I knew my schedule was jam-packed for the next several weeks. I didn't know when I would be able to see her, again. She had an upcoming appointment with the pulmonologist on Friday, with tests scheduled in the following weeks. This was one of the most difficult "see ya later" moments I could recall.

I had many things to think and pray about, on my long drive that night. I was facing a real test... prayer from the heart and leaning on the faith which comes from my prayers.

More testing was ahead. As our lives paralleled, Mother and I were "taking the next steps" in our lives.

+ + +

Chapter 6

WALKING MIRACLE

With a successful hip replacement and a less than successful knee replacement, Mother was walking remarkably well, in spite of her knee becoming more tender and painful. Trying to take one health issue at a time, she forged ahead praying for strength, courage and an incredible ability to maintain her positive attitude. Her focus was on an unsuspecting health dilemma. Lymphoma was the first life threatening diagnosis for Mother. She was learning to face her troubles with deeper and more meaningful prayers to God.

After we departed on January 16, she headed north while I headed south. When I arrived at my destination, I called to see how she was doing, hoping to offer her encouraging words. As much as she was concerned about her own health situation, she was also very concerned about my work situation.

Again, she was the encourager, offering me words of wisdom to cope, as she knew how my life's work was beginning to deteriorate. Mother was well aware of how much I loved my work. She was not seeing the happiness she had once witnessed several months after I first started working. She began sensing what I had begun sensing; this job was for a short season, for whatever reasons.

In talking with Mother late that night, I was very surprised at her optimism after the sad departure earlier that evening. With so many alternatives available, with all the latest medical technological advantages, I believed she was in good hands with her specialists, as God was the Great Physician.

For the next three days, I worked closely with a state-wide communications emergency ready preparedness team, including other State of Alabama agencies and departments who would be directly affiliated with media relations in case of a emergency occurrence. This was a team of approximately 50 individuals working together to coordinate every possible response to any negative event in a timely and highly professional manner, whether it was an actual emergency, or any organizational issues involving public affairs.

We were all dedicated to ensuring the public's safety. This was the top priority. The emergency ready preparedness team was required to practice a mock set-up if an incident occurred, keeping the residents and businesses in the area notified routinely of a situation.

One of my responsibilities was to be readily prepared to work with the media in the event of an accident or incident. My company continues to be the safest and most prepared organization I have ever been affiliated with. They maintained stringent safety policies for employees at every level of work.

My work related challenges were not in any way associated with the company's incredible core values, ethics, and integrity. That's what made it the most difficult to think about leaving. I loved my job and the organization's goals and objectives for the communities.

Tuesday morning, I arrived at our work site. Learning Mother's newly probable diagnosis was hard to absorb and focus as I had to put on my PR mask to maintain a professional face and demeanor.

At times, I was required to wear a hard hat on my job. But I was also wearing my "helmet of salvation" as I trusted in God's divine protection, as stated in Ephesians Chapter 6.

It was absolutely imperative to keep anything from diverting my attention to do the very best job I could, as I worked on this very important preparation assignment. With this new job, in a completely new working environment, I had just passed my first six month's evaluation with positive marks which gave me the much needed reassurance to stay upbeat no matter what I was facing.

At the end of the day I called Mother. In her voice, I could hear her obvious concerns, as if she were slipping into a mental struggle to keep her optimistic outlook. How I wished I could be at her pulmonologist's appointment on Friday to hear firsthand the results. There were so many questions that intermittently crossed my mind. My agenda included heading back to my plant after our Thursday morning's work review briefing to report to work on Friday.

I approached my manager and shared my Mother's health dilemma with her. It was a gratifying and inspirational conversation. She said I should be with my family during this trying time. She shared a personal story from her life about a health situation when she had helped another. Sharing Mother's story seemed to touch the depths of her soul. She seemed to emphatically understand how I was struggling with the news.

My manager was supportive as I listened to her endearing words of comfort. As our friendly chat concluded, she told me to head on out as soon as the meeting was over that day and in addition, take Friday off. She said to let her know if I would need Monday off as well.

As previously stated, our team members were entitled to a make-up day with our manager's permission. Our division worked on a federal holiday the previous Monday of that same week.

Without thinking, I hugged her, as tears streamed down my face. It was the first time we had shared personal information versus work related business. I was extremely appreciative for her kindness and understanding. Her approach in my time of need will always be remembered, as she illustrated compassion sincerely from her heart.

After our briefing, I was anxious to quickly leave. I called Mother when I started on the road to her house. Her spirits were uplifted when I shared I was on my way to go with her to the doctor's appointment the next day. Hours later when I walked into the house, it felt so good to be home! We spent the rest of the evening talking and sharing. I was looking forward to crashing in my own bed, which always guaranteed me a good night's sleep.

The next morning, Poppa, Mother and I got up early and drove to the specialist's office. Shortly after our arrival, we were escorted to an unusually small exam room. As usual, Mother's wit and humor lightened the gloomy waiting time. That was a reminder of how her laughter was her way of releasing stress when we went through the hip and knee times. I wished I had inherited that trait! She was jovial, picking on Poppa, who is always a great sport. When Mother gets wound-up with one of her funny routines, she always keeps us entertained.

We waited what for seemed like two hours, which was a mere 20 minutes. We heard a tap on the door. The doctor entered as we began to exchange introductions. I instantly noticed his long facial expression, appeared distressing. He immediately sat down. His head dropped slowly with a watchful eye on Mother's medical records versus the patient. The dread of sharing news about her condition became evident as he began stammering while reporting the specifics of Mother's CT scan. He explained, "The results verified my suspicion. Mrs. Harton. There is a 99.9 percent you have Lymphoma based on your test results."

You could have heard a pin drop. The silence was deafening.

This was too surreal. I had hoped Mother had been misinformed when she first told me the news. I held onto a tiny sliver of the possibility that she had misunderstood. She correctly heard the probability the first time. This appointment revealed a follow-up to confirm what was highly suspected, and what action needed to be taken next. It was not the news we had hoped.

Granted, the 00.1 percent was in her favor; yet the 99.9 percentage appeared to carry a tonnage of weight in opposition. Immediately, my heart's desire was to pray that the test results were wrong! I asked many questions as I was trying to believe what my ears just heard.

As I have shared, before working for my current employer in the nuclear industry, I worked in the healthcare industry for over 10 years. This experience exposed me to all types of medical issues, writing health articles and interviewing physicians about new, innovative, and cutting edge medical procedures. I learned to ask detailed questions from a patient's standpoint, and requested explanations to medical procedures using layman's terminology in a non-clinical format. My first question directed to the pulmonologist, "How can you be so sure when you have not performed an invasive test or surgery?"

He replied, "We repeatedly placed your Mother's CT scan and chest x-rays beside other patients' results who have been diagnosed with Lymphoma and they match." That was a definitive answer to my only question, as all other questions escaped me after hearing his response.

It appeared Mother did indeed have Lymphoma based on his report. This was really happening. Cancer of the lungs! It just did not seem possible! Many people face learning they have some form of cancer or some other debilitating disease every day. This was all too bizarre. My mind was spinning, "Why Mother, Lord?"

Before we left the clinic, her next surgical procedure was scheduled in two weeks. On that same day, I was scheduled to be at a major internal organizational forum hours away. Missing my work event was not an option. I also believed God was going to take care of Mother, so I accepted the fact I was not going to be with her this time.

As we traveled back to the house, we were all very quiet. I sensed fear beginning to consume Mother. It was evident in her lack of actions, her dazed expression and her loss of appetite. As the pulmonologist said the words "99.9 percent Lymphoma," it created the illusion that she could not overcome this, even with a strong faith in God.

Sometimes you can't overcome huge physical obstacles, because it is not His will. "But how do you know unless you ask Him?"... I thought.

When we arrived home, Mother had the same distressed look I captured when she initially shared the news with me. Now the rest of our faces looked stoic. Being deeply discouraged about a dire health diagnosis is a normal human reaction loaded with emotions. Anyone would experience these same reactions and fears.

Being home was always a comfort to me. I hoped it would be where Mother could find solace, peace of mind, and the ability to adapt to these new circumstances. Until we received the confirmed reports, I didn't know what else I could do, much less say to her.

One of my dear friends in the ministry refers to himself as a "fixer" for others. That was also my role in life when it came to my Mother and my brother, when he was much younger. Now, I couldn't "fix" anything. But I could surely pray.

Mother and I found ourselves sitting at the kitchen table where it seemed all our world's problems were solved! I reminded her about the time when I had pneumonia several years ago. She didn't tell me until later, but she had placed me on several church lists for prayers that went out all over the county. Maybe that was the answer.

So I grabbed the phone and began to make some calls, but I didn't sense it was the best direction. Then, I suggested Mother phone one of my friends who was a Christian counselor, hoping her advice and recommended Scriptures would ease Mother's mind. When Mother hung up, I sensed that wasn't the best direction either.

Poppa had settled in the sun room to watch TV and fell fast asleep in his recliner. There we sat at the kitchen table as I noticed Mother's eyes had an even more frightening look. I knew fear would not help. Fear always makes things worse. II Timothy 1:7 states "...fear is not of the Lord." The adversary was having a good time pushing our buttons, as we appeared in a panicked state.

While sitting at the kitchen table, we were quiet and very still. Within moments, an unbelievable spirit-filled awakening surged through me, and brought me to my feet. I stood up and said, "Mother, I don't know what I am doing, but come with me!" I grabbed her hand and we headed to my bedroom. I closed the door. I suddenly knew what to do without thought and without instructions.

My bedroom was located in the front area of Mother's house. It was a special place for me. It was the room where my maternal Grandmother stayed at night until she moved in full-time for the last two years of her life.

Grandmother was a "rock" and the "true matriarch" of our family. She was the hub before Mother inherited the position. However, Mother was more like her Daddy than her Mother.

Granddaddy was a quiet man with a great sense of humor and wit. He was a strong and solid Christian with unshakable values like Grandmother. They were quite the couple. He was a farmer and she was a homemaker. Both were faithful to their belief in God, read their Bible daily, and taught all of us the importance of prayer. They were extremely active in their small country church. There were no finer people than my Grandparents: salt of the earth. So it was easy to understand how Mother was the best mixture of both parents with high standards and strong Christian values.

But don't kid yourselves thinking I had placed my wonderful Mother on a pedestal. I saw her for who she was, which included a bit of mischievousness due to the fact she was watched like a hawk as she was an only child. I believe that was the reason Mother was so close to my brother and me. Her Mother treated all three of us more like siblings. But, it made for a great friendship with our Mother.

It was this front bedroom, where Hospice brought in a hospital bed for ease in helping Grandmother with all her needs. Once that bed arrived, it would be where she remained until she drew her last breath. She was someone that never gave up easily. She sought God's will and it stayed strong until He called her home. Within a few days after Grandmother lapsed into a coma, I was strongly led to stay beside her. She was as close to me as my own Mother. I didn't think I could bare the loss of her passing from this earth; but she left behind a sign, which would later continue to reassure my choices.

The night she passed away in July 2002, she was surrounded by Mother, Poppa, Jack, Bridget, and me. All of us were closely beside her. That was exactly the way we knew she would have wanted it. I held her right hand and Mother held her left. The others placed their hands on her as she drew her final breaths of life. We all kissed her and told her that we loved her. Tearfully, as grief was already upon us, we proceeded to leave the room. Mother shut the bedroom door. Grandmother's body was respectfully left alone.

Mother made the appropriate calls notifying Hospice and the funeral home. She then went back into the front bedroom before anyone else arrived. I stood silently in the kitchen while Jack, Bridget, and Poppa went outside to the back deck.

Mother quickly came to get me and said, "You have got to see Mother." With tears streaming down my face, I said, "I can't go in there. I want to remember her just as I saw her. I know what a body looks like when life has left it after a few minutes. I really don't want to go in there." Mother insisted, "You must go. You will regret it if you don't." She was adamant, which was not like her. Finally, I asked her while still crying, "Why?" She said, "You need to see her face...you really won't believe it."

As I headed down the hallway, I followed Mother. Hesitantly, I began entering the room. Total fear was welling within me as I was almost paralyzed trying to go forward. I crept in so slowly, afraid of what... I didn't know... the unknown, I suppose. When I entered the front bedroom, I was finally able to make myself look up at Grandmother. Then I completely understood why Mother insisted upon my returning to the front bedroom.

I was in complete shock. My fears were gone. My tears were no longer sorrow, but sheer elation! Grandmother's facial expression revealed her natural smile!!! I couldn't believe it!!

I was baffled, thinking, "How is that possible!?"

When we all left the room, she had a comatose look. Her face and her mouth were partially opened, as if her tongue was lying against her right cheek.

That was not what I was witnessing! Her mouth was almost closed with her lips barely apart with just enough space for her teeth to show. It was Grandmother's natural smile! There was no way anyone could have created her natural smile!

As Mother and I stood on each side of her bed, I looked at Grandmother, then I looked at Mother. I said "Only God could do this. It is a sign that she made it to the other side!" There was no other explanation for me, or for Mother. It was something I needed to see with my own two eyes. Mother's urgency for me to witness her smile was incredible. It was so not like Mother to be insistent. But I will be forever grateful that she insisted!

Seeing Grandmother's face lifted a heavy burden of grief which was so intense because we were so close. This was a phenomenal sight for my eyes to behold!

Since that moment in 2002, I never entertained any doubts in my mind that her spirit was heaven bound! I witnessed God's handiwork and peace. Since that moment of seeing her smile, it changed my entire perspective as I placed more and more faith in my personal relationship with God. Have I got off course in my life? Of course, way off at times! But each time, God pulled me back closer to Him.

The front bedroom... that's where Mother and I were headed, as I grabbed my Bible. The Scripture laid on my heart to read was Matthew 9:23... "All things are possible to those who believe in Him." I read it aloud, repeating it several times.

The words that came to my heart were far from any request I had ever prayed in my life. I began praying earnestly like I never had before! Again, tears came streaming, as I shared specific details with God. Undoubtedly, He already knew my heart's desire. I prayed sincerely for Him to please heal my Mother. I have no idea how long the prayer lasted. And I could not repeat the words if I had to! It was not of me!

Never once did I ever ask God to specifically heal any one area of Mother's body or from Lymphoma. My request included everything that needed His healing touch! The words flowed, as if I knew exactly what to say out in the open, as if it were an announcement or declaration. It was the most mysterious prayer time I had ever experienced. Never once did I doubt in my heart or mind, that Mother was healed when the prayer was completed.

Then the Scripture that came to my mind afterwards:

> *"For I am mindful of the sincere faith within you .... For God has not given us a spirit of fear, but of power, love and sound mind." II Timothy 1:5-7*

It was fear we needed to rid in our minds! In unison, we were seeking His power, His unconditional love as we needed sound minds to go forward versus any scare tactics the enemy would try, should God bless our fervent prayers.

Mother and I had already been placed together twice when she experienced joint replacements. First with her hip surgery, and then with her knee. So, I don't believe it was an accident for me to be the one to go with her to the doctor's appointment that day.

I believed God gave me an opportunity to pray as I sought Him with every fiber of faith I had in me. And I did! When I knew I had said everything that was on my heart, I closed my prayer believing Mother was healed! Yet, it was not me that created any healing. It was God.

WHAT??? We were raised in the Southern Baptist Church!

Where did that come from???

It came from the change and commitment I made to God since I began a sharp 180-degree turn which initially started in 2005. I learned to pray with complete devout faith. I believe God hears me no matter what church I chose to attend and worship as long as they believe in the Trinity. In understanding the Trinity; it's about accepting Jesus Christ in my heart first, then building a one-on-one relationship with God, the Father. Communication from God for any Christian is through the Holy Spirit, which is what I refer to as my "gut feeling." The "gut feeling" I refer to, is when I sense the Holy Spirit nudging me to do things in my life.

As Mother sat on the side of the bed, she said, "I am healed. I know I am healed." We joyfully laughed and cried as we hugged. All I did was simply and sincerely pray my heart's desire to God.

I could not explain how I knew the words to speak or Mother proclaiming adamantly she had been healed, before I asked her how she was doing. We both believed an incredible miracle was performed.

Mother's next door neighbor returned her call. Mother had left a message sharing the doctor's report. Right after we had completed our prayer time, our neighbor said she just read the exact Scripture as we had read after our prayer time. I believed it to be a huge confirmation of God working in His miraculous ways.

Mother and I both experienced a peaceful, calming feeling following our prayer time. We knew everything was going to be better than we could imagine. It was faith. It was positive thinking.

Mother called her Sunday school teacher to see if I could share the testimony of our prayer time with their class. He was enthusiastic for me to speak. So, I shared the amazing story of Mother's current diagnosis, and our faith in knowing Mother was healed. We never doubted it. That Sunday afternoon, I drove to my home to report to work on Monday. I departed from Mother with peace deeply embedded in my soul.

Mother's 69th birthday was fast approaching and I was scheduled to participate at the company's internal training forum within the same week. So I was missing both her surgical procedure and birthday, which were just days apart. Knowing I would not see her again, until after both occasions had come and gone, it was an emotional goodbye even though our special prayer time together had greatly changed our perspectives. The fear on Mother's face was gone. Her coping mechanism of witty humor had been reinstated. Her faith was strong, and her outlook no matter the outcome, was stronger!

While I was at the company outing, Mother's pulmonologist was going inward. He believed he could reach the swollen lymph nodes with a flexible bronchoscope and mediastinoscope. For such large words, my simpleton grasp interpreted the procedure as a needle aspiration using a tube placed through Mother's nose in an effort to reach into her lungs, while under anesthesia.

Unfortunately, the spot on Mother's lungs was in the extreme lower lobe, so the pulmonologist's attempt was unsuccessful. He aspirated fluid for pathology studies from other surrounding areas. The specimens retrieved were benign. If the fluid had been malignant, then the outcome would be less optimistic, but this was indeed encouraging news.

Mother personally called me to share the excellent report. When I received her call on my cell phone, my manager was standing nearby. She saw my face light up with excitement. To my surprise, she grabbed me without any hesitation and we hugged. It was nurturing, and a super nice gesture, as I was feeling very distant not being at Mother's side.

Even as Mother crossed this barrier with encouraging news, the pulmonologist explained the immediate need for a more invasive inpatient surgery. Mother requested the general surgeon that our family had used in the past - a reputable physician we trusted and a family friend who shared our Christian faith.

The surgery was scheduled in two weeks which was close to the end of January. Prior to Mother's surgery, I came home after the company's extended forum for a long three-day weekend. Her surgical date was on a Monday. Once again, the timing was perfect to be with Mother to hear the results firsthand.

The surgeon performed a biopsy by creating a small incision in the lower right lobe of her chest and lungs. As Poppa, Bridget, and I sat in the general waiting room hospital, Jack was on standby. Within a little over an hour, the three of us were called back to a private family room. Not once since Mother and I prayed together in the front bedroom did either of us doubt God answered our prayer request, as we believed she was healed. It's difficult to describe such a tremendous and powerful feeling of knowing Mother was healed. I had no doubts she was going to be alright.

The surgeon greeted us before he sat. Listening attentively, he began, "She is doing fine. The swollen lymph nodes are in the last stages of an infection healing itself. She will not need any antibiotics, but I want to

keep her overnight due to the incision. She can go home in the morning."
I knew God transformed Mother back to a healthier state. The doctor
looked very pleased being able to deliver such excellent news! We rejoiced!
Later, when I received copies from the general surgeon's medical notes, the
documentation states...

Her mediastinotomy has shown non-necrotizing granulomas within
her mediastinal lymph nodes. I suspect that given this it is all a totally
benign process for which we have nothing to support obviously primary
malignancy. I will defer back to the pulmonologist for any further
management he deems necessary.

There was so much more ahead for Mother's life. I robustly thanked
God during my return trip home late Monday evening, recalling the
surgeon's thought provoking words... "the swollen lymph nodes are in the
last stages of healing itself..." He said no further medication was needed.

Imagining the Lymphoma had somehow changed its course, was
God's doing. He heard our prayers in the front bedroom, and from
everyone praying for her healing. As I continued to pray my heart out to
Him during my travels that night, "Please render redemption from the
culprits we had encountered as we give You praise for all things!" I was
more serious and very willing to do whatever was necessary.

Returning to work the next day brought me back to the reality of
sheer anguish. My work situation intensified. The more I grew spiritually
devoted to God's will, the more "every little" thing seemed to be coming
against me.

Have you ever thought "I am not in the right place, as much as I want
to be here... but this is not where I am to be!?!"

No matter how much I wanted to be an active worker bee in the
corporate world of communications, to accomplish my major step on my
career ladder... it just wasn't working. It was becoming evident: this is my
will, not God's will, for my life.

A couple of months earlier, I had been contacted by the CEO of a
not-for-profit organization based in Washington, D.C. It was a contract
position to develop their national marketing brand. When first approached,
I turned him down. I was flattered but had a great job. Having placed his
genuine offer aside, it began lingering in my thoughts. Maybe this work

opportunity was exactly what I needed to move closer to Mother. I could not have began to explain why the transition was offered to change jobs, even though she was declared "well" by her physicians.

However, with the flexibility in this new position to work from anywhere, once again I was led to re-open my own business and utilize my reliable laptop, which had been primarily set aside since working in the corporate world.

After a tremendous amount of thought and prayer, I did the unthinkable. I resigned from my once golden career position, and was able to start the contract work immediately. I never missed a paycheck. There were no regrets, even in the following days after my decision. I knew God wanted me to follow His direction in my life. But there were selfish ties I needed to break, such as my ego.

By letting go of my occupational dream, I had to change and rearrange my thinking quite a bit. Emotions are always intertwined with our thoughts. That is what I had been praying for Him to show me the way! "Make a way, dear Lord!"

I'll be the first one to tell you... the transition was nothing close to easy! I was willing, as difficult as it was... I was willing! Ultimately, I didn't know why He was leading me; only that it was time to go home.

There were many questions from family members with serious concerns and doubts as if I had gone cuckoo! Lost my senses! After all, I had many opportunities in life which seemed rare and unique considering my success in marketing with a non-clinical health degree. And at my age? How could I walk away at "my" age? When I knew God tapping me. I didn't flinch. I obeyed! The peace I felt was astounding!

At first, it seemed neither Jack nor Bridget understood my life's dramatic change. I imagine, I would have wondered the same if a major life-changing decision had developed in either of their lives, not understanding what may have seemed "unstable thinking." I knew I was following my heart even though many never understood how I could walk away from a worldly secure corporate job, which was a highly coveted nuclear communications position, as there are few in the U.S.

The answer was simple. I was called to come home. It was easier said than done as I had to learn to adapt to several new changes with less income, without benefits or great business trips. I knew I was being obedient to what God was leading me to do, and at some point in the near future, we would understand. I learned to grasp a deeper level in obtaining peace with patience, which was a **major first** for me.

One month to the day after my evaluation when Mother shared her Lymphoma diagnosis, I submitted my resignation to my vice president. My manager was out of town. The timing seemed right, as everything fell perfectly in place.

When I walked out of the corporate headquarters after handing over my hard earned VIP badge to enter extremely secure areas of nuclear operations, I felt as if a huge burden was lifted off of my shoulders! The closure was ideal. I gained a lifetime of experience in a few short months, both professionally and personally.

When Mother shared how relieved she was that I was coming home, it confirmed my actions. There is more to life than professional achievements and high paying careers.

My "dream job" led me to a path for the redeemed. My brother has always said, "Chris always comes out smelling like a rose." As I continue to walk through the briar patches of life, it only appears to be a rose garden. The pathway can be complex at times.... and even more difficult to explain. Everyone has to walk their own walk.

Mother's alarming health warning had, indeed, shaken me to the core. It was our private nuclear reaction as she was our nucleus... our hub... our dependable encourager... our close friend and confidant, always displaying inexhaustible bounds of love for us.

I discovered life is not about what others think you should do; but what you know you must do... follow your heart... doing what you know is right for you. I experienced the beginning of this change just before Mother fell and broke her hip.

It was time to act on what I "knew." This was another fork in my life's road. Leaving the security of the corporate world, with its excellent steady income, the house I loved, and friends I deeply cherished. It was emotionally difficult. But it was what I was led to do.

My change of pace began with a new eye opening awareness of God's grace.

It's no wonder things began breaking apart, just like Mother falling and breaking her hip. My life had to be rebuilt, with a strong foundation in God's Word. God provided an eye opener, in my walking away, which wasn't seen as a miracle in my life at that time. Soon we understood more as Mother was becoming a "walking miracle."

+ + +

Dear Father

"It appears life has taken me by complete surprise,
Things don't appear as I surmise.
When I accepted Your call to follow You
First, You taught me about Christ's Rules…
To show hospitality and love at all times,
Walk with a 'Christ-like' conscience in my mind,
Never judge one another as we think we see,
To look beyond what others can be,
To love in my heart as I, Your Child, has changed,
To take up the Cross as my life is completely rearranged,
To always forgive others before the sun sets us apart,
To pray with You before, during, and after we embark,
To pray for all who hurt with such pain,
To pray with thanksgiving as I praise Your Name.
It seems I often ask in my devoted prayers,
For safety when others set traps and snares.
You taught me not to judge any one from the outside,
But to love unconditionally as the Holy Spirit within me guides.
Please understand my Lord... I am trying to fit in,
But I am not sure I am sensing where I was to begin.
My struggles have become double-fold,
Than when I told you 'YES' oh so bold!
I fight constant hurt and suffering as the 'new' me,
Not wanting to give you less than I should be.
You, I turn to pray on my bended knees...
'Help me My Lord, as I try to live more like Thee!'
I knew it was not going to be an easy road,
But I have been caught in an undertow!"

"My Child," He said, as I heard My Master's voice…
"You always had your way, your life was your choice.
When I called for you to pick up the Cross and follow Me,
I am the One who taught you how I want you to be.
Many of my Children are not as they should live,
They don't take the time to understand or give.

They see you as they knew of you years ago,
Few are willing to see any different as you continue to grow.
It is their perspective that has not changed,
For your life with me is completely rearranged.
Now you understand the struggles that I face.
It seems most of My children have forgotten their place,
From when they too accepted My Son,
Somewhere along the way they lost what was to be done.
I know you see life differently in your new walk,
And I am glad you turned to me to talk.
Your mission is not an easy one at best,
But remember as you keep trying...I am here to do the rest.
Go forth and do your work in My will...
Life is challenging offering little warmth, with some hard chills.
I feel your pain deep within your soul,
When you said "Yes," you've discovered what you were told.
Many days are filled with hardships as you walk for My Son,
Continue to lean on Me as Your Father in the Triune.
I will never forsake thee and will always be near,
For I am with you always, as you subside your fear.
With your faith instilled in My ways on your daily walk,
Remember to keep coming to Me when you need to talk.
I will always comfort you, guide, and direct your way...
Remember I love you more than I could possibly say.
I am your Father and I will show you how to cope,
For life isn't easy when you take up the Cross of Hope."

I replied "Thank you Father for Your time this very day.
I will continue to follow You, as I choose to walk Your way.
I must I admit, I thought coming home would be with open arms,
Instead You sent me where I sense dissension and harm.
It is amazing to see so much work is to be done,
As the mission is to teach others... 'Your grace is sufficient for every one.'
In others' lives as they ponder within their hearts,
I see them gather near You, yet all seem so far apart."

DEAR FATHER

Father said, "Do your work and continue to seek Me,
For I am the One who called you wherever I need you to be."

My Master told me it would not be an easy road,
As I was prepared for hardships… but not this heavy of a load.
The decision for me was to live through God's direction,
Since within I experienced Christ's resurrection.
I struggle for happiness, truth, and tremendous repair,
As I deal with daily hurt, distance from loved ones… as I despair.
To be seen as the continued old "Chris"
"Christa" now seems to be far from bliss.
What He has asked of me leaves no option,
For I vowed to do His will, His way, as I try to function.
Christ died for me and I chose to follow in His steps,
How hard it can be as I struggle to find my pep.
I face each day afresh in His Spirit as I strive to move on,
Living as a new "me" leaving behind my "old self" to be gone.
I have lost friends and family deeply ingrained in my heart.
As I sense we might not be close again, perhaps further apart.
I will try to work harder lifting up my burdens as I pray,
Discerning in others "What could she possibly have to say?"
"Who is she to teach me anything on this… or any other day?"
As I continue to completely commit to live in His will, His way.
I asked Father, "What happened to peace and fun?
Why do I long for You to allow me to run?"
I asked Him to send me on another mission far away,
As the hurt continues to mount… almost too much to stay.
I remain home for now, doing the best I can,
Knowing without my God, I could never withstand.

Father said to me,
After He heard my plea…
"I love you, My Child, and one day we'll go,
Stay a little longer, and soon you will know.

By: Christa (Chris) Davis   August 6, 2007   3:16 a.m.

Chapter 7

GOING IN EVERY DIRECTION

For the next two years, as I continued to live in the same house with Mother and Poppa, she experienced numerous health obstacles. With little to no warning, each time, it left an indelible mark on our lives, never knowing what to expect next. The absolute truth of what was happening could have been bone chilling, and downright frightening. It was our hope in God, that kept us stronger than anyone could fathom!

Our compassion for others in pain, grew immensely. A further in-depth understanding of those suffering remained in our prayers. A new understanding of caregiving certainly made us more acutely aware of just how much patience, no matter how much you love the person you're caring for, was needed to keep your peace of mind.

Crossing paths with strangers as we sat in physician waiting rooms became an induction into a larger "family" for patients seeking answers, needing relief and consoling, as we utilized our listening skills. Our interaction with other patients was incredible. Almost everyone we met who had metal implants, were now facing health issues after their implants. It was a staggering number of people. There was no doubt; this was a larger mission that I could have ever surmised!

Mother endured so much in ways I can only share by observation, or as I was told by her. To put myself in her place was not possible, but it certainly tilted my perspective towards a deeper compassion in caring for her, wanting to protect her. After her 2006 hip-breaking fall, tremendous adjustments developed in her life. It was a jolting reminder to reevaluate the vulnerability a person can experience in an instant.

Most likely, no one ever expects a fall resulting in a broken hip, much less any tragedy, unspeakably worse!

Mother's changes, which had occurred, were not something easily written off as "old age." Her spirit and personality were still too young to categorize her as "at this age, things begin to happen." As I was personally discovering, at any age, things begin to happen!

Yet when it does… stop to realize the brokenness and necessity to repair a person's ability to cope, much less adapting to new ways of doing the simplest of things physically. Squatting was no longer an option for Mother. Bending over to put on her shoes or to pick up something she dropped was now a chore versus done with ease. Even the thought of losing her balance, now created an underlying "on guard" instinct that was never an issue prior to her replacement surgeries.

At the core of her persona, it would be a far greater adjustment when the world wasn't looking. Desolation tried many times to creep in, but hope always prevailed as her spiritual walk with God was as essential as the correct food she consumed along with a good nights' rest. Her faith gave Mother the ability to get through what she believed was a never ending battle. And she was right. Once you embark in a deeper healing, the battle never ends. A weak will becomes stronger only if you seek the Source of strength to replenish your nourishment in mind, body, and soul.

Mother was always good at hiding her insecurities and her feelings. Now they were exposed as she had no choice but to be dependent on others. A massive eclipse in Mother's wide range of physical symptoms increased. She began to have some level of pain at all times.

In the latter months of 2007 smaller problems began to surface, in addition to Mother's periodic knee pain. Getting past the fear of cancer was hindsight. Currently, our concern was slowly being diverted to her overall gradual weakness as it discreetly began to consume her energy. Everything seemed harder for Mother; from feeding herself to being herself. Nothing was easy. Her every move triggered pain in what appeared to be a faulty left knee replacement which she stated "never felt right from day one." Almost every medical test or procedure required Mother to be placed on a physician's exam table or lying on a gurney. This was a huge accomplishment considering how low her energy level had dropped. Lifting herself was not an option. Her care was almost constant as her health worsened.

I placed great emphasis for those handling Mother's body to please remember both replacements, especially while in surgical procedures requiring anesthesia. All of her medical charts were well documented about which leg and where the joint replacements were located. One wrong way turn and her knee could become worse or the ball of her hip could easily become dislocated, requiring an additional surgery.

There are successful breaks in life that can make things so much better. Then there are bone-snapping breaks that seem to take the life right out of a person.

One day you are healthy. The next morning you wake up realizing a fall caused your world to be turned upside down. The latter created a subconscious phobia for Mother as she applied her emotional and physiological brakes in her life.

It wasn't just the breaks she learned to contend with. Mother's body weakness in her upper extremity never seemed to stabilize for any length of time.

She became a regular patient in and out of our local hospitals with an influx of kidney stone procedures. Her kidney infections dated back to 1958 when she was pregnant with me. But those kidney problems were an occasional health blip on the renal radar.

Beginning in July 2006 and throughout 2007, her kidneys became more problematic on a regular basis. At times, I was amazed at how well she maintained her optimism even when challenged with all her health hurdles.

She continued to rebound triumphantly, even though Mother spent more and more time in her urologist's office, or an ER. Treatments for her renal problems increased. She experienced several back-to-back lithotripsy procedures to blast kidney stones.

Mother drank more fluids and lots of water. She had always been someone who didn't drink much at meal times, or in between. But that fact alone did not explain the calcium increase which developed stones in her kidneys, or the additional infections. Her condition worsened significantly towards the fall of 2007.

Just around the corner was Mother's upcoming 70th birthday in

January 2008. What a great opportunity to celebrate her life! After many years of her making sure all her family's birthdays were special occasions; now it was her time.

The party was planned weeks before her birth date. Tim and Tina Gossett, owned "Simply Southern," a local restaurant they operated in Centre.

The Gossetts are dear friends; actually more like family members. Tina was a former psychiatric nurse, and Tim was a teacher in the "gifted" program, and named "Teacher of the Year" in the State of Alabama during that time.

Both are marvelous people with a deep rooted love for the Father. They were instantly dear friends from the moment we met. Kindred spirits. God obviously provided the way for our paths to cross. Their endless love and encouragement, before anything truly began to transpire with Mother's health, was like having angelic support on earth for human times. And continues to be!

Mother and Poppa met the Gossetts after they moved from Georgia. My first time to meet Tim, then Tina later, was the day I resigned from my corporate job. Mother met me at Simply Southern in Centre, and said I needed to meet some wonderful people. That was an understatement!

Tim and Tina transformed one of Centre's beautifully large older homes into a decorative and exquisite dining atmosphere with excellent food and special amenities such as linen tablecloths. Those types of services were a far cry from what Centre folks were accustomed to at the local burger places.

At Tina's suggestion, "Simply Southern" would be the perfect place for such a special festivity. Tina and Mother became dear friends the instant they met.

Tina recalled the first time she met Mother; "I always tried to seat her at a certain table so I could join her to chat for a few minutes between helping other customers. Patricia has such a sweet spirit with a genuine graciousness and wonderful nurturing appeal. She is so easy to talk to because she is a good listener, giving good solid advice. Since we attended the same church, I was always uplifted by her incredibly talented gift for playing the piano, as if it were a privilege to hear her music. In getting to know her as a friend and mother figure, I sensed God's presence in our conversations, which is a rare quality."

Since I was old enough to understand people's conversations, I have always heard so many similar compliments about my Mother, and her gift for playing the piano. Most everyone Mother meets, such as Tina, always shares the same view. Both ladies are faithful with an endearing spirit, tender and compassionate, illustrating a true sense of God's faith in His daughters.

As Mother's birthday was fast approaching, it seemed fitting when Tina initiated the idea to celebrate her birthday at "Simply Southern." Since Mother was not feeling well at the time, we hoped this event would put some pep back in her step with a fun and enjoyable party. This 70th birthday celebration seemed to be the perfect time to have an uplifting gathering!

While I helped to coordinate some of the surprise arrangements, Poppa ordered his beloved wife, a beautiful bouquet of fresh cut flowers. Tim and Tina made special food preparations of Mother's favorite dishes. They reserved the entire restaurant so it would be a private party.

Our surprise plan was for Poppa to encourage Mother to eat out that night since it was her birthday. As soon as she was to arrived and saw so many familiar faces dear to her, we would announce that it was her party and the festivities would begin. What a great plan!

Mother's birthday arrived! Everything was ready to roll at "Simply Southern," except the birthday girl. Instead she became sick during the day and by early afternoon; she was rolling on a gurney from the ER to the OR for a kidney stone removal blocking her right kidney. She was in serious pain and perhaps the sickest I had seen her in a long time.

I didn't have the heart to tell her about all the special birthday plans while she was heavily medicated, waiting for surgery. Although I knew Tim and Tina would certainly understand, I dreaded notifying them with the disappointing news. In less than two hours, Mother was expected to walk in the restaurant, enjoy the festivities and fellowship. No way was it going to happen that night! The surprise birthday party had to be cancelled. And the surprise was on us!

Once Mother recovered, I shared the details of the party. She replied, "They should have gone on without me and enjoyed themselves!" How selfless. How incredible. She could have said anything at that moment, but she sincerely wished happiness in a time of dire distress. Her outlook on life, whatever the obstacles, continuously uplifted my spirits!

As time progressed Mother had increasing problems in her left knee. The irony of her deciding to have a knee replacement was due to her fear of falling again. After her hip incident, increased weakness continued in her left knee. Before her knee replacement, it would give way without warning. That was the only reason she quickly decided to plan for another joint replacement, so soon after her hip replacement.

Her scheduled visits to Dr. Doubter averaged every six to nine weeks. During each visit, the same comments and test results were given after ordering x-rays and occasional lab work for a possible infection. He said the x-rays always showed her knee replacement to be intact, and the lab work always came back normal. This would have been exceptional news if her pain had not become increasingly worse.

Dr. Doubter seemed to be patient as he listened while Mother repeatedly described the intensifying pain located about four inches below the lower knee implant, which was tender to the touch. Her other main concern was her unstable mobility. It was evident that her knee was becoming more of a hindrance.

Poppa and I both felt something must be wrong, even with her good reports with the x-rays and lab work. Each time we addressed this issue with Dr. Doubter, his reply sounded like a recorded message, "Sometimes knee surgeries or other type of replacement surgeries don't always alleviate the pain. It's just something you will have to learn to live with."

Mother continued to be as active as possible. Without any further signs of redness, fever, or a rash, she never had a classic symptom as listed on most any reliable medical source for a failed or allergic reaction to a metal implant or replacement. The outside of her knee appeared to be normal looking. The previous fever only lasted a few days and the incision healed within 10 days after her replacement surgery. However, only

Mother knew exactly how her knee felt on the inside. We knew she was not just complaining to have something to say.

She continued to be faithful in following Dr. Doubter's directives. He seemed concerned with Mother's best interest at heart. Keeping that in mind, we never questioned his expertise… until later. For some, it would appear to be obvious to consult a second orthopaedic surgeon's opinion. With Mother's health issues started to vary, it seemed best to stay with the original surgeon.

Her physical ability was declining as her pain escalated. I began wondering if there was any correlation with all of her health issues. However, the progression was slow at best, making it extremely difficult to connect any specific cause.

It reminded me of the analogy Mother often used about a frog in water. When the frog is first placed in a pot of water on a stove, the temperature is not noticeable. As the temperature increases, the frog adjusts to the slow warmth of the water until it soon becomes hotter. Then it's too late, as the frog realizes he is in hot water. That described Mother's situation.

At this point, we were not aware of "revision" surgeries for metal joint replacements, which is the next surgical procedure if an implant fails due to a medical reason or health condition. We were not even aware of faulty devices! During this time, there wasn't any news or alerts of possible faulty joint replacements.

Since returning home, I began to see other signs and symptoms that I never would have been able to observe if I had not been living under the same roof. She was not doing nearly as well as I expected at this point with ongoing renal problems, and a joint replacement that didn't function as well as her hip replacement. Also, Mother began having numerous headaches, almost on a daily basis.

After witnessing her invigorating and awesome comeback from a hip replacement, to discover four months later that she was so slow in rebounding from her knee surgery, it was not making any sense. Continuing to pray for God to show me how I could help, the situation was becoming increasingly frustrating.

I knew my returning home was for more than just any one issue needing to be addressed because the God I serve, is a matrix. Often times, I refer to Him in an analogy like the pattern "plaid." He is everywhere at the same time, with crossing counterpoints weaving through the very fabric of our being, our world, and our entire universe.

Every day, Mother started with a better outlook, with little to no complaining. It was inspirational to witness someone who appeared to be experiencing many health oddities. She was told so many times by Dr. Doubter that her knee problem was "something you will have to live with." I believe she resolved herself to this fact, and this was how it was going to be.

She required more time to rest beyond her already slowed down daily routine as she was forced to adapt to her body becoming increasingly weaker. Resting or napping, was never a part of her makeup or habit. Now it was a ritual in the afternoons if she were home. This was quite an adjustment for me, knowing her as well as I did. At first, I thought it might be Poppa's daily nap time influencing Mother. Before her hip replacement, Mother was never one to sit still. Poppa was the only one who required a mid-afternoon snoozing refresher.

Of course, a hip break is a traumatic injury which can change someone's active lifestyle. But I kept sensing there was something more, a silent underlying factor still contributing to her demise. I often found the happy couple reclining in the sun room while watching TV with their eyes closed. I wondered if they left TV on, so no one would hear the snoring duo rattling the mini-blinds.

Having lived further away from home for the past few years posed a whole new way of adjusting to Mother's new leisurely scaled down routine. Life's tempo slowed down a bit for her, with the exception of when she played the piano for church or community functions. I later realized her "slowing down" process was a key indicator, or clue to her unknown health issue, which was lurking within, somehow attached but not showing itself.

Mother continued to need more care from her urologist. Kidney stones, kidney infections, and urinary tract infections were occurring more frequently. Each procedure also required a great deal of medicine to stop the infections. She learned to endure the severe pain, fevers, nausea and chills, which sometimes triggered a migraine. But every time her body went through another illness, her overall health declined as her weakness escalated. My concern was the frequency of the same problems which continued to emerge.

As her scheduled lithotripsy procedures also increased, the more concerned I became for the healthiness of her kidneys enduring the blast of large stones. Her urologist reassured me that the process did not harm her kidneys. Another method was a stone retrieval called a "basket" procedure surgically performed in the outpatient surgery department. The number of both kidney procedures was truly astonishing!

As I have shared throughout this true story, Mother has been a pianist for decades. Her talent had developed a great deal of muscle strength in exercising her arms, wrists, hands and fingers. She could play the piano two to three hours without stopping. No one would argue that her muscle tone and flexibility were stronger than the average person. So what were we to think when all ten of Mother's fingers, her hands and wrists became extremely weak?

The increased weakness progressed almost overnight! It was difficult for her to simply lift a plastic bottle or a glass to drink. Straws became a necessity. Yet, she continued playing the piano enormously well, even though her endurance level was at a much lower threshold. All during my life, I listened to her play when it seemed to be her way of expressing herself. I saw her playing as a sign of hope! But imagine... playing the piano extremely well, while battling to feed, bathe, or dress herself. Mysterious.

Poppa and I were sitting at the kitchen table one morning when we noticed Mother's difficult attempt to lift her hand to feed herself had become worse. At first, I thought she might be developing Multiple Sclerosis as I had viewed in others, diagnosed with MS. Her movements had become debilitating but her need to recognize this weakness had been scoffed by her own thinking. Until she could no longer deny she had some sort of a major health concern, which would require further testing, our hands were tied! Poppa and I had not discussed her condition with, or without, her. We simply looked at one another and knew she needed medical attention.

Mother finally agreed it was time to check further into the development of her hands weakening. She was referred to a hand specialist in Birmingham. After several visits and extensive tests including lab work and nerve conduction studies, we learned she did not have carpal tunnel, which was highly suspected. She was then referred to another specialist in the same medical group. After completing Mother's physical dexterity examination, both specialists began to collaborate because they were perplexed with Mother's test results.

We were told Mother's weakness was called distal, meaning it was away from her body. Proximal muscle weakness is located near the main trunk of the body, as in the upper arms and shoulders. If Mother had been diagnosed with proximal weakness in her arms, her condition would have been easier to identify. However, the odd route in which Mother's nerves and muscles were becoming weak, first in her hands, created a strange relay based on the body's anatomy from the brain and spinal cord as nerve and muscles move away towards the body's extremities.

Mother was referred to a neurologist, Dr. Young[14]. He specialized in unusual neurological problems. It was several weeks before she could be seen by Dr. Young as a new patient. However, Mother continued to deal with her urologists with frequent kidney related problems and visits to Dr. Doubter for knee replacement concerns. We spent hours traveling and sitting in waiting rooms, but again, it was in those times we found solace in talking with other patients. It was well worth the trips as those times brought healing to our souls.

As for my world, besides going in different directions carrying Mother and Poppa from here to there, my small marketing business remained stable, which kept me busy enough to pay my bills. Under the circumstances, it was not going to grow much past that point since my time was primarily increasing to help Mother. I continued applying for jobs on a steady basis at various places in the area, trying to get back into the work environment.

No matter how many doors I tried to open for a new opportunity, it was not in the cards. Not yet. To give you more insight on how jobs have quickly opened up for me in the past, my brother Jack has always made the statement, "You are like a cat, always landing on your feet." This time, I couldn't get a pounce, much less get off the floor!

I knew deep within, God had a reason for keeping me at home. Until I came to terms with His plans, I struggled with emotional pain while Mother struggled with primarily physical pain. It seemed obvious by now that it was a higher "design" for me to be at home for her. This gave me a process time to heal from old dusty childhood wounds, I had kept hidden away for decades.

Mother became more dependent on me for driving and doing chores, as her abilities became increasingly limited. She's such a private person. Not many people knew how much she had to depend on others.

As time marched on, we continued to pray for Mother's health. My prayer repeatedly became, "Dear Father, please reveal the culprit." Living in a house without a lot of privacy, I was drawn to make a place in my walk-in clothes closet for a private prayer closet. Oddly enough, when I returned home I was led to move into the middle bedroom of the house. As I have shared, the front bedroom had always been "my room." The middle bedroom was "Jack's room."

Although we had both grown up and moved on, we were still siblings that jokingly had territorial spaces as to who slept where; who sat in what chair at the kitchen table... and the same for the parking places in the yard. This unspoken rule also applied to which seat was who's in the den for a movie, or cheering on the Tigers as we enthusiastically watch Auburn University football games.

It was an integral part of our sibling friendship, which Jack and I had previously shared with one another before embarking on new lives with our spouses. It made it more fun, than annoying. Now, my close-knit friendship with him was on shaky ground, as he did not understand at the time what I knew to be true. My place was home. I have no doubts his concern was warranted from a natural state of mind due to my decision to resign away a long career. In time, I prayed he would come to understand, it was God leading me here.

Although, Mother was able to use her hands to some small degree, her dependency increased on my assistance to help her. Any attempts to do any tasks which required lifting and coordination were now disregarded as it became a tremendous effort. We prayed this situation would only be temporary as Mother's health was quickly spiraling downward. To our amazement through it all, she was able to continue playing. The piano became her sanctuary to those who watched her play magnificently while struggling to make it to the piano bench. We were richly blessed with sweet sounds transpiring peace and tranquility as if they flowed directly through her from heaven.

Throughout the winter, spring and summer of 2008, Poppa, Mother and I became more of a steady threesome with revolving physician appointments or procedures. Even though, I longed to be elsewhere... many times... it was obviously apparent my place was home. It became easier to adjust. My roommates were two wonderful people with great dispositions, as they napped most of the day! Life was no longer about "me" but learning to serve Him, by assisting others.

Without much warning, it was Poppa's turn to have health problems in the midst of Mother's problems. In spite of it all, they both kept their spirits up and remained light-hearted about everything. If they were ever down, they never expressed any negativity around me. Their pleasant personalities were a blessing. Something I could certainly learn more about on a personal level. That is where God helped me to "mellow" out from the rat race of the work world of which I had become accustomed, seeking a little cheese to go with my whine! Yet, I loved it! Or did I?

After several physician visits, we learned Poppa had prostate cancer. I printed off an assortment of reading material and diagrams so Poppa could understand what was transpiring with his body. The information proved to be extremely helpful, providing options in selecting a specialist.

Similarly, as Mother epitomizes Christianity, so does William Thomas Harton. He demonstrates it every day. So my concern for his well-being was as serious to me, as if he were blood-kin. He deserved the best medical technology available for his prostate cancer treatment plan with a medical staff demonstrating compassion and concern.

After reviewing the information and alternatives I had researched for prostate cancer procedures, Poppa realized a second opinion would be well worth his time. Late one night, Mother watched a news segment featuring an innovative cancer radiation machine. The procedure offered less radiation per dose than other existing treatments. The next morning, as she shared the information I began exploring facts about the machine, the outcomes, the doctors, and where they were located.

Living in Centre gave us a choice to go either east to Atlanta, Georgia, or head west to Birmingham, AL. Both metro areas offered the new procedure. Either way was about the same driving distance. Mother and Poppa chose Birmingham, mainly because the traffic was less of a hassle than heading towards Atlanta. Their positive attitudes and willingness continued to move them in the right direction.

The specialist in Birmingham was a female. I wasn't sure Poppa would be comfortable being seen by a female physician. He was naturally a bashful fellow. Yet, after they met face-to-face, he believed she was the best choice. Of course, she was young and attractive, "but a very skilled physician who knew her stuff," Poppa told us. Mother and I found it amusing, and certainly enjoyed any levity that came our way!

The specialist explained more about his condition and proceeded to check his status as a candidate. His prostate level and other factors met all the qualifications to be accepted as a new patient. It was wonderful news since this option offered less radiation per dose. This lessened the chances of him becoming physically ill from the treatments.

The hospital provided special temporary living accommodations at a place called "Hope." Mother and Poppa could stay together throughout his eight weeks of treatment. The atmosphere was very welcoming with access to the rooms with an elevator. In addition, there was a large kitchen area with food lockers for the patients, spouses or family members. The rooms were furnished nicely and the staff was very gracious.

Meals were provided by different church and community groups, three to four nights a week. To make things even more accommodating, "Hope" was located close to the hospital. It was a perfect arrangement for Poppa and Mother. Since I was living at the house, I took care of the animals and household chores, which included some cooking, cleaning, washing, ironing, etc., for three people. So, I was really looking forward to enjoying less responsibilities while relaxing, studying, and working on my client projects.

The first treatments were to begin the second week of October 2008. Poppa would be finishing up his last treatment the week before the Thanksgiving holidays. Everything fell into place. I believed Mother and Poppa were looking forward to some alone time, also.

Although, Mother was still having problems with her left knee as it continued to be painful, she was extremely supportive for Poppa versus thinking of her own health issues. "Just like Peas and Carrots," Gump[15] clichés best described the hearts of the Harton couple still sweet on each other.

During the first week, I enjoyed complete solitude in the house. I turned up the music a bit, and let the mini-blinds shake as the bass sounds rumbled. Freedom - a "college break" for an overgrown kid!

Unfortunately, Mother was not having near as much fun. Another kidney episode came about on Tuesday, the very first full day after their arrival in Birmingham. Mother said the pain radiated down her back and to her right side. She thought seriously about going to an ER. Although, the hurting was bearable, she decided to find an urologist in the medical complex adjacent to the hospital. She was successful with her choice. The specialist prescribed pain relief medications and antibiotics immediately on her first visit. By Thursday, her pain had completely vanished.

Thursday night, the phone rang at 11:15 p.m., which was late for phone calls at the house. Before checking the caller ID, I thought it was probably Mother needing medical treatment in the ER. Instead, it was a nurse calling from Centre's nursing home, where Poppa's sister-in-law Dorothy (his deceased brother's wife) had just begun living in the nursing home within last two weeks. She had become an adopted "aunt" and member of our immediate family before Mother and Poppa were married. They had visited Dorothy before leaving Centre, sharing their plans of returning home on the weekends for the next eight weeks. She knew I was available should she need anything, along with Poppa's oldest son, Rick[16], and his wife, Rachel[17].

Dorothy was quite the shining personality hued with laughter and plenty of short two-liner jokes. It was her way of starting a conversation, but primarily camouflaging her nervousness when going to physician exams.

Dorothy and her parents had lived in California in the early 1940s. That's where Dorothy met Poppa's brother Maurice. They fell in love and married. At the time, Poppa and Maurice were in the U.S. Navy and both were assigned to the U.S.S. Manchester.

One of the most memorable times Poppa recalls, was while he was in the Navy, a movie star came aboard their ship for publicity photographs while in port. Of all the men aboard dressed in their best decked Navy uniforms, Poppa lined up on the rail entrance of the gang plank.

Without any warning, Marilyn Monroe laid one heck of a kiss on Poppa's check while a photographer snapped his unforgettable moment in time! Mother claims to this day that Poppa never washed off that spot on his face! Dorothy still reminisced about those days often sharing stories about her beloved Maurice.

So when the nurse called and said Dorothy was being transported to Centre's ER, I was caught by surprise. With Mother and Poppa in Birmingham, I knew my place was to be with Dorothy. I called Poppa, changed clothes, and headed to town. By the time I arrived at the hospital, the ER staff said Dorothy had been sent to a private room. Quite honestly, I expected her to be sitting up, telling one of her funny jokes, ready to reassure her that I was close by.

When I first arrived, I approached the nurse's station asking for Dorothy's room number. The floor nurse warned me, "She is in bad condition." However, I didn't anticipate her being near death. To my unexpected shock, this vibrant lady I had come to know and love over the past few years, was laboring heavily with each breath. I was caught completely off guard seeing her in this condition.

As I approached her, it was obvious she was in a coma. This was an all too familiar scene as I had been with my maternal Grandmother while she was in a coma, and others during their life's last moments. I sensed it was just a matter of hours before she would succumb based on her heavy breathing, but only God knew when her last breath would be. There was no doubt where I was needed. It was midnight. She had previously told our family she did not want to be left alone when she died.

She believed and trusted in God. In our previous conversations, we had many talks about current events and Christianity. We had good lively discussions. She was more educated about the Bible than one may have surmised. She was not a regular church member, but that isn't a requirement to get into heaven. Dorothy knew it's a personal relationship with God.

Staying with her through the night was not a Good Samaritan act; it was because I loved her. For me, it was important for her to know she was not alone, just as she requested. During her comatose stage, the nurses and I tried to get her to acknowledge our presence. But she never responded.

I remembered when my Grandmother Williamon was drifting in and out of her comatose state, I asked her to open her eyes for me or move her hand… anything so I would know she could still hear me. Within a few moments, she slowly opened her eyes. Grandmother confirmed she could hear me. I believe she could hear everything until she drew her last breath. Based on that experience I never doubted that Dorothy could hear me, even if she didn't open her eyes or move a finger. So, I talked to her just as if she were sitting up and responding.

From time to time, I would step out in the hallway to call Poppa and Mother, as they asked me to keep them monitored on her situation. They offered to drive home right away, but there wasn't anything more that could be done. Mother and Poppa had already shown Dorothy unconditional love in many ways for several years.

They decided to stay in Birmingham for the night. Poppa would have his last treatment for the week early the next morning. They planned to return to Centre on the weekend for possible funeral arrangements. Poppa knew I wouldn't leave Dorothy's side, as he requested I call him every hour to give a status on her condition.

At 6:10 a.m., on October 9, 2008, Dorothy Harton passed. Before her last breaths in the final few minutes, I placed my arms around her head and neck, holding her as best I could. She loved hugs. I wanted to make sure she was held and loved as she departed from this world. Her service was on Saturday. Mother and Poppa returned Sunday afternoon to be in Birmingham for Poppa's treatment Monday morning. It was a hurried weekend for the "Peas and Carrots" couple.

Once again, the phone rang. This time it was early, about 6:00 a.m. It was Poppa calling. Mother was in the ER for the reoccurring back and right side pain she experienced the previous week. Her symptoms abruptly stopped just long enough for Dorothy's funeral proceedings. Since Mother had an amazing track record of kidney problems in the past two years, the ER physician also believed that was her health issue, once again.

Part of the medical center's protocol was to place a heart monitor on every patient. That was one area I felt certain she didn't have a health concern. Mother was in a great deal of pain with a slight fever so the ER physician admitted her.

Once again, there was no doubt where I was supposed to be. My laptop and Blackberry® gave me the necessary tools required to get my clients' work accomplished. Two years later, again, Mother and daughter at another hospital. I was beginning to understand more of "why" I was led home.

Many different decisions were fast approaching as we found ourselves going in every direction!

+ + +

Chapter 8

HUGE FEAT!

Have you ever wondered if perhaps your professional calling in life was something completely different than the career path you chose? Since 2006, I had gained a tremendous amount of practical health care skills as a caregiver by watching and learning, in becoming more aware of the human body from a medical-clinical perspective. It' came as no surprise when thoughts began to run through my mind about focusing on a specific area in the health care field, such as nursing.

In keeping our spirits up, we tackled each day with a new determination to seek solutions in spite of the mysterious onslaught of health problems, as Mother was admitted to a major hospital facility in Birmingham. She stayed determined, strong and championed every step of the way, never allowing any setbacks to detour her positive mindset.

When Poppa called me at 6:00 a.m. from the ER in Birmingham, I packed my belongings. It didn't take long to learn what essentials were needed when staying in a hospital, as I clearly remembered from our experiences.

I was heading out on yet another nomadic escapade. Packing efficiently has never been one of my strong suits. But, that was about to change to keep my bag light. Only necessary items were carried, or what I considered necessities, which included: my pillow; a favorite blanket; my warm Patagonia® pullover for times in the hospital waiting areas which are always cold; and my tooth brush. The cell phone was a given! Most anything else can be scrounged at the hospital or purchased at a nearby drug store.

My next stop was our local veterinarian to make boarding arrangements for our house pooch, Skippy. Then quickly, I was on my way to Birmingham arriving by mid-morning.

When I entered Mother's hospital room, the bed was empty. Not a welcoming sight. As I looked over at Poppa without uttering a sound, he immediately said she was taken for further testing.

Her symptoms included nausea, vomiting, and severe pain in her right side. The ER physician assigned Mother's care to an experienced general surgeon, Dr. Sue Wallershaw[18]. Just before Mother returned to the room Dr. Wallershaw came to share the tests results. The surgeon's primary concern was Mother's acute upper right quadrant where abdominal pain was radiating to her back. There were several suspicious possibilities; one primary possibility included a gallbladder attack.

Since Mother was examined by an urologist at a nearby medical complex for a kidney infection the previous week, Dr. Wallershaw placed Mother in his general care, until further testing determined the exact problem.

In the meantime, an ultrasound was performed to determine if the gallbladder was a factor. The results were negative. Since the pain persisted, a CT scan with contrast dye was the next test. The results revealed a questionable stone in the neck of her gallbladder duct in addition to multiple small stones seen in both kidneys.

The next analysis was a HIDA[19] (hepatobiliary iminodiacetic acid) scan. This test helps track the production and flow of bile from the liver to the small intestine. Bile is a fluid produced by the liver that helps the digestive system break down fats in the foods eaten. A HIDA scan creates pictures of the liver, gallbladder, biliary tract and small intestine, using a radioactive chemical, or tracer, that helps highlight certain organs on the scan.

Several years ago, I had a HIDA scan before my gallbladder was removed. Having experienced this procedure firsthand, I learned this test tries to emulate the same effects as a gallbladder to reproduce the pain. Mother's HIDA scan test results led Dr. Wallershaw to believe Mother had a diseased gallbladder.

However, the first priority was the kidney stone which needed to be removed surgically by the urologist. He believed a probable cause was one small to mid-sized stone visible on the CT scan.

The next day, Mother was taken to surgery. However, the kidney stone was not visible. It's my understanding, from Mother's primary urologist, renal stones can surface or move within the kidney making it possible for a small one to easily hide.

After the surgery, we were told there was not a stone large enough to cause the symptoms Mother was experiencing, especially since the stone easily retreated making it unable to be removed. As the process of elimination ensued, Dr. Wallershaw proceeded to focus on the gallbladder as the potential source of Mother's recent symptoms.

I arranged my sleeping space for the first overnight stay in Mother's spacious hospital room. Once again, with laptop in tow, I worked after Poppa was safely tucked away for the night in his private guest room, and Mother was sound asleep.

Another wonderful amenity offered where Poppa went each day for his treatments, was a guest transportation service from the hospital to the guest lodge. This was a huge help as it allowed me to remain by Mother's side, and gave us peace of mind knowing that he was safely entering a and exiting buildings at all hours. Once again, our needs were well taken care of, as our prayer list was growing!

To my surprise, my sleeper space was not a chair but a short couch. When pulled from the end, it created a somewhat longer semi-comfortable bed. At least I was able to stretch out full length, versus feeling if I barely moved, my bed would snap back into a chair position. While trying to rest, it's no fun to be tackled quite unexpectedly! I've wrestled with those contraptions, and the recliner usually wins!

This arrangement provided adequate rest when Mother didn't need my assistance. My first concern was her well-being and my attention was heightening, as her "wellness" was becoming further from reality.

Additional complications developed, which delayed Mother from getting immediate relief from a gallbladder surgery. She began having more severe tenderness in her right side as her fever began rising. Further lab work verified an elevated white count: a sure sign of infection. By all indications, Dr. Wallershaw said it was evident an infectious gallbladder was the culprit of her current illness.

Over the next seven days, Mother's health condition developed potentially frightening symptoms. With a fluctuating fever, there was no sign of it reducing to a normal temperature until the inflamed gallbladder was "cooled down" - a medical term used by practitioners. Mother was given stronger antibiotics intravenously 24/7 until her gallbladder "chilled." Once the inflamed organ was ready to be surgically extracted, Dr. Wallershaw would remove the diseased gallbladder by a laparoscopy procedure versus creating a four inch incision.

The risks were substantially higher considering all the details, as Mother's fever remained high. The strong antibiotics did not begin slowing down her inflamed gallbladder. Mother was monitored closely by the physicians and nurses. This should have been a major clue to her other health-related issues.

Her diseased gallbladder appeared to come from nowhere without any previous symptoms. Now, it placed her physical health in a vulnerable situation. If her gallbladder erupted, the infection would go into her chest cavity creating toxicity to other organs, which Dr. Wallershaw explained explicitly. She kept an especially close watch on Mother's weakening condition.

Although Mother received the absolute best care available, she was the absolute sickest I had ever seen her. Even with the best care, there was nothing else that could be done, except pray and watch. "Miserable" would not begin to describe how terrible she felt throughout this entire ordeal. She was unable to keep any food down. I kept cool wash cloths on her almost 24 hours a day. Mother was in and out of consciousness, as she would fall into a deep sleep.

She continued to lose everything she tried to eat or drink when I could get her to attempt a bite or two, or drink a few sips of liquids. Until her white blood count was in an acceptable range, Mother's gallbladder was not stable enough to be surgically removed. The longer the inflamed gallbladder stayed in an "angered" state, the more antibiotics were being pumped into her increasingly weakened body.

I kept thinking…. "There 'must' be another underlying problem. What are we missing?" However, we had to deal with first things first, before going in another direction searching for an underlying diagnosis. Mother's current health condition was the exact opposite of the health she had enjoyed for so many years. And it seemed to happen so quickly. Yet, there wasn't a medical specialist that could link the many physical oddities her body continued to encounter. With so many things coming against her at once, the thought kept reoccurring; there had to be something more.

Mother's arms and hands were repeatedly stuck with I.V. needles often due to her veins collapsing, or a vein bursting shortly after a new I.V. was attempted. It was crucial for her to continue receiving fluids and antibiotics intravenously. Prayer was the only open vessel working. It was distressing, as she appeared to be far sicker than Poppa and I cared to acknowledge to one another.

Finally, her left arm had a vein that cooperated. But once again within an hour of the I.V. beginning to carry the much needed medicine and fluids throughout her body, I noticed a large swelling bulge developing under her skin, as I was continuously trying to keep her wiped down with cool cloths.

I called for the nurse. She said Mother's veins were no longer viable for a successful I.V. insertion after so many unsuccessful attempts to start new ones. Mother would have to endure an uncomfortable "mini" surgery performed in her hospital room for a peripherally inserted central catheter (PICC) into her right arm. A PICC line is a tube placed directly into a large vein, allowing separate I.V. receptors to be used externally providing a smoother and less painful process of administering meds and/or drawing blood.

However, a physician's order was needed to have a PICC line inserted. At that moment, Dr. Wallershaw walked into the door of Mother's hospital room on a Sunday afternoon! She was a God-send! She agreed with the nurse's assessment and ordered the procedure immediately. It was a relief and answered prayer.

In order to replace her I.V. access, During her mini-surgical invasion, I left my "home away from cubby space" for about three hours. That was where I had been for days, other than going downstairs to the cafeteria or assisting Poppa.

I escaped the building to go outside for awhile. It was the third week of October. The weather had cooled off considerably since the last time I was out for any length of time. It was a nice breather and so refreshing!

When I returned from my short outing, Mother seemed to be doing much better. Just the thought of her not having to be stuck repeatedly with I.V. needles was comforting to know.

Consequently, Mother continued experiencing knee pain when she exited or entered her bed, or did any walking. She managed to take care of her personal needs as best as she could even though the weakness in her arms and hands persisted. At times she was stronger, able to feed herself, hold a phone, and drink from a cup using a straw. But her body was also filtrated with strong antibiotics! A clue we should have suspected.

At one point, while I was sleeping, "Miss Independent" was maneuvering around trying not to get her I.V. tube kinked between her arm and the I.V. machine. Unfortunately, she fell backwards onto the bed, landing on her left wrist. Thank goodness the x-ray showed nothing was broken; just bruised.

I asked Mother to please tell me when she needed help to get her in and out of the bed, no matter what time, day or night. Her reasoning was that she knew I needed to rest, and didn't want to bother me. It was a sweet thought, but now was not the time for her to try anything without assistance, especially with her knee giving way, periodically.

Hoping things might start settling down, Mother and I were unexpectedly awakened one night as a nurse quickly entered her room turning on the overhead lights. They began checking her vitals, stat! I woke up clueless as to what was happening, and looked over to see Mother was just as surprised.

The heart monitor was still attached from when she was first admitted from the hospital's ER. The heart monitor at the nurses' station was displaying that Mother's had fibrillation in the lower part of her heart chambers. Her heart rate was 39, which we were told was too low. When it dropped, the nurse's display monitor sounded an emergency alarm. Mother did not have any chest pain, no breathing problems, or felt any different than she had - so we tried not to panic. We continued to pray together each night for Mother's condition to get better. I continued to pray for God to "please reveal the culprit."

The next night, everything was fine with no surprises. However, the following night, the same scenario happened again. Without Mother realizing it, Poppa and I became seriously concerned. She had experienced two separate low heart rates in the 30s, within 48 hours. Mother's heart rate dropping into the low 30s was a strong indicator of a possibly of heart failure, which Dr. Wallershaw later explained to us. This scenario was not something I ever imagined would had happened!

Mother did not have a history of heart problems, no shortness of breath, and always passed her treadmill stress tests without any complications. Everything was way off base for Mother's past medical status, and now heart problems? Nothing was making any sense.

The following night, Poppa left for the lodge catching a ride with guest services. He called to talk to Mother every night before going to sleep once she began feeling a little better. That night before hitting the "roll away sofa hay," I walked to the first private corridor I could find.

As I have shared, prayer continued to be an essential part of our lives. Mother, Poppa and I would often make the time together to voice our concerns and our gratitude to God, as we desperately sought His guidance. But somehow I longed for a human voice, someone who knew about heart conditions, knew our situation, and knew Mother.

There was only one person that came to mind, "Berry." That was my nickname for Gail Winds[20], one of Mother's best friends. She was aware of all the details of Mother's condition, since as I kept her closely informed. So, I didn't have to explain anything by calling Berry.

Her husband Kemp[21] had passed away in recent years due to heart problems. Berry and Kemp were the couple Mother and Poppa hung out with on special occasions, or to have a double date night. Mother and Berry were close as friends and previous coworkers, before retiring. They are still the "best of friends," remaining close in working careers for nearly 26 years, in addition to church and social events. In earlier years, our families spent a lot of time together boating on Weiss Lake in Centre.

Berry was the most comforting and compassionate person God

could have placed on my heart to call that night. As I found an isolated corner in the hospital to share my concerns, she listened to my teary-eyed uneasiness. It was reassuring to hear someone who understood, as her words were comforting and encouraging.

At this point, we were on a 10 day streak hospital stay, as Mother battled a high fever, in and out of deep sleeps. I tried not to appear as if I was bordering on exhaustion, especially in front of Mother. Her needs were frequent. I was thankful I could be at her side. Her gallbladder was still not cooperating for it to be surgically removed, even with continuous antibiotics flowing through her system. However, the nurses were wonderful, encouraging and instrumental in keeping our spirits up just when Mother needed a boost.

Almost every physician who entered Mother's room was great, treating her with incredible respect and compassion. Every one of her nurses was a believer in our same faith. It was evident to us, that God gave us earthly angels during Mother's care. All of the staff were the most dedicated and kindhearted servants. It was like being on God's mountain top! At times I could just sense His presence, which was desperately needed. It calmed our fears and anxiety when we felt overwhelmed and bewildered by Mother's medical concerns.

Many of Mother's friends in our hometown did not realize she was having so many complications, or that she had an encounter with swollen Lymph nodes briefly diagnosed as cancer. As I shared, Mother was not one to complain, or to divulge information about her privacy. Unless the events were witnessed firsthand, no one would ever have known how ill Mother had become.

Jack was only a phone call away and I kept him posted as much as possible. A few of her close friends call periodically, including her first cousins, C. J., Taylor, - one in particular, John Adams, M.D. - literally our "family" practitioner who lives states away. He often called to check on her status. When she was awake, Mother kept her calls quick. I knew she was sick if she didn't feel like talking on the phone! "Shopping and talking"... when those two things stop, you have to wonder ... what's wrong with "Mother?"

I seriously began to wonder if she was ever going to be "finer than frog's hair," again. When could she return home? The big question I was too scared to consider was, "which home... earthly or heavenly?"

She was in a semi-critical condition, appearing to be closer to death at times than I wanted to admit. God knew our concerns. I believed with all my heart He heard our prayers. Witnessing His work through so many people and events; there was no way anyone else could have made things come together like the woven patterns of "Plaid."

Mother's condition became more tenuous. We were surprised she was not placed in ICU due to her status. Her gallbladder was being monitored closely.

Her suspected heart condition and persistent weakness made me question whether her body could endure more physical stress, and for how long? I had some time to sit back and ponder while staying close by Mother's bed side. I kept thinking, "How could all of this be happening since December 2006?"

Inquisitive thoughts crossed my mind during my breaks while working on my client's project. Taking care of Mother and trying to work was almost too much to bear, but God instilled a deep inner strength within me when I didn't know how to keep going.

Since the two heart alarm occurrences, Mother was placed under a cardiologist's care. Enter Dr. Hardheart[22]. Based on his bedside manners, I wondered if his heart was in the right condition! He was the only physician to enter Mother's room with a cold indifference, determined to call the shots, with no mutual patient discussion or questions to be asked.

He immediately informed Mother without relaying any alternative or choice, that she needed a pacemaker. I thought "Whoa! A pacemaker on top of everything else! Had her physical health indeed become this fragile?" Poppa and I were in complete shock! This was really off the charts, medical or any other!

"A pacemaker?" I kept questioning this medical decision. We had trusted the other physicians. They had been right on the mark with everything. Perhaps it was just his lack of people skills. Something didn't sit well about his insistence, but I wasn't the doctor.

As Mother's hospital stay was approaching the 12th day, the following plan was first shared with us by the general surgeon, Dr. Wallershaw. Then Dr. Hardheart made his visit… dictating more than informing.

First, a temporary pacemaker would be inserted, which was a surgical procedure placing Mother in the ICU. During her 24 hour observation period, she could not move her head or body for several hours. In ICU, no family members were allowed to stay at her side, as I had been doing. A catheter was to be inserted during surgery.

The second day, Mother was scheduled for the removal of her gallbladder, which began to "cool down," after the PICC line was inserted and allowing larger amounts of antibiotics to help rid the infection.

Day three included taking out the temporary pacemaker and replacing it with a permanent pacemaker.

It was hard to fathom… "Three surgeries in three days!" Especially after her body had been through so much!

After the third surgery, Mother would return to ICU and in 24 hours, she would be moved to CCU for the remainder of her hospital stay. Then she would be discharged if everything went according to plan, within 24 hours.

Mother had four major surgeries and one minor surgery in 17 days. I evaluated the amount of medications she was given, the number of times she was put to sleep, and the amount of lab work she had gone through. It was utterly astounding!

I thought about her ICU and CCU stays, her right hip and left knee replacements. It was as if I could hear Mother's cry in my mind as if she were a little girl unable to understand why she had to go through so much. All I wanted to do was hug her, comfort her, and reassure her that I was near. When you go through so much together, it is difficult to separate when you know someone is dependent on you; speaking for them when they're not able.

I hoped somehow a miracle would come from this hospitalization showing us any underlying reason with all the tests, as to why she was having continued weakness. At the present, our miracle was that Mother was surviving and still thriving.

During the time Mother was in ICU, it was evident God was listening to our prayers for her continued healing and protection. With no warning, I came down with a 24 hour virus including fever, chills, and vomiting. I was so miserable, but so glad I was not allowed to stay by her side causing any further problems while she was somewhat quarantined in ICU. She had already experienced so much… with more on the way.

. Mother heading to ICU meant I needed to find another foxhole. Thank God for having an Aunt Boo and Uncle Bob, with a condominium within a few miles of the hospital. The same week I needed a place to stay, it was vacant. How absolutely amazed I was with how everything worked out so well. Yet, another prime example of how great God is when you give Him your problems. Often times, before even asking. Witnessing His ways of demonstrating His great and unconditional love, often left me in awe when I could not think due to exhaustion.

Working on my client's project was difficult at best with all the challenges, and very little sleep, or quiet time. However, my client was extremely gracious since he personally knew Mother and Poppa in business dealings. The work was close to completion. I received an email at 9:00 p.m., the same night I had a fever and was light-headed from medications.

With all the United States' economic concerns beginning to increase, the financial world went into a tailspin. This was right before the 2008 Presidential election which was looking to be a very tight race. No one knew how the country was moving forward as a nation. Due to my client's unexpected business accounts dropping like flies, I was notified my project was dropped. Things were so focused on Mother. I couldn't do anything, feel anything, or blame anyone. I knew I gave it my best.

That night, I was so grateful to be in a place where I could sleep in a bed and have a private bathroom. It didn't even affect me that the majority of my income had just stopped. Mother's health was my foremost concern. My virus lasted for 48 hours, and then it was time to pack-up Mother and Poppa and head home to the farm.

Since Mother walked into the Birmingham hospital's ER, I was so appreciative for her to be in an excellent medical facility providing superb care. Poppa also had unbelievable support as he continued his treatments, doing everything in his power to assist in Mother's care. He was going through a serious time with his own recovery. It was exhausting for him to experience his own serious procedures, while watching his wife suffer through so much in such a short time. I was extremely thankful for God's protective watch over us, in meeting and exceeding, all our needs.

I was also grateful for Poppa's sons, Ryan and Rick, as they made arrangements during Mother's hospitalization in helping to transport their Dad (Poppa) from Birmingham to Centre and vice versa. On the last trip from home, Ryan and Poppa retrieved Skippy from our local veterinarian to surprise Mother. She had sorely missed Skippy, and was concerned about him staying away for so long from anyone he knew. Mother's love for her pets is immense, as if they were her true best friends at heart.

Mother asked for special permission to be rolled outside in a wheelchair so she could see her best little buddy. He was as happy to see her as she was to see him. Skippy was also wonderful company to me when I became suddenly became sick. Again, the timing to use Aunt Boo and Uncle Bob's condo, in addition to having a beloved family pet, was all wonderful blessings easing my concerns, and illness at this point!

Poppa completed all the required radiation treatments. He was released with a healthy prognosis. Mother was discharged on October 31, 2008. Finally, we were headed home. I truly wanted to believe the "trick" was for Mother to literally get back on her feet, and the "treat" was having both parents with greatly improved health!

Things began to settle down. We all were extremely grateful to be crawling into our own beds, again! I hoped our medical adventures were getting past us, with high anticipation Mother would soon rebound. Instead, she would again be plagued with another onset of extreme physical weakness.

For the first time, Mother became extremely discouraged. Poppa and I decided it was time to follow-up with the neurologist she had planned to visit before her unexpected hospitalization.

Her ability to get around the house or go places was becoming a more difficult task. She began losing weight due to a serious lack of appetite. Mother's naps were more frequent.

Yet, her desire to have a clean house was evident as I was given a list of chores! Even with a contagious sense of "spring fever" in the fall months, she was still not able to enjoy being outside very much. Her new hobby was watching the cardinals and hummingbirds as they swooped down from a nearby maple tree to land briefly on her yard's bird feeders.

One particular day, Mother was emotionally lower than she had been in a long time. It was rare and unusual for her. She spent the majority of her time in a recliner positioned where she could look across her back yard with several acres of dense woods. Our old barn was built on large boulder rocks which is located next to our corn field, was also in her viewing range. Her landscape of a beautiful outdoor scenery helped her to have some small connection with life beyond her own concerns, almost as if she had her own private sanctuary.

It was a beautiful day, but her body was easily fatigued with just getting dressed. When she needed a lift of encouragement the most, she prayed for God to give her a sign she was going to get better.

She shared that special moment with me:

"A hummingbird showed up in front of me, just outside the glass storm door of the sun room as I sat in my recliner. Out of nowhere, he appeared and was at eye level, rapidly flapping its tiny wings. He seemed to be looking straight at me, hovering in the exact spot for several seconds." Mother said she knew in her heart, it was a sign from God for reassurance that she was going to recover fully. Even though she didn't have a clue what exactly was continuing to pull her physical strength down further and further, often times it's the smallest reminders that can transition us to keep flying, keep going!

As I continued to pray for God to "please reveal the culprit,"... I believed in my heart Mother would fully recover! For some reason, I couldn't give up on her. It was deeply within my soul not to give up on trying to understand her real health issue.

The idea of her not making it, seemed too much to accept. No matter my outlook or desires, ultimately it was in God's hands, and Mother was the one who had to have the fight within her. Even with all the encouragement in the world, it was ultimately her will that would be the determining factor in her recovery, as long as God provided her every breath!

By now, the winter months had come and gone. Mother again was hit hard on her 71st birthday in January 2009 with another kidney infection and kidney stone removal. This time, Poppa and I didn't dare plan a surprise party since Mother was so good at surprising us!

The toil of her physical weakness was starting to create more problems with Mother's physical abilities. It became an emotional abyss of frustration. Not knowing why she had experienced so many sporadic physical afflictions causing her body to simply wear down. As a daughter and caregiver, it was the hardest - yet one of the most helpless times I've ever shared with Mother. Despite it all, she tried desperately to stay chipper, which was difficult at best.

The journey would soon become more bizarre.

Too soon, we would again find ourselves back in Birmingham sitting in another exam room waiting on the arrival of news from yet another specialist. We were meeting with Dr. Young, a neurologist, referred by Mother's hand specialist months earlier. So much had transpired since our journey began with her symptoms of hand weakness. Now her overall weakness was creeping throughout her entire body.

During his exam, Dr. Young shared that he was also puzzled with Mother's weakness. He said what we previously were told, "Both of her forearms, wrist and hands have distal weaknesses, which is uncharacteristic for a typical muscle disease."

He ordered a series of extensive neuromuscular tests at a research medical center in Birmingham. It required Mother to have another nerve conduction study and EMG by Dr. Luke[23], a specialist in neuromuscular diseases, medical research and associate professor.

The Electromyogram (EMG) and Nerve Conduction Studies[24] measure the electrical activity of muscles at rest and during contraction. Nerve conduction studies measure how well and how fast the nerves can send electrical signals.

Nerves control the muscles in the body by electrical signals (impulses), and these impulses make the muscles react in specific ways. Nerve and muscle disorders cause the muscles to react in abnormal ways.

Measuring the electrical activity in muscles and nerves can help find diseases that damage muscle tissue or nerves. EMG and nerve conduction studies are often done together to give more complete information.

An EMG is performed to find diseases that damage muscle tissue, nerves, or the junctions between nerve and muscle (neuromuscular junctions). These disorders may include a herniated disc, amyotrophic lateral sclerosis (ALS), or myasthenia gravis (MG). Also EMG studies attempt to pinpoint the cause of weakness, paralysis, or muscle twitching. The EMG does not show brain or spinal cord diseases.

Nerve conduction studies are done to find damage to the peripheral nervous system, which includes all the nerves that lead away from the brain and spinal cord and the smaller nerves that branch out from those nerves. These studies are often used to help find nerve disorders. To determine the source of extreme muscle weakness and fatigue, these particular tests were required to evaluate her muscle reaction to the intense and painful testing done by needles being placed at key points on her body.

Two weeks after the thorough muscle and nerve conduction studies were performed by Dr. Luke, we returned to Dr. Young's office to learn the results. He said, "My conclusion is a muscle disease called Myopathy[25]. However, the specific type is inconclusive." A muscle biopsy was warranted.

The next step was an informal surgical procedure. It was scheduled two weeks later where Mother had her previous muscle and nerve conduction studies performed by Dr. Luke.

One of the first persons Mother called was our cousin, John, as she shared every step of her medical mystery with him. He had continued to closely monitor her condition since her admission to the hospital in October 2008. John, and his brother Taylor, have always been more like brothers to Mother, since she was an only child. John and Mother discussed her in-depth and strange medical symptoms and possible diagnosis.

He asked "Has anyone ever had muscular health issues on your Dad's side of the family?" His Mother and my maternal Grandmother were sisters, so John was familiar with their history of long healthy lives. My Granddaddy lived to be in his late eighties. All of his family members lived long lives with no visible signs of muscle weakness, according to Mother. Again, nothing made sense.

"Dear Father" I prayed, "What is the culprit?"

Mother was devastated to learn she had a muscular disease. This independent lady, always managing to do for others, was continuing to rely on others.

It was not the way she imagined life to be in her later years, nor was it the way Poppa or I imagined her life to be. But more times than not, life is never the way we imagine.

Again, I found myself in a complete loss as I repeatedly fervently prayed for understanding, "Dear Father, What is the culprit? Please help reveal the link between Mother's assortment of illnesses and the underlying issue."

During our "de jour" of physician meetings, a couple of the doctors referred to Mother's age and her challenges, "It's just a part of the body getting older."

In other words, just because she was 71 years old (at this point in time), she was just to "accept" her condition?

They had not witnessed her vibrant life, and the way she touched others' souls with her unique God-given piano playing.

Were we just supposed to accept her condition? I thought, "Who is going to fight for her livelihood, and quality of life, if this is not the correct diagnosis?

Was this the reason God directed me home?

Was it to help unravel her problem?"

Instead of accepting a treatment plan with no solutions and giving her medicines, which can lead to other health complications, we opted to thoroughly consider the medicines the neurologist said she would have to resolve to take the rest of her life.

There was no offer of hope, while the quality of life was escaping Mother daily. We became more determined in depending on God's infinite grace and hope, with all ten toes working perfectly in the HUGE feat!

+ + +

Chapter 9

FOOT WORK

Learning of Mother's latest diagnosis seemed too peculiar. Once again, a visit to a physician specialist was too familiar of previous scenes as I remembered when Mother, Poppa and I sat in a pulmonologist's exam room to hear a diagnosis of Lymphoma.

Two-plus years later in the spring of 2009, again the three of us were sitting in another specialist's exam room, listening attentively to yet another astonishing health discovery. When Dr. Young announced "Myopathy," it came across like shock waves. "Is this really happening to her again?"

Mother was an extremely emotionally stable lady. She had demonstrated her strengths throughout my entire life. Nevertheless, everyone has a breaking point. My heart was breaking for her, as we were told about the medical findings. She was speechless. I think Poppa and I were on the verge of numb-stopping mindlessness, as if the wrong report had been given.

Months later, while retrieving Mother's medical records to share the true account of her medical story accurately, Dr. Young's notes revealed that after his initial examination of Mother's weakened muscles, he had suspected ALS (amyotrophic lateral sclerosis) or Lou Gehrig's disease. It immediately carried me back to a time when I witnessed an extraordinary physician diagnosed with ALS.

During my public relations career when I worked in occupational health care, there was a young surgeon with a flourishing practice. He was perceived as friendly, approachable, and caring towards his patients. Dr. Ehle was in his late 30s when diagnosed with ALS.

At that time, this town was quickly developing into a medical hub in Georgia. There were a multitude of diverse specialty practices working as partners with the main health care providers. The medical community was similar to a college fraternity. He became known as one of the most admired surgeons in the region. When it became noticed by the public that Dr. Ehle had ALS, his motivation to keep practicing medicine was admirable. He worked until he could no longer carry his own weight.

I recalled his health declining; unaware I would be studying more details about this disease years later in my Mother's journey with her medical mystery. This surgeon who had practiced with productive and skillful training, found his own capabilities diminishing as his young body grew thin and frail. Yet, his smile and direct eye contact illuminated his spirit, which camouflaged his disabilities.

He was undeniably bright. He was diligent and determined to continue practicing medicine. I had the highest esteem for our medical organization's administration to maintain his employment. A highly reputable skilled surgeon was now the most respected and highly skilled trained "doc in a box," as walk-in clinics were labeled at the time.

Dr. Ehle knew better than the rest of us what was ahead as an ALS patient. He never gave up, continuing to demonstrate integrity and character. My deep admiration for him remains a vivid memory. He kept going until he was not able do for others. What a living inspiration to achieve beyond the norm.

He remained faithfully devoted to his patients and the medical profession throughout his entire short-lived career. I saw a quality of strength in him I needed to find in myself and reach for everyday. Especially on days when I didn't think I could go on any more. He demonstrated perseverance to make the most from his life, his education and training. He kept going, fighting, and believing.

When I reviewed Dr. Young's medical notes documenting that he believed Mother had ALS before her muscle biopsy report was returned, Dr. Elhe's inspiration was a brilliant reminder of courage under duress. I knew how extremely fortunate Mother was to be diagnosed with a type of Myopathy versus ALS.

After Mother, Poppa and I left Dr. Young's office, I continued to suspect there was a deeper health issue possibly causing her muscle weakness. Again, it was a "gut feeling" that was blatantly tugging at my heart. The only other time I can remember a gut feeling being so incredibly strong was knowing I had to be at Mother's side, hours before she fell and broke her hip!

Since March 2007 when I made the decision to return home, too much had happened to Mother's body in too short of a time span. It seemed there was something every day on our agenda, whether a physician visit or medical procedure.

It was March 2009. Mother had been healthy for so many years prior to the onset of all these odd physical symptoms. I continued to ask myself, "What were the events leading up to her hip fall in March 2006, that would create such a medical mystery?"

Dr. Young stated Myopathy was rare for her age range. My thinking was the neurologist was giving his best academic guess of how Myopathy could have developed at her age while healthy. "Or did Myopathy appear after she was no longer considered healthy?" I continued to speculate every angle of her situation.

In spite of the dreadful news when she was diagnosed with Lymphoma, we continued to strongly trust in the 0.01 percentage and Mother's life turned around. Having the faith of a mustard seed is what comes to mind. It was insurmountable hope adjacent to a driven curiosity which I sensed was instilled by the Spirit by God. That was the force which kept me digging deeper, with questions until the specialists were absolutely positively sure about Mother's condition.

To better understand every single aspect of Myopathy, I researched reliable medical sources, continuing to pray for God to lead me to the root cause. My "gut feeling" to keep searching, when I ran into barriers at times gave me the gumption to keep striving. "Think outside the box, or the box could be your coffin," was my attitude. My boxed theory doesn't mean a person dies. But when you box yourself in, not allowing intervention from God through others with so many available resources to keep you moving, thinking, learning... it can debilitate your mind, body, and soul.

Whether you believe in God or not, valid facts are true and difficult to dispute; perhaps controversial, if not fully convincing.

God directed my every step, as I eagerly sought to learn more about

Mother's mysterious medical madness. I read every article available I could find. From highly clinical-based medical research journals and case studies, to easy to read for any non-clinician lay person, to understand about the details of Myopathy. Anything that was remotely close to her diagnosed muscle disease, I tracked to read for any clues that might help to understand a missing link or connection. There were an abundance of web sites, but the key was knowing which ones were reliable. That's when I depended on God's guidance for my search direction as key words would come to mind.

The most in-depth medical research was in the United Kingdom and Europe. At the writing of this chapter, the United States did not have a data registry for failed, or troubled, orthopaedic cases.

The United Kingdom research was conducted over a span of 20-25 years. Based on their data registry, the studied cases had more definitive symptoms, as well as precursors of physical reactions, which far surpassed any information on web sites originating in the United States. Whenever I was motivated to learn more, I was extremely grateful to all the medical researchers who began this process over two decades ago!

What was mind blowing was the seemingly lack of progress with any detailed investigation in the United States among medical practitioners and research clinics available to the public in spring 2009!

There simply was not any data results of metal joint replacements related to metal allergies that I could find. Everything I found was neat and tidy classic symptoms. It was if there had never been a failure in the United States.

Now, it appeared as if Mother was the only one who had been linked to a possible metal allergy linked to a severe muscle debilitation. The mystery became more compounded due to the lack of data or personal stories sharing anything like Mother was experiencing.

Waiting for physicians to speculate the root of Mother's unique health situation and rare symptoms, was not a viable option. She was becoming weaker almost daily to some extent. Her arms reached the point where they were barely useful to feed herself, much less care for her own physical needs in any other capacities. It was more evident than ever, she needed someone by her side, 24/7.

I was compelled to continue my own research. Witnessing her personal struggles, as physical barriers became more challenging over the past two years, was enough to fuel my inspiration for answers - if at all possible! Watching her health and her body's capabilities diminish sparked a deeper commitment to do everything I could possibly do for her. As I had made written and mental notes, I became her walking diary. Why not take the clues and try to figure out the puzzle? With my devout faith in God, there was nothing to lose and everything to gain.

Albeit, God is in control, and I believe prayer is the unequivocal power in communicating to the Almighty Father in Heaven. As I sought answers, I continued to be enthused from His miraculous healing Mother in January 2007. "All things are possible to Him who believes." Mark 9:23 I believed!

She was diagnosed with a 99.9 percent rate of Lymphoma. Upon having surgery, there was no sign of cancer as we had been previously told by her pulmonologist. There had to be a smidgen of evidence at some interval exposing the culprit's façade. If the arch rival working against her physical health could be revealed, then hopefully others with similar mysterious declining health problems relative to muscle diseases with metal allergies to certain metal implants, could be forewarned.

Why not pray for God to work through Mother as an example of how science and prayer work together to reveal a key link? Anything is possible! Doubt was impossible!

Nothing was more important to me than devoting my energy to understanding this medical mystery. The timing was crucial, especially at Mother's age, even though no one knows which breath will be the last.

My non-clinical health degree provided an easier learning curve when reading medical information. My personal drive became more pragmatic.

Every day, Mother's weakness became my strength.

Her medical condition became a driving desire within me to find some light in order to expose the dark secrets of her health mystery. In our mother-daughter relationship, she never stopped giving her time and energy to me. Why would I dare hesitate to do the same for her?

In reviewing Dr. Young's medical notes where he strongly suspected Mother having ALS, I became more intrigued in researching ALS factors. From his perspective, why did he think she had ALS?

My cherished memories of a young surgeon's courage, channeled the needed motivation to keep pursuing. In reading more about ALS, I was led to a trail of connections that incorporated a better understanding of how Mother's knee replacement could be a factor in affecting the weakness in her upper torso. Her entire body was being plagued by a deep-seeded root, which appeared more like symptoms for Chronic Fatigue Syndrome.

Naps and frequent periods of rest were required for her to be sustained at best. But her resting was not enough for the much needed respite her body was missing. In my observation, there was no other explanation of how she could have kept going without being supernaturally blessed.

Research regarding Myopathy and other muscle diseases, state the proximal muscles, which are closest to the trunk of the body, are the first to become weak. However, as discussed in the very beginning of her weakness after being examined by a hand specialist, Mother's distal muscles including her forearms, wrists, and hands, which demonstrated weakness. This same pattern of weakness was now confirmed by Dr. Young and Dr. Luke in their medical examinations.

At this point, Mother was not yet diagnosed with a specific type of Myopathy. However, the only one matching Mother's symptoms when I explored the types of Myopathy, pointed towards "Inflammatory" Myopathy.

"What is Myopathy?" Myopathy[26] is a term used to describe muscle disease due to neuromuscular disorders in which the primary symptom is muscle weakness due to dysfunction of muscle fiber. Other symptoms of Myopathy can include muscle cramps, stiffness, and spasms. Myopathies can be inherited or acquired.

"What were the signs and symptoms?" General symptoms of chronic Inflammatory Myopathy included slow but progressive muscle weakness starting in the proximal muscles - the muscles closest to the trunk of the body.

Inflammation damages the muscle fibers, causing weakness, and may affect the arteries and blood vessels that run through the muscle. Other symptoms include fatigue after walking or standing, tripping or falling, and difficulty swallowing or breathing. Some patients may have slight muscle pain or muscles that are tender to touch.

With so much emphasis placed on researching Mother's physical condition, it was amazing how my marketing business dropped to allow the time. How my bills were going to be paid was something that lingered constantly in my thoughts. It was not easy at times, but I continued to place my faith in God for provisions. And in the most mysterious ways, all my needs were met... Your "wants" are another issue!

If I ever became discouraged, I could look at Mother and a burst of energy took precedence over any pity-party. The incredible drive within me to help her was phenomenal. Without any great hesitation, I kept moving forward as I studied her medical records, called friends and family for support in learning more, as I prayed for answers.

As time marched on, I lived at my computer desk reading, searching, hunting, and digging. With such descriptive words to give a better idea for every rock I turned over and living in the South, my scenario could appear as if I were engaged in a sporting event. The workouts were similar. But, this time it was my brain being stretched as I learned some incredible mind-boggling facts. Some of the information had been long forgotten from my physiology and anatomy college classes at Jacksonville State University, Alabama.

The research was extremely enticing as every link or bit of information kept turning up new possible connections. This led to an exhilarating insight, as I delved into long hours of Internet searching, organizing, drafting charts, and began compiling a list of Mother's overall health problems she had experienced since March 2006.

Every facet about Mother's life was listed. I tried to think of any possible repetitious exposures to anything that could have triggered her muscle weakness. It was time consuming. Overwhelmed and tired, I had a fleeting thought of walking away, but again, one look at Mother and I could not leave her, or the work I was driven to research. Where it was going to lead if anywhere? I wasn't sure, but I could not give up. I was quite certain of one thing - something greater would come from this experience, even if it was not successful for Mother's health issues.

Although my business slowed down tremendously due to the recession, spring time means tax time for most Americans. As much I dreaded interrupting my research, I knew I had to get things organized to send to my CPA.

I reluctantly placed my research papers and files to the side, as I began organizing all my receipts and statements to verify my business expenses. Along with the long hours of research and doctor visits, I still pursued clients for any small business projects whenever possible. It was a full load, but as Mother's condition worsened, her health issues became my sole priority.

As I pulled out my proverbial shovel to start "digging" through another pile of sorts, I discovered an unusually double-folded piece of paper. Curiously, I began to unfold what appeared to be a time line in my penmanship dated from January 2005-07. As I stood among the mini piles of paperwork scattered across my table, I suddenly found myself sitting down in amazement. I couldn't believe what my eyes were reading. It was hard to imagine I had written this time line since I had no recollection of compiling the insightful documentation of information. My memory did not recall when I would have scribbled the notes. As I began reading, I realized it was a snapshot … a time line… a treasure providing a major pivoting clue!

The once folded piece of paper had events paralleled in two separate columns detailing my life, and the other column was notes about Mother's life during the same time frame. As I studied the notes, I had listed my previous residences with a couple of facts beside my whereabouts from 2005-07. In the adjacent column, I documented Mother's surgeries, starting in March 2006 with her hip replacement.

The next date under Mother's column was July 2006 when she had a left knee replacement. I could not believe my eyes! In the margin next to "knee replacement in July 2006," I had a note … "Hand weakness began in the same month after knee replacement." Bingo!

Bursting at the seams, I ran to Mother sharing the discovery! You'd thought I had found a check for a million dollars! This was a huge breakthrough! For nearly two years, I repeatedly asked Mother, "Do you remember when your hands became noticeably weaker?" She was never able to pinpoint an answer or remember when it occurred. Poppa and I couldn't remember, either. Her weakness was so vague and so slow in the beginning, I really thought she had a case of carpal tunnel. Anyone that can play the piano all over the key board, as she did, could easily had carpal tunnel.

The mysterious part of it all, is that I did not clearly remember writing the time line. Although I did stay with Mother during the surgeries and rehab recoveries, I was living in the middle of Georgia at the time. I was surprised... ecstatically, I might add... that I would had noticed the onset of her hand weakness. Or did I?

This was the information needed to assure the direction to go with the research. Needless to say, I contacted my CPA asking her to "please file an extension." I was eager to begin major research in this direction.

Dr. Luke, the neurologist who performed Mother's muscle biopsy, was an approachable medical researcher. He worked with rare medical cases focused on muscles. In our previous discussions, I found him to be open-minded with an exuberance to listen to any possibility. His care and compassion for his patients was of the highest regard.

Before our next appointment with Dr. Luke for Mother's biopsy follow-up exam, my immediate task was to find the link if possible between Myopathy and Mother's knee replacement. The thought became stronger as it hovered in my mind - her knee replacement, or what transpired during her knee replacement - was the problem. With the time line, I was reassured to stick with my strong discernment.

When I went back to the factors which cause Myopathy symptoms, there were only seven[27]: autoimmune disorders; endocrine disorders; exposure to toxins; infections; vitamin deficiency; medication; and metabolic disorder.

Out of the seven listed, only one could possibly link to Mother's health issues: toxins. All the other factors had been previously ruled out through lab work. So, my focus was centered on her knee replacement.

"What types of metals were in her joint replacement?"

Inflammatory Myopathy was the only type of Myopathy which fit Mother's atypical case due to her symptoms pointing to toxins. Therefore the toxins would inflame her muscles and create the weakness which leads back to Myopathy. However, at this point, we still did not have a specific Myopathy diagnosis.

While leaning back and reeling in the quietness of the moment with a half-baked grin on my face knowing in my "gut"... I knew we were on the right track. Out of the blue, a stunning memory linked more key information to Mother's condition. I remembered when I was a little girl, Mother wore a silver ring that made her finger turn green.

Here I go, again! Jumping out of my chair, I headed towards Mother and Poppa's hangout a.k.a. the sun room. When I shared with Mother about my memory of her ring, it never occurred to either of us that she might be allergic to certain metals in jewelry. She recalled when wearing her wedding rings, made of platinum and silver; they caused a reaction working with certain foods in the kitchen. Based on further research, that's not always an indication of a metal allergy, but a reaction to a metal.

Still, trying to connect the links somehow - my next thought, "What keeps someone who is allergic to jewelry from being allergic to a type of metal in their body?"

It had never been a topic of discussion with any of her physicians, not even her original orthopaedic surgeon, Dr. Doubter. Mother said she had always been allergic to any jewelry other than gold. At last, it was all starting to make tremendous sense to me!

When I tried researching toxicity and muscles, the only signs and symptoms listed were for heavy metal toxins.

The web sites repeatedly stated the same information - "You may have heavy metal toxicity if you are experiencing any of these symptoms[28]:"

- Chronic pain throughout the muscles and tendons or any soft tissues of the body*
- Chronic malaise – general feeling of discomfort, fatigue, and illness*
- Brain fog – state of forgetfulness and confusion*
- Chronic infections such as Candida

- Gastrointestinal complaints, such as diarrhea, constipation, bloating, gas, heartburn, and indigestion*
- Food allergies
- Dizziness*
- Migraines and/or headaches*
- Visual disturbances
- Mood swings, depression, and/or anxiety
- Nervous system malfunctions – burning extremities, numbness, tingling, paralysis, and/or an electrifying feeling throughout the body*

"*" Indicates the symptoms Mother experienced.

Over the next several days at a non-stop pace, I searched the Internet, practically wearing in the same clothes, as I was driven to link some connection. I researched more specific articles, going to new web sites and investigating more details.

God continued to place key words in my thoughts. I had studied health anatomy, biology, kinesiology and physiology extensively at JSU, although I was blessed with marketing and communications skills. To promote a health product or service, I learned very detailed information and statistics, often using medical terminology to create promotions, publications, and Power Point presentations, for physicians or the health organizations where I worked.

In my continuing pursuit, all the information available discussed heavy metal toxicity but nothing was stated about metal allergies to the metals in joint replacements. The most common heavy metals humans are exposed to include: aluminum, arsenic, cadmium, lead, and mercury[29]. I remembered Dr. Doubter mentioning Mother's knee replacement was made of Chromium and Cobalt metals when I accompanied her during a follow-up visit.

Given the circumstances, I contacted Dr. Young to share the information and time line. I also asked if he would order lab work showing metal allergies. When we talked on the phone, I shared Mother's metal allergies to jewelry and the possibility she was allergic to the metals in her knee replacement. To my surprise, he was very receptive to the idea, and believed I was on to something new in Mother's particular case.

However, outside of the heavy metal toxicity lab work, he was perplexed how to check for other metal allergies. He did not have a clue where to begin, but he was glad to order lab work for heavy metal toxins. I knew it more than likely would not show an allergy to Cobalt or Chromium since neither was even remotely related to heavy metal toxins. However, Mother and I were willing to make the trip to Birmingham for the lab work. In a few days, we were notified with the results which were negative, as I suspected.

During this time frame, I had a doctor's appointment with a neurologist, Dr. C at a major healthcare facility in Atlanta. He was very open-minded in regards to researching new and unusual connections. In my follow-up visit, I mentioned what was happening with Mother. She decided to ride with me to get out and enjoy the scenery. Mother was also a previous patient of Dr. C's for migraine headaches, which he helped to get her on the right track with a new medicine.

As I began sharing more details cased on the information I shared about the research involving Mother's health issues, Dr. C shared a previous study he had learned about some adverse effects of Cobalt in the body. Although the medical case he elaborated in discussing with me was rare, Dr. C suggested Mother have lab work specifically for Cobalt. Perhaps it was a link or the possible culprit. After all, we knew she had Nickel-Cobalt-Chromium metals in her body. He was gracious enough to make the arrangements for her to have the lab work that day.

About a week later, we were notified that the results proved negative. However, we were extremely grateful to Dr. C's open-minded approach that anything is possible! He supplied a great dose of encouragement for me.

However, it was disheartening to discover that not one of the medical practitioners we encountered thus far had any idea how to test for any other types of metals that were placed in the body, such as joint replacements. If in fact, her muscles were inflamed due to the type of metals in her hip and/or knee replacements, creating an allergic or toxic reaction, we were clueless as to how or where to acquire the lab work.

Mother's case appeared to be extremely rare. In today's leading edge of technology, I believed there was a medical institution somewhere in this world that could detect and distinguish lab results based on the metals used in joint implants.

As I shared the facts, I learned from my research, specialists never considered or had any reason to consider if a patient with muscle problems could have a metal toxicity leading to sporadic side effects such as: increasing fatigue; severe muscle aches in shoulder and neck; muscle cramps; sundry organs abruptly needing immediate medical attention; headaches; muscle pain; slight to severe muscle weakness; joint pain; burning sensation; occasional redness over healed incision; slow to heal incision; inflammation throughout entire body; loss of appetite; weight loss; or unusual paleness in skin color and cloudiness in the sclera of eyes. Amazing discovery.

With so many odd symptoms, I could understand that if not living with someone 24/7 for an extended period, how difficult it would be to get in the vicinity of the problem, much less pin point it. Instead of Mother's health digression discouraging me, it became an even bigger challenge to dig deeper.

As disappointing as it was that there didn't seem to be a metal test, or any test, that could detect metal allergies or toxicities from metal joint replacements, her quality of life depended on finding an answer or viable solution. So, I didn't let the lack of lab reports stop me from being aggressive in seeking, not just the link or connection, but a physician who would and could help.

It was imperative to know exactly which metals were used in all of Mother's replacements. I called Dr. Doubter's office and was directed to speak to his Physician Assistant. The PA was gracious in sharing the information which included the specific metals, manufacturers, lot numbers on the implants, and type of spray used on the polymer cup placed in her hip. There wasn't any need to mention the possibility of trying to link the metal to Mother's recent diagnosis of Myopathy, or the possibility of metal toxicity during our conversation. I needed more information or research, first. Getting the facts or sufficient evidence to strongly suggest any connection between the metal and her recent diagnosis was vital to disprove Myopathy as being the primary culprit. All along, I believed her extreme muscle weakness to be simply a side effect of a larger health problem.

Two prevalent thoughts kept repeating; "If Mother has Inflammatory Myopathy, what was causing it?" "How do I link Inflammatory Myopathy to metal allergies if I cannot prove an allergy through scientific testing?"

Everything pointed to metal toxicity creating her muscle weakness. And I was still determined to have a valid theory prepared, if Dr. Luke could further research what clues I had unearthed.

We returned to Birmingham for Dr. Luke's exam to perform Mother's biopsy on April 16, 2009. Previously, I met with him on Mother's initial visit and shared more details in her health's decline. In our discussion about this unusual health occurrence at her age and her healthy medical history, he was also curious as to why she was diagnosed with Myopathy if the biopsy did validate Dr. Young's medical findings based on the other muscle tests. But, Dr. Luke was more curious as to which type of Myopathy. In comparing her current situation with her medical history, this case appeared to be something out of the ordinary.

Dr. Luke displayed a genuine interest in his patients' longevity, comfort, and dealing with the possibility of serious declining health. What I liked the most about Dr. Luke was his innate ability to "think outside the box" and his humanitarian approach in striving to help his patients. He demonstrated a very humble personality, highly unusual compared to many specialists we had been talking with over time.

So, before Mother's biopsy that day, I asked the nurse if I could meet with him for a moment. I wanted to share the information I gathered which included my time line. My hopes were high for his lab to be able to test for metal toxicity with muscle samples, but Dr. Luke said it was not possible because his lab was not set up for that type of testing.

However, he strongly agreed with my theory based on the research and symptoms I had noted about Mother's knee replacement being relative to her muscle weakness, especially since it was discovered to be in the same month as her knee replacement. He urged me to return to the original orthopaedic, Dr. Doubter, with my time line, research information, and theory. I was very encouraged and almost ecstatic, as I believed we were closer to shedding light on the core of the culprit!

After the muscle biopsy, Dr. Luke shared with me that he had to cut deeply into Mother's left arm known as the brachial area, for muscle tissue samples to be thoroughly tested for pathological results. The cut was deeper than Dr. Luke initially believed would be necessary to provide tissue samples for a diagnosis.

However, due to Mother's muscle tissue being white versus pink, he had to go near her bone for healthy samples. It would leave a gapping area not quite visible from just looking at it, but her left arm was now difficult to move and bring towards her chest, as if she were trying to pick up a glass to drink. Something no one ever thought would occur from a muscle biopsy. But it was a necessity to diagnosis her possibly ill-fated muscle disease.

One morning shortly after the muscle biopsy, Mother and I discussed the possibility of legal action if things did link together. I knew if the culprit was the metal in her knee or hip replacements, she might have enough evidence to litigate with possible malpractice. But my "gut feeling" was leading me away from that route.

During our morning prayer together, we both agreed not to seek legal action. We believed God knew exactly how to take care of everything and everyone, should anything be proved other than for Mother's best interest. We were not bargaining with God, but making a promise to give Him our burdens in helping others learn more about metal issues related to health problems. We prayed for His continued blessings to connect the links. We continued placing our faith in Him.

Within two days after the muscle biopsy Mother became pale, feeling even more fatigued then previously. She started to look like she did while hospitalized for 17 days in the fall of 2008. It was about 6:00 p.m. when I noticed her left arm, where the biopsy had been performed. The swelling was similar to when her veins collapsed while hospitalized.

I called my close friend Tina Gossett, RN, BSN. She and her family returned to Georgia after two years of struggling to keep their restaurant "Simply Southern," profitable. Tina suggested we call the neurologist, Dr. Luke, and watch closely for any other signs. She said if it became worse, we needed to take her to an ER.

It was Mother's weakest point thus far since March 2, 2006. For hours I kept a vigilant watch on the swelling, as it appeared to stabilize. It was all she could do to sit up due to the lagging fatigue and overall weakness. However, Mother wanted to do her daily Bible devotion. This particular night she began the devotional reading for April 20, 2009. Her voice was so weak. When it came time to read the Scriptures, she actually misread the suggested reading but didn't realize it until much later.

Mother had skipped down two verses, reading:

"Therefore, strengthen the hands that are weak and the knees that are feeble, and make straight paths for your feet, so that the limb which is lame may not be put out of joint, but rather healed." Hebrews 12:12-13

After hearing the Scriptures, Mother, Poppa and I believed it provided insight. Maybe Mother was not going to have another knee surgery. I was led to gain further insight so I read my study Bible's interpretation: "meaning to make peace through strength of character."

The Scripture reading was not a mistake. In our immediate future, Mother, Poppa and I would learn more about character and integrity within ourselves, and in the physicians we would soon encounter with our genuine plea for help.

It was crucial for Mother to have the best medical care available. But the real importance was her attitude and faith as she garnered a deeper inner strength from her soul and her will. Mother did not have any control over her physical weakened condition. She did however, have control over her inward approach, as reality stepped in presenting callousness through professional caretakers.

Mother's testing included more than medical examinations. She learned to discern professionalism, or the lack of professional traits, while being introduced to a variety of views and perspectives from medical practitioners.

A man-made metal implant inserted into Mother's leg was just as toxic as Dr. Doubter's decision to do nothing, through lack of professional character and integrity. Intentional or not, he lacked assertiveness to assist in giving proper care, in my opinion.

Integrity and character are strengths that should never be allowed to fail, particularly if your occupation is to serve others. The true corrosive source was about to be revealed, after nearly three long difficult years.

Mother, Poppa and I would be facing two healthy able-bodied surgeons who could have learned a great deal from my previous coworker, Dr. Ehle, the young surgeon diagnosed with ALS. He never allowed his integrity and character to be tarnished. Instead he illustrated everyday how to give your best. It's all about taking one step at a time in directing your "foot work" in life's walk!

+ + +

Chapter 10

ON A ROLL

It had indeed been a long haul; but finally the time line provided hope for a major breakthrough for Mother's medical mystery! Pertinent information was pointing towards her declining health beginning with her hand weakness, which was now linked in the same month when she had knee replacement surgery. The probable root cause was narrowing a type of metals in her implant, or something related to the surgical procedure, or the device.

Since her hip replacement was four months prior to her knee replacement, it was surprising that she never complained of any problems or pain until after the knee replacement. If there was a correlation between the knee replacement metals and her pain, what, if anything, was different about that replacement? The same type of metals were used in the head and hip support structure attached to her pelvis as in the knee replacement.

Based on my time line, her complaints of pain in her knee, and the information I had discovered in research cases from the United Kingdom, stating the types of metals used in implants can lead to serious health issues, every thing was supporting the possible connection between the types of metals in her knee replacement and why she was experiencing so much discomfort. Mother stated, "My knee has bothered me since 'day one'." And it continued to create a great deal of pain. It seemed this was the obvious connection. I was sure of it.

The next hurdle was directly connecting her hand weakness to a specific type of Myopathy, which Dr. Young had diagnosed. Of all the types of Myopathy, her symptoms only aligned with Inflammatory Myopathy. In doing more research about Inflammatory Myopathy, I found that it was the only one which stated "toxins" affecting muscle tissues would create a severe weakness. But, how was I ever going to convince a physician of this rare correlation which did not appear to be reported in the United States?

Add the fact that I am not a doctor, nurse, or a clinician, but most likely seen as an over-eager daughter trying to "fix" her Mom! What were my chances of getting over this hurdle? Try 100 percent. Not 99.9, but 100 percent.

The Great Physician was knocking down barriers I probably didn't have a clue that were trying to block our journey to the core of the culprit. There were many David and Goliath moments in this journey.

During the night, Mother's arm became more swollen where she had the muscle biopsy. I immediately called Dr. Luke's office the next morning. I was concerned since her veins previously collapsed while hospitalized. Dr. Luke returned our call within a very short time. He believed her blood vessels were blocked or obstructed creating an embolism. He urged us to come to Birmingham so he could examine her arm, ASAP. By this time, it was already mid-morning as we prepared for a two-hour drive.

With Mother's extremely weak physical state, she was not able to walk any distance beyond 20 feet without stopping to rest. We didn't have a wheelchair, but had previously obtained Dorothy's (Poppa's sister-in-law) medical equipment when she passed away.

One of the pieces of equipment was practically brand new. It was a "sitter-walker," type vehicle for walking assistance. Basically, it's a manual mobile four wheeling cart, which allows the user to temporarily park with adjustable hand brakes. The user can sit down securely on a padded seat covering a wire basket as a storage compartment. The detachable basket could also be fastened on the front of the cart to be used for a variety of needs. The hand brakes and hand grips on the handles of the cart steered the wheels, which had two rotating in the front for ease of mobility. It was lightweight, durable and when not in use, it collapsed together, and easily fit in a backseat or trunk. I had noticed this device used by others with physical disabilities when in public places. It appeared to be very functional for folks sauntering along needing support for walking, but still independent.

Mother and I decided to use this modern day gadget instead of taking the time to rent a wheelchair. I placed it in the back of the SUV and tried to make Mother as comfortable as possible as we headed for a quick exam with Dr. Luke.

One of the much needed blessings during all of our parking anywhere and everywhere, was Mother's handicap parking permit issued after her hip replacement. Everywhere we traveled, a handicap place on the front row. That was an added blessing!

Once we arrived at Dr. Luke's medical building, my exercise chore for the day was to get Mother up three flights to the third floor by elevator then push her to his office which seemed like several, several miles away.

Realistically, it was a long trip down a long "haul"-way extension connecting to another long "haul"-way. It was a lengthy and invigorating hike! Mother did not feel like sitting up, much less trying to walk. How grateful I was to have the "sitter-walker" cart! Anything with wheels, keeping us on a roll, was well worth its weight in gold. Even a wheelbarrow would have been great on this long haul day!

Talking about being on a roll, not only did I get my much needed workout quota met for the next few months, but several gut wrenching laughs were exchanged between us, as well. I am more than grateful for Mother's wonderful personality. She may lose her ability to physically take care of herself, but not her sense of humor. Seeing this part of her persona at some of the worst times in her last two years, simply amazed me. Humor is the best medicine! For Mother, humor is often the first reaction when the going gets rough.

Of course, I had a "back seat" driver sitting in front of the sitter-walker cart. The disadvantage to this new fang-dangled four-wheeling invention was having no place to prop her feet. So, we stopped for "mutually" needed leg rests along the way. But I didn't mind at all. A picnic lunch would have been nice to have on our many stops, in this seemingly unending building.

Finally, we arrived at Dr. Luke's office. He was quickly summoned and immediately came out of an exam room and checked her arm, then decided she needed an ultrasound to check her blood vessels. This meant an extended "outing" on the medical campus by venturing to another major clinic two blocks away.

We returned to the SUV for the short drive. Loading Mother in the vehicle was more difficult because of her additional weakened state. It was taking a toll on my physical abilities maneuvering her in and out, up and down, and then reloading everything again. "No problem," I thought as I was already exhausted from one sightseeing tour of a large medical building. My intention was to stay focused on Mother's care and her needs. I could always collapse when we got home and take a quick nap.

We were in a rush to get to the radiology department before they closed. When Mother sat in the sitter-walker cart, it made the wheels on the back of her cart free rotating with two stationary wheels positioned in the front. The 360 degree turning range on the back rotating wheels made the ride for her a bit exciting. It was like a reality video game trying NOT to hit the indoor pedestrians.

As we rolled across a corridor to radiology, the foot traffic was heavy. And that's not counting Mother dragging her feet, or me just dragging! People were headed directly towards us seemingly without a clue, not realizing that they were risking their lives with me behind the rotating wheels of the cart, with Mother onboard with a heavy purse that could break a foot if it dropped! It was like we were invisible. I'm not sure how they could have missed us! We were good-sized moving targets. I'm not short and Mother is not small. That's the vision!

Swerving was the only way to avoid hitting people as they appeared to be racing to a huge fire sell extravaganza. I thought I did pretty well considering Mother never once fell over or out of the "ugh" cart, which I began to affectionately refer to it. Finally, we arrived safely to radiology.

While Mother was having the ultrasound, I kept thinking about Dr. Luke's advice to go back to the original orthopaedic surgeon with my "hunch," as he called it. He said there was a good possibility the metal implant was causing the reactions in Mother's body. My mind was going a mile a minute, even though a glazed over daze may have appeared on my face. I probably looked more like a Crispy Creme donut while sitting in the waiting area due to my eyes being so glazed. I could have easily played stare down and won that day! There was no rest for the weary, as I was determined to try every way possible to figure out her problem, or at the very least, give it my best effort.

After thoroughly thinking things through, Dr. Luke was right. It was time to return to the source and talk to Dr. Doubter. More research was required to prove the theory of a possible muscle-metal-toxicity connection. Several doctors, including Dr. Luke, told me this was not an easily proven factor to determine. It appeared Mother was just a rare case, if that were the problem.

Dr. Doubter had stated in every exam that Mother's x-rays showed her knee implant to be intact. The bone scan she had requested, in her earnest plea to find out why she continued to have left knee pain, returned with a negative report.

"How do I link the metal possible allergy or toxicity with Inflammatory Myopathy?"

I had no answer and needed further direction. I waited eagerly for Mother. Dr. Luke instructed for the ultrasound technician to share the test results with us. If there was an embolism, Mother would have to be admitted to a hospital, pronto.

While I waited, the thought occurred for me to call my friend, David. We had known one another since I was 13 years old, which is a stack of decades! In the past three years, we had talked more often when things began to happen with Mother's health situation. He and Mother had also remained good friends through the years, so I kept him updated on her condition.

As I sat in a rather large waiting area, I shared my theory of the "muscle-metal-Myopathy" connection, and the desperate need to connect the dots before presenting the facts to Dr. Doubter. I could hear the tapping of keys while David listened to the theory details. He had been researching "Chromium and Cobalt" on the Internet. He sent three web sites to my email address. Those sites initiated an greater in-depth search linking metal toxicity to the bone which could prove to be the root cause behind Mother's diagnosis of Myopathy.

My friend, David and I concluded our conversation just as Mother came from radiology with an excellent report. The embolism in her arm had somewhat dissolved and her vessels were not completely blocked. The swelling had gone down considerably. This news was a huge relief. A real horror at this point would have been if her veins had begun to collapse.

Serenity and peace began dwelling deep within my soul as I sensed God was sustaining Mother, until we had more information and a physician on the same page with a new possible medical breakthrough. Forging ahead, I continued to lean on His guidance and direction. Mother's current physical situation made me more acutely aware of her body's frailty. The main priority it seemed, was to get the metal out of her knee. If her health rebounded, it would confirm a type of metal was indeed the culprit.

We headed back through the building and into the parking lot, loading up as we set our sights for home. During the two-hour drive, I continued to think about the metal and the Myopathy theory. Mother began dozing early-on during our return trip home due to exhaustion. She was completely washed out, but had been a really good sport. Realizing the strain our "outing" had placed on her physically, I knew Mother's limitations were completely opposite than before her knee replacement. Even though her sense of humor was intact, her ability to do things, and recharge her body was not as it had been.

There was so much more work to be done to prove her prosthesis was the culprit. I just knew her replacement had to be the issue. It was the only possible link to the her health issues, after reviewing everything in addition to discovering the time line.

Dr. Luke did give me a tremendous boost of inspiration in his comprehension of the potential connection. His encouragement added enormous credibility to Mother's rare health condition, and we greatly needed his reassurance. It gave Mother hope, which she desperately needed at this point. She knew all too well, that she was not "too" well.

I kept thinking... "Dr. Luke had called it a theory or 'hunch.'" I had no doubt God was revealing the culprit.

After returning home, I was extremely anxious to research the web sites my friend, David, had previously sent by email. Everything he sent reassured our strong suspicion, that Mother needed to return to Dr. Doubter to review her medical case. It was the only route.

There was enough evidence to substantiate a good review of Mother's problem. The web sites regarding Chromium and Cobalt medical studies and effects on patients, led to an entirely new wealth of pertinent information. We were "on a roll." If the metal implant was the issue, Mother still had to contend with having a type of Myopathy until the metal implants could be removed. And that was if the metal was creating any metal allergies or toxicity and had not hopefully destroyed any healthy muscles tissue on a permanent basis.

Dr. Young had previously planned for Mother's care after the muscle biopsy results were disclosed, which included placing her on continuous rounds of large doses of steroid medicines on a permanent basis. Steroids would have boosted Mother's muscles for a short interim. But, over a long period of time, it would not be worth the risk. Steroids have a high probability rate. Webmed.com[78] is one of many reliable health and medical web sites providing an overview side effects of prednisone or cortisone oral medicines, which can lead to additional serious health problems such as the presence of sugar in the urine, impaired would healing, enlarged liver in addition to other issues with high risk factors in the body when taking the meds for a long term basis. At the time it was the only alternative drug offered by a physician who was open-minded about what could be causing her Myopathy.

After we returned home from Birmingham, I shared more about my theory in greater detail and the incredible research data I believed God had directed, with Mother and Poppa. I suggested we return to Dr. Doubter, as Dr. Luke had advised. Placing Mother on steroids was not going to "cure" her problem of Myopathy. We needed to look at all of the options, if any others were plausible, to make sure we were on the best path of her return to health - should that be a possibility!

Mother and Poppa were very open-minded about what I had learned, and believed the new information and time line revealed a new found hope to connect her medical mystery. There was no reason not to investigate this route further. I also conferred with other physicians and nurses I knew as friends. Based on their clinical insight, it continued to make sense from a medical standpoint. However, "proving" a medical connection was the most difficult task.

Scientifically, there had to be a culprit causing the Myopathy. The physicians we encountered didn't have any ideas or medical findings, so why not dig deeper. In my faith, God is the Creator[30] of everything, the Author and Finisher, the Great Physician! Why not follow the leads I believed only He had placed in our path?

We moved forward expeditiously. Mother and Poppa shared the same sensing. "Just like Peas and Carrots"... they prayed together for answers every day, which instilled faith stronger keeping their dependence on

God, as in one.

The time line I found scribbled in my penmanship, stated her hand weakness began AFTER her knee replacement. It had to be the metal implant or some form of bacteria on the metal implant which caused her pain and her health to have a rapid descent. We were in agreement… "Let's keeping going with God's direction," and that is exactly what we did.

The month of April 2009 was almost gone. Our only hope was to keep our deeply instilled faith intact. My earnest prayer was for God to sustain Mother's health, as He guided me on this research. And He did.

Research and Revelations Reviewed:

After researching Myopathy in trying to understand the muscle disease, I learned this was quite possibly a hereditary disease. But neither side of Mother's family had any signs or problems with muscle issues.

With Myopathy, the proximal muscles (shoulders, head and neck) are the primary muscles to become weak. In Mother's case it was distal (lower arms, wrists, hands, and fingers). This was a mystery, although it was not a complete rarity in Myopathy signs and symptoms.

Mother was checked for carpal tunnel. Since playing and practicing the piano regularly for decades, her muscles should be stronger than the average female in her age range.

Inflammatory Myopathy was the only type of Myopathy which possibly fit Mother's health issues. Without having a specific diagnosis of her muscle biopsy, "inflammatory" of all the types of Myopathy seemed clearly evident.

Since witnessing her increasing muscle weakness, the information stated about Inflammatory Myopathy provided only one possibility: metal toxicity.

Each of her physician's offices were called to learn which specific types of metals were placed in Mother's body during her right hip replacement (March 2006); left knee replacement (July 2006); and pacemaker (October 2008).

While preparing for my 2008 tax return, a time line was unearthed noting Mother's hand weakness began in the same month after her left knee replacement. Being with Mother during both of her replacement surgeries, in addition to her 17 days while hospitalized with numerous health oddities, resulted in her receiving a metal pacemaker and her gallbladder extracted.

Although I lived hours away, I "happened" to be with Mother at the times for both replacement surgeries, it was my beginning role as her "walking medical journal." Once I returned home, things provided further insight to odd symptoms during her health's spiral descent. I was able to be included in all of her physician visits as her "walking diary" and caregiver.

All the evidence at this point indicated a probable failed prosthesis in her left knee. This replacement was comprised of "Nickle-Cobalt-Chromium" as reported by Dr. Doubter's PA.

Mother's pain was well documented by Dr. Doubter's medical notes and in her hospital records. "Since day one..." was again documented in his medical records, after a follow-up exam of her knee replacement on March 31, 2006.

Dr. Doubter's medical records noted there was "a slight uptake (or shift) in the bone scan" on August 2008. The bone scan was only physician-ordered after Mother's repeated request to see if there was anything the scan could pinpoint after two years since her knee replacement. He said, and it is documented, "There wasn't any change based on the bone scan results."

In 33 months, Mother's health had deteriorated greatly with constant renal issues beginning within a short time of her knee replacement July 2006.

Either her knee replacement surgery - or possibly - Mother's serious health dilemma was initialed by her hip replacement surgery, since it was the first replacement. Anything associated with her replacements raised suspicions.

Mother never had any major health issues in her life except occasional migraines and occasional kidney stones. Now those two "occasional" issues had turned to "significant" issues.

Once the theory was presented to Dr. Luke, he suspected the strong possibility that there could be a connection. He encouraged us to return to the original orthopaedic surgeon to review her medical case while she was in Dr. Doubter's care.

Considering all the facts and any additional information, I created a new time line for any physician or clinician to gain a clearer understanding of the health and medical occurrences. This tool gave me a wider perspective and ignited a more investigative and definitive research.

At the end of three long days of reading everything possible which was pertinent about Mother's known symptoms, I had enough evidence to suggest a strong connection between metal toxicity to Nickel-Cobalt-Chromium. Was she experiencing a reaction creating toxicity in her body which were affecting her organs? My next step was to call Dr. Doubter, as Dr. Luke suggested.

Mother already had what appeared as a near miss with Lymphoma; her kidneys were continuously problematic with frequent infections; her gallbladder was removed and a pacemaker inserted. She had been through the gamut in 33 months since various types of metals were placed in her body. I was told by Dr. Doubter's PA that her hip replacement had a Nickel-Cobalt-Chromium head, Titanium stem and polymer cup.

Ironically, her hip replacement did not appear to be causing any pain; but, her focus was completely on her knee, as it was extremely tender and very sore to the touch.

Mother had so many other things to contend with during the last three years, it was if someone was using her for target practice with invisible darts hitting certain areas of her body. Her faith kept her strong in mind, in heart and in knowing whatever was to come about, she would continue to hand her problems over to the Great Physician.

As I reviewed an abundance of available lists on the Internet from reliable medical web sites for metal allergy symptoms, none seem to align with Mother's health issues. She did have a slight fever and redness, but every article or medical journal I read stated a rash would be evident in over 90 percent of orthopaedic metal immune hypersensitivity[31] cases.

In the research studies, "Allergy to Metals as a Cause of Orthopedic Implant Failure," provides more scientific insight - "A constantly growing social demand for orthopedic implants has been observed in Poland. It is estimated that about 5 percent of patients experience post-operation complications. It's suspected, that in this group of patients, an allergic reaction contributes to the rejection of metal implants.[31]"

At the time of this information entry in *Steel Standing*, the long-term effects were just starting to be under scrutiny because of the potential biological effects of metal wear debris which causes poisonous microscopic ions to be released throughout the blood system.

My review summarized documentation describing the biological activity of metal wear from her orthopaedic devices, which pointed to great concerns and potential, creating microscopic debris releasing from Mother's metal implants, creating metal allergies and toxicity throughout her body and it's reactions.

The introduction of risk assessment for the evaluation of metal alloys, and their use in patients with joint replacements, includes potential harmful effects on: immunity; reproduction; the kidney; developmental toxicity; the nervous system; and carcinogenesis (cancer)[32].

Mother's pain was the most evident when she attempted to take a step using her left knee. It was particularly difficult when she tried to climb or come down stairs or short step entrances. She had begun to show weight loss. Although she was never a large woman in an excessive size, but her body's frame was mid to large at with her height at 5'6".

Her appearance was transforming. Her face was worn with pain, as she had been through tremendous amounts of suffering - more than she wanted Poppa, me, and others to know to keep us from being overly concerned.

The day after we returned from Birmingham, when I had received a good healthy dose of encouragement from Dr. Luke about my "hunch," I called early in the morning to make an appointment with Dr. Doubter. The receptionist asked the purpose of the visit, since Mother had not been examined by him in several months.

I was honest in stating, "I believe Mother is having some type of reaction with the metal in her knee replacement, possibly metal toxicity."

The receptionist scheduled an appointment the very next day.

Every day, I depended on greater faith as I continued to place everything in His Hands. Every day, we believed we were one more step closer to seeing her return to a healthy life, again. Faith is believing without seeing. Our faith in God showed us we were able to persevere.

As a caregiver, I wanted to do anything and everything for Mother until she could return to a better quality of life. Or at least keep her spirits up, as well my own, knowing that we were giving it our best shot in trying to understand what was happening.

Mother needed tremendous encouragement. At times it was overwhelming and exhausting; but how could I possibly think of walking away when Mother was not even in a position to walk?

What I learned from this new "walk" in my life traveling beside Mother, is everything in life is NOT predestined. If life was predetermined, then why would God give anyone on the face of the earth the gift of prayer to communicate with Him, whether verbally, or in our thoughts... at any time, any place?

He is still in control, but He also listens IF we try talking to Him. That's what I continued to do.

Prayer was the key of recognizing God as the Almighty.

This journey began with a sincere heartfelt prayer in 2007.

We *WERE* on the right track towards the specific answers needed. God was keeping us "on a roll" as we began to go in the right direction.

+ + +

Chapter 11

JOINT DISAGREEMENT

In preparing to meet with Dr. Doubter, I made copies of all my medical information and research which aligned with Mother's rare and obscure health issues. Based on the credible research, I was convinced her problem was caused by some specific type of the metal in her knee replacement. Also, based on the research, all indications were evident Mother had a severe metal allergy, quite possibly metal toxicity. With all my heart, I believed our meeting with Dr. Doubter, listening to the medical information would somehow champion him to assist Mother any way possible.

Her previous visits totaled 11 follow-up exams, all because of her repetitious pain with her knee following the replacement. Each time she returned, he responded to her concerns repeatedly stating, "You will just have to learn to live with it." Poppa witnessed hearing Dr. Doubter's same statement for the majority of the visits. I attended three of the visits, while listening to his reasoning. Yet, he never offered any alternatives other than a mild pain medicine.

I also unmistakably remembered his first reaction when Mother stated "something does not feel right with my knee," in the hospital during his evening rounds July 12, 2006. Previously, it appeared by Dr. Doubter's gestures, that he was not concerned. His lack of compassion to assure Mother that her knee replacement should improve was obvious. He seemed oblivious to her complaint, as if it didn't matter what she shared. His quick reply appeared to be a canned remark, as he turned to see my Mother's look of despair while in dire pain.

So, why would I think he would be any different when we presented our concerns to him about possible metal allergies than any time before? Good question. Perhaps we wanted to give him the chance to recapture the same caring role we experienced after her hip replacement when a patient-doctor trust had been established. Dr. Doubter had also stated, on previous occasions, that he was praying for Mother's physical health. Why not give him another opportunity to solve the problem when the thorough medical research pointed to the knee replacement he implanted?

To be fair, it certainly makes sense to allow time for any surgery to heal before jumping to conclusions. But a considerable amount of time had passed... 33 months... it was time to jump!

For over a period of two and a half years, Mother asked during each visit for him to please check further about the odd pain in her knee as it was intensifying instead of improving. She was seeking answers from her highly skilled surgeon, but Dr. Doubter continued his "routine" exams. His pattern was like a revolving door, with only one opening.

Perhaps Mother should have sought another orthopaedic surgeon's advice for a second opinion, but she really wanted to believe Dr. Doubter was giving her the best possible care. Not once did it ever occur to me, or anyone else, to acquire her medical records or any x-rays from Dr. Doubter until after our last visit.

Thursday, April 23, 2009

Finally the day arrived to meet with Dr. Doubter. Mother, Poppa and I were ready to share what we perceived as great news, evidenced with printed research data. The first fact I had planned to present after his initial exam, was her allergy to all types of metal jewelry, except gold. According to the information his PA shared when we talked three weeks earlier, Mother had "Nickel-Cobalt-Chromium" metals in the upper and lower implants of her left knee replacement. Her right hip included a Titanium stem with a "Cobalt-Chromium" head.

In October 2008, when I investigated the pacemaker metals, I was told by Dr. Hardheart, Mother's pacemaker was 100 percent Titanium based on the cardiologist's medical reports. However, there was never any mention of Titanium "Alloy," which is comprised of a small percentage of other metals, such as Nickel. I discovered this fact by going to the manufacturer's web site and checking the specifications on Mother's particular pacemaker model. All the facts were available for anyone to confirm on any pacemaker manufacture web site.

In learning more about "alloy metals" vs. "pure metals," expanded my comprehension of all kinds of metal uses in all types of ways, throughout the human body for various reason. At first, it was really overwhelming.

As we sat patiently in Dr. Doubter's waiting area, Mother was the last patient called back before they started closing for lunch. Like three blind mice, we were headed to the exam room exhilarated with hope and excitement to share the news of what we believed was Mother's problem. Since Dr. Doubter had been Mother's attending physician for her orthopaedic needs, we gave him the benefit of the doubt. Perhaps he was as frustrated as we had become. Maybe this would encourage him to help her feel better. After all, that's all we wanted. We weren't there to threaten him or present ourselves in any way other than be willing to share information and work together with him as the lead specialist.

In all the other exam follow-ups, Mother had to have an x-ray for his review before examining her. This was the first time his ritual procedure was not part of the exam. His PA entered the exam room first. Oddly enough, he never closed the door. Having worked in medical facilities, I was acutely aware of HIPAA regulations and patient confidentiality. So, I found this lack of professionalism to be strange. Again, due to believing we were going to the source that could help Mother, I gave the situation the benefit of the doubt. It seemed obvious that Mother was the last patient in the office, other than the front office staff, as it was very quiet with a sterile sense.

The PA was friendly and proceeded to chit-chat. He asked the purpose of our visit, as he was ready to document Mother's answer on a medical chart. Mother began to explain in great detail about her previous health adventures, but primarily, the pain increase in her knee. She shared in a nutshell what I researched in addition to the time line. I briefly shared what I witnessed since returning home in March 2007, plus the other additional health problems Mother experienced the past fall of 2008. He continued taking notes. As the PA began exiting the exam room, he stated Dr. Doubter would be in shortly, and then he shut the door. It was about

45 minutes before Dr. Doubter entered, again leaving the door wide open, which was noticeably unusual. Perhaps others were listening? It appeared that way at the time.

Everything was different that day. We arrived with high hopes, perhaps even a bit naïve in believing we were in the right place. As I reflect on the mere mention of metal toxicity to his receptionist when making the appointment, perhaps Dr. Doubter was more than likely on the defense. In his double take, as he looked at her when entering, it didn't take much to convince him Mother was not feeling well because her skin color was a pasty pale.

The trip was an exhausting two hour ride for Mother, much less preparing for the day's meeting with Dr. Doubter. She was extremely weak. To make matters worse, her left knee began "clicking" the night before, as if something was loose when she walked. The main purpose of our visit with Dr. Doubter, was to ask for his help and support as we tried to convey the rare symptoms Mother had experienced. Again, our intent was never to enter his office with an ounce of hostility, or with any suggestion of placing blame on anyone.

In proceeding to exam her knee more thoroughly, Dr. Doubter placed his hand on the calf of her left leg to check her knee mobility. He twisted it, then moved it from side-to-side and front-to-back. She voiced that he was causing pain while he examined her range of motion and flexibility. He bent her knee to check for knee replacement's bending extension. She was obviously in pain when a spontaneous outburst caught all of our attention as she would quickly respond, "That really hurts!"

Dr. Doubter never asked Mother to walk around so he could check the clicking noise she had just shared. While Mother continued to sit on the exam table, he placed his thumb on the lower bone between her knee and the front of her foot. Again, she unexpectedly reacted, "Oh... that's sore right where you have your thumb." It was obvious, due to the apparent tenderness she felt, that her knee was not alright.

Dr. Doubter leaned back on his stool with both hands cupped on his knees and his legs crossed. Poppa and I just sat quietly, as we waited eagerly to hear his summation.

He stated in a calm demeanor, "I don't see any problem with this knee." Then he justified her pain by stating that too much time had elapsed since her knee replacement surgery for any type of metal allergies or toxicities to be evident. He reassured us her knee was intact. He strongly suggested her problems were coming from another part of her body since she had been going through so much.

I immediately and politely brought to his attention the length of time she had been complaining, and reminded him of her "day one" complaint. I vividly recalled her stating this to him when she became more alert after the surgery. He sat there in the same position like a statue. I shared my theory supported with copies of scientific medical data from the United Kingdom, explaining how the metal in her knee could be the culprit causing her other unrelated health problems. As I pulled out a set for him to read and keep, Dr. Doubter appeared to be fascinated with the theory and information. "Without Ms. Harton having the classic 'textbook' signs, there was no way, she could have a loose knee replacement," he said.

How odd that Dr. Doubter mentioned a "loose knee replacement" when we had not conveyed any concerns about the implant being loose. Our main concern was the pain and tenderness, which we shared with him!

In Dr. Doubter's medical opinion: in two and a half years of x-rays - in addition to his physical exams - and stating there was no indication from the bone scan to support any signs of looseness - it appeared nothing was convincing to him, that Mother had a bad knee implant. At the time, I did not have a copy of the bone scan report or his medical records regarding Mother as his patient.

Again, Mother asked about the recently developed clicking noise in her knee when she walked and bent her leg. Dr. Doubter simply brushed it off as part of a knee replacement's motion adjustments over time.

Needless to say, we were all three in complete awe of his standoffish approach, with what was an apparent urgent situation to us. It was obvious by Mother's lack of energy, she was in trouble with her health! I could not comprehend his lack of necessity to do something for her. I was totally befuddled.

I emphasized Mother's acute pain reminding him that she was not one to complain. It was frightening to see how far she had digressed in her physical state, just making this trip. Yet, he did not seem the least bit fazed.

The research I had compiled seemed to point to the metal in her knee creating a toxin, as the microscopic ions released into her bloodstream increased each time she bent her knee. The medical research from Southmead Hospital, Bristol, United Kingdom, stated concisely in the abstract:

> "This review summarizes data describing the release, dissemination, uptake, biological activity, and potential toxicity of metal wear debris released from alloys currently used in modern orthopaedics. The introduction: If risk assessment for the evaluation of metal alloys and their use in anthroplasty (prosthesis) patients is discussed; ... includ(ing) potential harmful effects on immunity, reproduction, the kidney, developmental toxicity, the nervous system and carcinogenesis (cancer)[34]."

Based on applicable medical studies of a valid connection derived from renowned orthopaedic researchers, Mother's case was in the category of a rare metal allergy leading to toxicity with the probability of the toxicity leading to cancer.

But Dr. Doubter did not indicate he was onboard with this theory. "Her knee is perfectly fine," he reinstated.

Dr. Doubter was provided fact-based evidence which validated further testing of the metals in her body for allergies. In addition to Dr. Luke, a prominent neuromuscular researcher, advised us to return to Mother's orthopaedic surgeon to further investigate if the metal was the source of her health demise.

It was as if Dr. Doubter was experiencing "information overload."

He appeared nervous as his face blushed as he continued to sit as a statue, with clasped hands propped on his crossed-legged knees. He turned to me and asked, "What do you want me to do? What is the next step of action I should take?"

Honestly, I could not believe my ears. A seasoned orthopaedic surgeon was asking me what he should do! His appearance of innocence and naivety baffled me. He was considered one of the best in his field with an impeccable outstanding reputation. Perhaps, I had hoped he was going to advise us, not the other way around.

Instead of saying what I was thinking, I calmly suggested Dr. Doubter order blood labs. My suggestion was based on what I read in a medical journal's research study checking for metal allergies. He replied, "I don't know of any labs in this area or in this state that performs lab work to show any allergies to metal. I have no idea where to find a lab that completes blood work to test for metal sensitivity or toxicity."

I replied, "You're telling me there is not a medical facility, or lab, that can test Mother's blood or offer any type of lab work, that monitors metal allergies to check if the metal in her knee replacement could be the culprit of her health problems??"

His response was "Maybe the Mayo Clinic. I just don't know. This is not a subject I have been made aware of." I remembered the lab work Dr. Young ordered to check for heavy toxic metals. Although the results were negative my point was, if those metals could be tested, there should be a way to test other metals used in joint replacements in humans, especially with highly advanced medical technology in the past decade.

He continued to sit, dazed in the same paralyzed position. I expected pigeons to come through the wide opened exam room door and land on his head at any moment.

Completely and utterly astonished, I realized he did not have a clue. Not one clue. For the first time, my eyes were open to his limitations. We were no longer three blind mice. I could sense Mother and Poppa had the same revelation. It was very clear Dr. Doubter was not the physician to help Mother. He knew how to do orthopaedic surgery replacements, but anything beyond that specialty area, was totally out of his realm of experience. Dr. Doubter said he did not do revision surgeries. In my desperate attempt to get any help, the idea came to mind to ask Dr.

Doubter if another surgeon could examine Mother since he had stated he did not do revision surgeries.

He appeared to be glued to the exam stool. He said he needed to read the detailed research information I had brought for him. We asked how soon he would be able to get back with us since Mother was obviously becoming weaker. After a moment of what appeared confusion in his attempt to answer my simple question, he finally instructed us to stay close by, until later in the afternoon.

Hesitantly, yet hoping for a solution to help Mother before we left his office, I proceeded to ask what his plan might be. I asked if hospitalization with lab work to check for infection... or drawing fluid from her knee, might be able to provide Mother with rest and an opportunity to regenerate. Anything would be a huge help at this point to stabilize what little physical strength she had remaining. Ideally, a diagnosis to the problem and his offer to possibly fix her problem was our anticipation.

The wheels appeared to begin turning in his head. I was hoping to see smoke any minute, as if he were going to state something brilliant to help Mother. Instead, Dr. Doubter said he couldn't admit Mother to a hospital since he did not have a specific diagnosis to correlate with a billing code. He suggested we go to a nearby ER and he would be contacted.

But that plan didn't make a lick of sense! Since he didn't know where to begin to do testing, why go that route? The medical information I provided practically gave verbatim instructions as to what steps were necessary. It wasn't that I was trying to tell Dr. Doubter how to do his job. I was trying to relay information based on a medical documented case almost identical to Mother's problem. It was becoming very clear to me, that he was grasping for straws, that is if he could get his hands unclasped from his knees long enough.

After a few more minutes of futile discussion, it was as if a lightning bolt jarred him into reality. He shared that a colleague, who was a best buddy from medical school, and was very familiar with doing revision surgeries. Dr. Doubter said he might provide insight if the knee revision was indeed the problem.

He said he would call him to discuss the case if we would continue to wait. I'm not sure how Dr. Doubter was able to get up, considering he had sat in a locked position for a good 20 minutes. Off he went, as he politely closed the door.

Mother sat on the exam table for the duration, while he called his colleague. Periodically, she would glance over at me as if I were going to say something that would reassure her Dr. Doubter was going to return with an answer. I said everything I knew to say without presenting myself as a "know it all" or "a problem child." What more could I offer?

He seemed genuinely impressed with the information due to the fact that he admittedly stated, "I've never been exposed to any metal information or researched it." His acknowledgement stunned me for some reason, as did his ability to sit in one frozen and apparently uncomfortable position for 20 minutes or longer. As we continued to sit and wait, it seemed as if we were on a physician game show. His one phone call was his only lifeline.

Maybe Dr. Doubter didn't know what to do, or say, because I was seeing something for the first time that perhaps he had not seen, nor tried to previously visualize. Perhaps, Mother was the first of his patients to ask about any metal allergy issues, related to a joint replacement.

After a rather long wait, he finally returned explaining more about his medical college buddy's partner, a top-notch orthopaedic revision surgeon named Dr. B. M. Logger[35]. Dr. Doubter said he was excellent in performing joint revisions and if there was anything wrong with Mother's knee replacement, Dr. Logger was one of the best. He handed me the contact number of the practice written on his physician script. We were emphatically instructed to specifically ask for Dr. Logger's nurse as Dr. Doubter stated, "She will be expecting your call."

By the time we left Dr. Doubter's office, I hoped he was guiding us to the right orthopaedic surgeon to solve Mother's dilemma. Perhaps another physician, new to her case, may be more prepared to understand exactly where I was coming from based on her symptoms, condition and the medical information I had gathered. All the research gave us valuable and valid information strong enough to be given consideration versus going to a physician with no direction in trying to figure out her health problem.

Acting as a "layman" clinician was not what I aspired to be!

I drove the vehicle to the front door of the medical building of Dr. Doubter's office. Mother was barely able to make it. She was exhausted, physically, and emotionally.

As we headed home, I believed we were finally making some progress. Although Dr. Doubter did not appear to comprehend what to do next, we were hopeful Dr. Logger would understand our dilemma. We knew "time was of the essence." Anyone that looked at Mother, physician or not, could easily see her weakened physical state.

We were about halfway home when Mother suggested we go ahead and call, since it was a Thursday afternoon with concern that Dr. Logger's office may be closed on Friday or close earlier. Mother picked up her cell phone to make the call. The medical practice receptionist answered and immediately connected her to the nurse, "expecting our call."

While driving on a curvy mountainous road towards home, I noticed Mother was repeating her problem as if the nurse didn't understand. I thought, "Odd," especially since the nurse answered in less than three rings, which is an almost impossible feat to get a live voice on the first attempt! Mother motioned for me to pull over to the side of the road, which had steep cliffs on each side. She proceeded to ask the nurse to please hang on for just a moment. I turned off the road at the first place where all four tires were on solid ground versus partially hanging midair. Mother quickly passed the cell phone to me, as if we were playing hot potato. I knew this was not a good indication considering her conversation had been less than five sentences. That was way too short of a conversation for Mother!

As I began speaking with the nurse, I introduced myself and explained my relationship to their new patient, in thanking her, for her time. From the moment the conversation began, she demonstrated rudeness, arrogance, and hatefulness in her tone… and those were the nice adjectives. The nurse questioned everything I said. It was a good clear cell connection. There didn't seem to be any reason to repeat what I stated since we both spoke English. I really couldn't grasp what her problem seemed to be. What was up with her haughtiness and condescending tone?

When she finally asked the question why we were calling, I said Dr.

Doubter referred us to Dr. B. M. Logger. She said, I am making you an appointment with Dr. E. Z. Jiffyluber[36]. He is equally skilled in his abilities as Dr. Logger. I found that to be another odd change of plans based on Dr. Doubter's high recommendations for Dr. Logger. However, Dr. Jiffyluber was Dr. Doubter's college buddy.

While I tried to give her requested details about Mother's problem, explaining that we had just left from a visit with Dr. Doubter, she adamantly professed Mother did not have any allergy or toxicity related issues with her knee. (Really?)

First, the nurse did not have any medical information that we were aware of unless Dr. Doubter faxed copies of his medical files to their practice. Secondly, I was given the impression by Dr. Doubter that we would be welcomed in a friendly medical practice environment.

However, it turned out to be a horrible conversation, as I tried desperately to be as nice as possible. The nurse seemed determined to make this dialogue difficult. Her responses caught me completely off guard. She then told me to get Mother's medical records from all the doctors she had seen in the past three years. I scrambled to find a pen and paper to write down her direct orders.

Please note: This was on a Thursday afternoon and she made the appointment for Monday morning at 8:00 a.m. I explained how difficult it would be for Mother to get dressed so early in the morning since she was extremely weak, so the appointment was moved to 9:30 a.m.

Without allowing another word to be squeezed in edgewise, she instructed me to go to their web site, get a map of their location and then print off the required "new patient" paperwork with emphasis placed on making sure it was "completely filled out."

In addition to the paperwork for their office, she reiterated to be sure to bring all the medical records from the past three years from all the physicians who saw her including test results and x-rays.

Did she really think we, or anybody else, could accomplish her demands in four to eight hours during medical office hours the next day... which was a Friday. That was IF all the doctors' office were open!

I knew time was crucial for Mother to be seen by a specialist to possibly help her. Perhaps this was a test to see if we could be civil even if the nurse was not. I hoped her example of how she treated me on the cell phone, was not an indication of their office behavior. As Mother and Poppa listened, it was apparent this was a one way conversation by my lack of being able to response... "Yes, but..." and "If..." and "Well, I'll..." - No it did not go well for me.

I was able to ask one last question before we ended "her" phone call. Since she was in a physician's office, all I needed to do was give her the physicians' names and numbers. They could fax Mother's medical records to Dr. B. M. Logger's medical practice without Mother's written consent! She refused, stating they were closed on Fridays. Oh, well.

The last thing Mother needed was to hear my voice level rising to the same tone the nurse vented. It appeared that we disturbed her day's agenda by her having to stop and talk with us. Her scathing manner exuded the perception that we were not bright individuals. Perhaps on Monday morning we should have shown up barefooted, with uncombed hair and having consumed multiple cans of beans the night before to make sure we left a trace of "country folksy" perfume in the lobby area!

Is this a dose of sarcasm? Absolutely! Even as a Christian, why on earth make something smell like a rose when it was more for fertilizing rose bushes! I just got off the phone with the "Chief Thorn!"

Even at my worst point when I felt I was pushed to the edge of my patience, I still hoped these capable surgeons would turn their behavior to the Savior, as truth and hope would emerge for Mother's health.

We did exactly as Dr. Doubter instructed by calling Dr. Logger's office. Then one call connected us directly to Nurse Thorna Hornet[37] who had a bee up her hinny's bon-bon. Wonder if she placed the bee in a jar at night so she could reinsert the poor creature the next day to keep her "bad-titude!" I wondered if her interaction, which was "far from gracious" was the same towards everyone. When I got off Mother's cell phone, I comically visualized it starting to melt from Nurse Hornet's raging fury. Lovely lady!

With the instructions to obtain Mother's medical records, the first place I called for copies was... you got it... Dr. Doubter's office! They were extremely polite. I was tempted to share our encounter with Nurse Hornet, but decided not to, especially if they were close colleagues. Mother gave me the number of a friend's office in Centre so we could easily retrieve the faxed medical records on our way home.

As suspicious as I was about heading to this orthopaedic practice based on Nurse Hornet's conversation, I was excited to be obtaining Mother's medical records, hoping they revealed some link to all of her health problems.

Friday morning, April 24 rolls around. I arose exhausted but eager to do whatever was necessary to gather as much pertinent information as possible before Monday's appointment. Taking into consideration that Mother's past three years of medical records were located in four different cites and hours apart, there was NO way I could travel to all of those locations in the same day. In addition, the trips would have to include Mother traveling with me, for her to sign consent forms. Some physician office policies require at least 24 hours to 5-7 days, for advance notice to comply with a patient's request.

This appeared to be an impossible task. How in the world could we begin to get all the information without Mother's consent, or a fax machine at the house? Instead of panicking, we gave our concerns to God.

We prayed together, asking Him to please help us make it possible for things to work out to acquire the needed medical records requested by the revision surgeon's nurse. Most importantly, I knew we were handing over our burdens to a God who makes the impossible, possible[38]!

It worked out that Jack was in his office that day. As her son, he was a legitimate receiver for Mother's medical records. Usually he is out of his office on the road traveling a great deal in his job, meeting with physicians in his organization's network. Jack greatly assisted by receiving her records faxed to his office, which automatically converted to emails. Then Jack forwarded the records to my email address which I saved and printed.

Everything worked smoothly all day. It was completely amazing. But we needed one more set of medical records from a surgeon's office. It was closing in 15 minutes. I shared our urgency with the office manager. At 4:55 p.m., the medical staff agreed to fax the records to Bridget at their home's fax machine. It was a very long and unbelievable day with seamless communication from one or more offices, using the house phone and our cell phones. The pace was quick, as if we were "bookies" taking bets before a horse race began!

We did not have the original x-rays, but we had the radiologist's reports. God made all of that happen... it was a miracle! Once again, having worked in medical organizations, I knew this was a close to impossible task with so many offices and people involved, in addition to their work schedules assisting other patients in the medical offices. To obtain what was requested in a short time frame, was pure gratification to accomplish such a huge task! And it was all done on a Friday, while some revision surgery offices were closed!

The most important barrier to clear with approximately 12 medical offices was HIPAA, which mandates stringent patient confidentiality. There is no other way to explain how everything came together than giving God the credit.

To my surprise and disappointment, as I reviewed Dr. Doubter's medical records, his documentation revealed the opposite of genuine care. It appeared Mother had been more of a hindrance than any possibility of helping her, even in her repeated pleas for help with her knee pains. Perhaps, I was naïve as Mother, but she desired to be treated with preeminent care, exceptional medical skill sets and genuine follow- through for her optimum health outcome.

Dr. Doubter was provided valuable insight from our contributions in sharing details about her personality and living habits. Her family was attentive and involved, supporting her needs. He had met each of our family members.

No - Mother was not just another patient! She was an individual in need of excellent health care for her palpable signs and symptoms. As a family, we stepped up to the plate in giving Mother the best care possible in the hospital, through rehab and at home, why should he... as a practicing professional... treat anyone with less than his best? We had certainly respected and followed his physician orders.

Baffled by his medical records when I later reviewed them, I was hesitant to share them with Mother. She had placed endearing trust in this physician as his façade was remarkably well portrayed. The medical notes concurred exactly word for word what Mother had said all along about her continued pain in her knee, especially making it difficult for her to climb up or go down stairs. Nevertheless, his reported reaction stated; "Mrs. Harton has returned again with the same complaints." Why did he not see these symptoms as a signal of trouble with her knee replacement?

Mother was not the type of person to sit by and not get involved with life, especially when it came to her family and her active community responsibilities. Always extremely energetic, she enjoyed trips with three of her former female coworkers, planning long weekend getaways where shopping and shows were plentiful. Mother's church responsibilities also kept her on the go, playing for special occasions. Resting was not in her nature, but now longer naps were a routine part of her daily agenda as a requirement, not a luxury.

Backsteps to Review:

Mother desperately wanted more testing - any type of further testing - besides x-rays to check for possibilities that something could be wrong. Up to this point, nothing was formally investigated although evidenced by her physical decline.

Finally, Dr. Doubter agreed to proceed with a bone scan at Mother's urging. This would indicate if there were any problems with her bones and the metal replacements. He also explained to Mother that her blood work would show any infection or problem with her knee.

However, every time the lab reports were in normal ranges. He saw no reason to offer her anything more because she did not fall into the classic "textbook" signs and symptoms.

The medical records revealed more insight. On August 6, 2008, Mother returned for a bone scan. Two weeks later on August 12, 2008, an office visit was scheduled with Dr. Doubter to learn the results. The notes below were in Dr. Doubter's medical records, as stated in its entirety:

"Ms. Harton is back in today with the results of her bone scan which showed a slight increase in uptake but nothing too specific. Her white count is 4.45, SED* rate 21, and CPK* 0.5. As such, I don't see any real indication of infection. I told her the next thing to do would be to aspirate it if she continues to complain of enough of pain. She has a lot of neurologic issues going on. She is scheduled to see a neurologist. I told her to go ahead and make that appointment and see if he was able to come up with anything. Otherwise, I feel fairly comfortable watching her knee. We will see her back in another year for repeat x-ray and exam. In the meantime, I gave her a prescription for 30 Mobic 7.5 mg one a day."

*Foot Note Terminology:

SED Rate [76]: Sed rate, or erythrocyte sedimentation rate (ESR), is a blood test that can reveal inflammatory activity in your body. A sed rate test isn't a stand-alone diagnostic tool, but it may help your doctor diagnose or monitor the progress of an inflammatory disease. The sed rate test measures the distance red blood cells fall in a test tube in one hour. The farther the red blood cells have descended, the greater the inflammatory response of your immune system.

CPK: Creatine[77] - When the total CPK level is very high, it usually means there has been injury or stress to the heart, the brain, or muscle tissue. For example, when a muscle is damaged, CPK leaks into the bloodstream. Determining which specific form of CPK is high helps doctors determine which tissue has been damaged.

Eight weeks later Mother was carried to an ER in Birmingham for mysterious health emergencies, high fever and abdominal pain. Her 17-day hospital stay was the beginning of serious but sporadic issues within her body's system.

The next scheduled visit with Dr. Doubter was March 2, 2009, with the following medical documentation:

"Patricia Harton is back in follow up. She has had a lot of

health issues since we last saw her. She had her gallbladder out, pacemaker put in. She fell in early November when entering a restaurant landing on her right knee. She has gotten better since that time and is now ambulatory back to her normal levels. On exam the left knee looks good. The incision of course is healed. No significant swelling, full 0-120 degrees of motion, good stability to varus and valgrus stress. Her hip on the right side moves freely, no significant swelling in that lower extremity. X-rays (two views) of her hip on the right side show a well cemented bipolar hip anthroplasty in good position. X-rays (two views) of her knee show a well positioned total knee anthroplasty. I think she is doing well. I have encouraged her activity wise. She takes only a baby Aspirin and stool softener. I will see her back in a year for repeat x-ray and exam of the right hip and left knee."

It was amazing to think that Dr. Doubter believed Mother was "doing well" based on his medical notes, yet she continued with complaints of her pain in her left knee replacement. Her next appointment was scheduled one year later as a "follow-up." At this point, Mother had gone through quite an ordeal never regaining her strength or the sparkle in her eye. Yet, Dr. Doubter believed she was "doing well" although, her physical appearance showed otherwise.

He also said to her in my presence, that he would continue to pray for her health. It's rare to find a physician who believes in God and professes it to his patients. This was the reason Mother was hesitant to pursue another physician for a second opinion.

From a story-sharing standpoint, it's easy to read this information and say "Well, I would have done this or that…," but again, I refer back to the illustration Mother has used from time-to-time. When a frog is put in warm water, the heat becomes so gradual, that the frog doesn't realize the water is getting hotter until right before he is cooked.

I continued to pray for God to "please reveal the culprit." I sensed there had to be a valid link connecting the metal in her knee to her overall weakness. Again, I reference the importance of the time line I unearthed on March 8, 2009, while I was preparing taxes for my business. The time line revealed when Mother's hand weakness began in the same month she received her knee replacement. In addition to her recent diagnosis of Myopathy, it seemed the keys were handed over to unlock the floodgates of research connecting the types of metal in her knee replacement to her overall health decline.

One of the more enlightening medical research discoveries was by "The Journal of Bone & Joint Surgery[39]," Lund University, Lund Sweden. The abstract states:

> "Patients with inflammatory conditions have twice the risk of developing lymphoma. This seems to be further increased if they have metal-on-metal joint replacement. Prospective studies should be undertaken in patients with chronic systemic inflammatory conditions after the implantation of a metal-on-metal implant to investigate lymphocyte function and the risk of developing haematopoietuc malignancies."

The study further explains cellular toxicity and the immune system. This is how I made the connection. If Mother's knee replacement was a metal or a comprised substance of a metal, which she was allergic to as I have already documented in a previous chapter, then her body would reject the metal in the knee replacement, creating major problems throughout her body.

This was just one of many articles that were extremely enlightening. Rare and unusual health problems seem to have a tendency to fall into the category of "I don't know what to do with you, so we'll just keep giving you medicine."

I prepared over 40 articles of valid information and research which I shared with Dr. Doubter in our last visit on April 23, 2009. My theory or "hunch" was further validated when I shared my idea with Dr. Luke before he performed Mother's muscle biopsy April 16, 2009.

As I have also shared, nothing else appeared to fit the symptoms for Mother's Myopathy diagnosis, except Inflammatory Myopathy due to metal toxicity, which was not formerly diagnosed at this time.

The biggest drawback was not having a orthopaedic surgeon as her attending physician to keenly monitor Mother's care, or look beyond classic "textbook" signs, or symptoms. Although she did not show any signs - it was obvious she could not walk well due to inflicting pain.

Three years was fast approaching since her knee replacement surgery, and she appeared to be losing hope at times. Somehow, through the remarkable essence of it all, she would quickly rebound and keep going.

Monday's Exam, April 27, 2009

To concisely summarize a long office visit and physician exam: Mother was handled with boxing gloves versus with a physician's gloves of care. Dr. E. Z. Jiffyluber was condescending, giving Mother an unnecessary unsympathetic exam. He treated Mother's painful knee and sore leg without any compassion, as if he had never heard of the word. Dr. Jiffyluber bent her knee every way possible, which brought tears to her eyes a multitude of times. His bedside manners were "badside" manners.

To make matters worse, the newly healing incision in Mother's upper left arm from the muscle biopsy just days prior, was given no consideration. Mother clearly forewarned Dr. Jiffyluber of the tenderness in her arm. He placed his hand on the very area she had asked him to please not touch, squeezed it as he rolled her body for further examination. He was callous. And that seemed like one of his finer qualities that day. Poppa and I sat, repeating for caution, as we felt we could do nothing but watch her suffer.

To share Mother's journey in this particular chapter of her life by using sarcasm to describe her treatment, is the only way I can share the "Doubter and Jiffyluber Duo."

The passion I have for Mother, and for Poppa, runs deep. After being by her side and witnessing the hostile treatment right before my eyes, created an anger in me that I had to let go and give to God deal. The hardest part is that I allowed the most insensitive exam to occur! It was most inappropriate.

Mother has a high tolerance for pain, but when Poppa and I saw her cry, it was obvious she was hurting from Dr. Jiffyluber maneuvering her body as if it were a large duffle bag of laundry. Poppa and I promised, "Never again!"

We believed we had been sent to a professional, whose Hippocratic Oath states that he will listen to his patients, and do all in his power to participate in a patient's healing.

He allowed me to share very little with him before he took most of my research papers to made copies. He had the audacity to tell me the Internet was not the place to find any answers, and was too inadequate for doing any kind of research.

This was the wrong path, but we were headed in the right direction!

There was no better place to send our extended hurt but to God, with as much sincere forgiveness as we could muster in our hearts. We earnestly prayed for all their patients' care… past, current and future, the physicians and their office staffs.

Clearly, we had a joint disagreement.

+ + +

Chapter 12

"BEND" THERE DONE THAT

In spite of the difficulties we experienced by seeking Dr. I. M. Doubter's expertise and assistance, only to be referred to an orthopaedic surgeon such as Dr. E. Z. Jiffyluber, our briefly dampened hopes had gained a vivacious source of energy once we had a good night's rest. The entire transition proved to be exhausting as we worked feverishly to obtain the required medical records before going from Dr. Doubter's care to Dr. Jiffyluber.

Honestly, I had my suspicions based on several clues, but was so desperate for Mother to get help, I wanted to be wrong about their care obviously being less than the best. The quick appointment set-up, and unrealistic time frames with volumes of medical records to be obtained to meet Nurse Hornet's request on behalf of Dr. Jiffyluber, was virtually an impossible assignment. It seemed to be laid out far too smoothly as a part of a bigger plan to distract our intentions.

Were actions calculated between two physicians to coerce a plan to help cover improper care monitoring in 33 months? There were plenty of facts to substantiate a lack of concern, along with constant urging precipitated by the patient. My guess is neither one of them ever believed, or cared to investigate into the real possibilities of what could be going on with Mother's knee pain and if, in fact it could be associated with her metal implant.

Legal steps could have been an alternative for Mother. We had decided not to take legal actions against any medical practitioner. We did not want to be a part of a world that seems to be constantly looking to sue others. Sometimes, it is called for when justice is warranted.

We believe there are excellent physicians currently leaving their practices due to many factors with our existing health care changes and challenges. It did not make any sense to go down the path of more trouble and legal battles. It made more sense to keep walking forward, allowing God to work through us on this medical journey. We chose to take the "Utmost High" road.

We sought His way of keeping peace in our souls by giving our revengeful anger to Him. When God places vengeance on others, He does so perfectly, whether we ever know it or not. When we as individuals seek revenge, we may do too much or not enough. I believe the Almighty knows exactly what, when, where, and how to express our burdens to those who hurt us. But only when we learn to give Him our burdens versus taking things into our own hands, and forgiving those that hurt us.

Dr. Doubter's PA made a point to call the day after our visit with Dr. Jiffyluber. He wanted to know what happened in the exam, and what was our next move. Mother was polite and said we were still weighing options. Mother and I continued to receive calls from Dr. Doubter's PA, on separate occasions. Each time, he brought up if we were seeking legal action. So, it seemed Dr. Doubter was thinking a possible malpractice suit was looming. However, Mother and I both made it perfectly clear - repeatedly - that we were only seeking medical information with no other intentions. We were calm in conversations, while Dr. Doubter's PA conducted a seemingly nervous inquiry.

Our meeting with Dr. Jiffyluber was on Monday, April 27, 2009.

The last exam visit Mother had with Dr. Doubter was on Thursday, April 23, 2009. The following is a medical record I received a day later by fax:

> "Patricia Harton comes in; apparently she has gone downhill quite a bit from her overall medical standpoint since we last saw her. She is with her daughter and her husband, who are both very concerned about her condition. Apparently she has gotten weak to the point she had to almost use a wheelchair to get around. Her appetite is suppressed and she complains of multiple aches and pains. Apparently they have done a good bit of research and they are convinced that this is an allergic reaction to the Cobalt-Chrome [Chromium] in her knee joint. Although I am

certainly aware that this does exist, it is very rare case and this has been in for some time. I would be skeptical if this was the cause but told then (them) we would do everything we could to rule that out. She has had a muscle biopsy out of the left and brachial area. We actually took the sutures out today so that she would not have to go to Birmingham to have this done tomorrow. She says traveling really wipes her out. I looked at her knee and there is no significant effusion. She is having a slight click in the knee which I think is just due to the polyethylene on the metal. It does appear to be abnormal. It is not warm at this point although she says it sometimes is. No x-rays were obtained today. I have talked to Dr. Jiffyluber by phone. He says his partner is one of the experts on this and would be happy to see her and to discuss it with her. They will make an appointment to see him next week. We gave them the phone number to set this appointment up. If they have problems prior to that time they can always go to the hospital and be admitted for further evaluation. I told them I would review the literature in the interim and be available should they need us."

There are five discrepancies in this medical record based on what Poppa, Mother and I heard in the exam room with Dr. Doubter:

1) Mother never mentioned her appetite, much less it being suppressed;

2) We were never told to go to an ER or hospital later if we had any further problems, but it was suggested Mother go that day until Dr. Doubter realized that was not a good alternative;

3) Dr. Doubter said the knee did appear abnormal in his medical notes, yet he repeatedly told us that he didn't think her knee was the problem, especially the clicking noise and as evidenced that he was skeptical of our theory of rare metal allergies or toxicity;

4) We were told we would see Dr. E. Z. Jiffyluber's partner, but we never had the opportunity to schedule an appointment with Dr. B. M. Logger. Nurse Hornet made sure we saw Dr. Jiffyluber instead of giving us a choice, even when I was insistent

on following Dr. Doubter's instructions to see Dr. Logger; and

5) Dr. Doubter stated, "I've never been exposed to any metal information or researched it."

However, refer back to Dr. Doubter's medical records. He must have cramped in an overnight review, quickly learning about metal allergy reactions and toxicity since he made sure the record stated "it was rare and he was skeptical."

Also, his medical notes stated this replacement had been done for some time. Would that in any way insinuate that because "he" didn't catch the early signs, or listen to the continuous complaints from Mother since "day one," it was impossible for her to have an allergic reaction to metal? Nah… surely Dr. Doubter was not a serious doubter at heart!?!

After experiencing what we felt like were two professionals putting on sideshow stall tactics to alleviate any concern on our behalf as they reassured us Mother did NOT have a metal allergy, or any toxicity problems based on their visual acuity. Could we have been wrong? Yes, most definitely. But, let's rule out some real possibilities first!

What if we had listened to their professional inflexibility presented as if we were completely out of our gourds, stopping any further medical investigation of Mother's continuous knee pain? Even if the knee replacement was not an element in her muscle weakness, she still suffered with every step. Where would Mother be today had we not pursued other avenues?

It is frightening to think of what she could have lived through knowing there were two practicing physicians who possibly decided to be uninvolved because of the fear of a potential malpractice claim. I strongly questioned their professional integrity.

How in the world was Mother supposed to keep believing she was going to be alright when she went through hell on earth that day with Dr. Jiffyluber and his deviance of her pain, or any possibility that something really could be wrong? It was simple. She continued in a walk of faith, not fear.

As aggravated as Mother, Poppa and I became with the situation, we immersed ourselves in believing the best was yet to be… better known as "hope." We stayed focused with a positive outlook. What seemed like a setback was just a slight downward slide before springing back in an upward direction.

There was never any doubt, and no longer a "Dr. Doubter," guiding us away from the culprit of Mother's problem. We were previously encouraged as Dr. Luke reinforced the "hunch," which I referred to my "gut feeling" which led me to continue my research even further.

Yes, perhaps Mother's case was rare at the time. But I do not think her case was as rare as the those orthopaedic surgeons might have believed Mother's condition IF only they would have been "practicing" versus "procrastinating" physicians!

Yes, my sarcasm in recounting my Mother's medical journey has continued because it is how I learned to insert levity versus animosity. The entire charade tilted my views to become more defensive rather than accepting offensive deception. We were determined to exhaust the possibility of metal allergy and/or toxicity.

Dr. Jiffyluber's exam was unforgettable at the moment, but forgivable. Mother had been spoken to in a condescending tone. She experienced treatment anyone would deem, completely unnecessary. She was agitated and aggravated. This extended two-hour trip made her weaker.

Imagine her great anticipation meeting a new physician who would hopefully somehow provide a new idea to her mysterious health issues, or at the very least, address the pain in her knee. Poppa and I could NOT believe we allowed Dr. Jiffyluber to "handle" her in the ways he seemed to be examining her knee. Poppa was adamant when he firmly stated, "I will never let any physician treat her that way, again!"

Remember, Mother and Poppa were like "Peas and Carrots." The happy-go-lucky couple with little, if any complaints, about their world as one union. While they seemed to be gaining their emotional composure, I was boiling feverishly at the outcome, needing desperately to chill.

Mother decided to call John to discuss what occurred sharing her great disappointment. As close first cousins, John made kept continuous updates on Mother's status and the medical mystery, which seemed to continually consume her life as the culprit was draining her rapidly. He was a great source as a voice of experience in the medical world, in listening to Mother and a physician and as her close relative.

John graduated from the University of Alabama, Tuscaloosa, 1961; the Medical School of Alabama in 1966, Birmingham; and served in the U.S. Navy Medical Corps from 1966-69. Afterwards, he started his own private practice. After 43 years of medical service and compassionate care to help as many of his patients and their needs as possible.

John knew Mother as an individual, very well. And when she was in fact, she not feeling very well. He was tremendously helpful encouraging Mother to keep moving forward. John asked Mother to give him a couple of days so he could do some research on the best orthopaedic revision surgeon in the southeast area. Mother agreed. She always had complete respect for John personally, and professionally.

As a family, we continue to be grateful to our cousin, the physician, who looks out for her best health needs and interests. He had always been faithful, caring, patient, and understanding. How fortunate we were to have John and his family, especially when we had become so frustrated with all Mother's health upheavals.

Within three days, John called Mother with a name and direct number to the nurse of one of the most reputable orthopaedic surgeons within our region. Dr. Mullinsworth[40] had a long waiting list for new patients, but we were extremely fortunate to get a quicker appointment due to John sharing Mother's circumstances. Based on previous blood work reports, surgery was imminent if her SED (infections) and Creatine (muscle mass) rates stayed in the abnormal ranges.

Since I had the majority of Mother's medical files, I thought it was imperative to scan and place them in my computer to create a better organization of the information under each physician or medical facilities' name for quick access. Every page was scanned and placed on two backup drives, plus a USB micro vault.

This became extremely beneficial when visiting a physician specialist who would not have immediate access to Mother's medical files. Another key factor was providing her on-going medical facts and how they tied in with her current problems.

Every physician I gave copies of Mother's other physician records about her other health issues, were extremely appreciative. It established a better physician-patient relationship illustrating open communication. Now, everyone could be in the "know," even if they were skeptical, or willing to learn what we were trying to determine.

In helping to unite all the many known pieces of the puzzles together, Tina's nursing skills were instrumental as she worked with me to link the connections with the medical information I had gathered from Mother's medical history. Primarily, I benefited greatly from her teaching me how to interpret Mother's lab profiles, as she explained how each result affected Mother's health, normal or abnormal.

She was also a prayer partner and dear friend. I believe God made it possible for her involvement to encourage me when I needed a strong faithful believer. Her excellent nursing education from the Medical College of Georgia, Augusta, helped to provide Tina with an already gifted medical ability for tremendous insight, understanding the scientific aspects interwoven with God's human design.

Once all of Mother's medical records were gathered from every medical facility and physician she had seen since March 2006, Tina also helped to interpret some of the medical language in which I was unfamiliar, in addition to Mother's test results. When I understood the root of certain words, familiar study habits carried me back to my JSU science study days. The research and my comprehension started giving me a grand overview of Mother's medical mystery and how it was quite possibly linked to the types of metals in her knee replacement.

I gained a possible "why" factor when her gallbladder became so inflamed without warning; her veins collapsing; and the overpowering physical weakness she had endured. Her low immune system was overriding her body's ability to heal. Everything happening to her kept pointing to a silent culprit known as "metal allergies," creating metal toxicity; and if not found and fixed in time, it could lead to cancer[33].

The research was solid. The mission ahead seemed a daunting task at best. It would be so much easier to just give up, find a job and move off, again. With my reduced funds, my bills were piling up and my own physical energy was more easily drained as I tried to keep many things going at once.

Within two weeks we were to meet with Dr. Mullinsworth. I had a copy of Mother's medical files in a notebook with highlighted areas for a quicker review noting other specialty physicians' concerns, which would correlate with probable orthopaedic health issues.

As Dr. Mullinsworth examined Mother's knee in a very caring and compassionate manner, he then checked her bone scan which looked like an x-ray image. Above the top implant, there appeared to be an inch of space. He believed, based on the darkness on the film, Mother had infection in her knee. Although the blood work and previous fluid from her knee did not reveal any infection, her SED rate was abnormal. Reflecting on her situation, it could have been her kidneys creating the infection since her renal system was hit almost biweekly with one problem after another.

However, he did convey skepticism in regards to Mother's knee replacement being correlated to Myopathy. He did not necessarily rule it out - but - he was not convinced the two were connected. Either way, Dr. Mullinsworth did not want to see Mother suffering which was obvious from his exam of her knee mobility. He then proceeded to examine her knee. Then asked for a current x-ray view while she was in his office, and also wanted current lab work completed at his facility.

Based solely on her appearance and slowed actions, it was apparent something was wrong in some area of her health based on his review.

She was always one to give 100 percent, but her performance was continuing to diminish. Dr. Mullinsworth informed us of how he planned to proceed with her revision surgery. After first removing her knee replacement, a spacer knee would be inserted with her leg positioned straight in a cast for six weeks, or until the infection was completely gone. After the infection was cleared, Mother would have a follow-up surgery to replace the spacer knee with a permanent knee revision.

Compared to the last two orthopaedic visits, we were encouraged yet concerned about the lengthy process Mother would endure. Mother was eager to proceed, if for no other reason than because of her increased pain. I admired her courage, as I witnessed how difficult it was for her.

One of the latest symptoms Mother started experiencing was muscle cramps, knots, and cricks in her neck and shoulders. It was becoming increasingly annoying and bothersome, so she decided to see a chiropractor in our local area. Once she started experiencing some relief due to his therapy sessions, Mother continued on a weekly basis until her surgery. It was the only reprieve, as her tiring muscles were tensing more as she tried to hold her head up straight.

In the research I had studied, no one had ever mentioned this particular problem or annoyance. The only thing that made sense was her muscles were so weak, it required more strength to hold her head up in a correct posture. We applied ice packs, in addition to over-the-counter muscle relaxant patches in an effort to provide continued relief for her.

Mother's primary care physician, Dr. James, was also receiving copies from all of her specialty visits, with the exception of Dr. Jiffyluber. He had told us at the end of Mother's exam when we requested Dr. James be included with his medical review, he would only forward medical documentation to Dr. Doubter. Somehow, Dr. Jiffyluber's remark wasn't the least bit surprising.

Dr. James asked Mother to periodically follow-up so he could visually inspect her physical condition and not just receive the reports. Mother called the day after Dr. Jiffyluber's examination to make an appointment with Dr. James. To her surprise, there was a time slot open prior to lunch.

Jack and Bridget were also kept informed of Mother's journey and at times, nightmarish ordeal. Their family obligations and full time jobs kept them extremely busy. It continued to make more sense for me to be the designated caregiver, working at home, while taking care of Mother.

Jack was able to meet with Dr. James, Mother and Poppa carrying the additional information I was led to research. Of all the days of being available for Mother's doctor appointments, tests, etc., I became sick and had to visit another doctor the same day. It worked out great for my brother to be able to attend the meeting, hear the latest updates, and be a part of the discussions. I was relieved, for many reasons.

Afterwards, Mother shared the exam discussion with me. She said, Dr. James agreed with Dr. Mullinsworth's idea to go ahead and do a revision since she had been in so much pain, which was evident to him. Mother had been his patient for several years.

Mother continued to share with Dr. James about Dr. Doubter's exam, in addition to Dr. Jiffyluber's exam. He was very surprised to learn the feedback. It was good for Mother to hear encouragement face-to-face from a physician who appreciated Mother as a patient. With Poppa and Jack at her side supporting her as Dr. James did, she seemed to gain a great deal of confidence from the pep chat! The previous weeks were really difficult when she knew something was severely wrong, but could not find many sources to help her figure out what was happening to her body. Dr. James gave her a virtual booster shot!

While discussing the replacement/revision process and prolonged agenda, Dr. James mentioned a new orthopaedic surgeon in the area, Dr. Christian Seymour[41]. While discussing the replacement/revision process and prolonged agenda, Dr. James mentioned a new orthopaedic surgeon in the area, Dr. Christian Seymour[41].

Dr. Seymour had completed additional training in minimally invasive total joint replacement, computer-assisted total joint replacement, total hip resurfacing and the Oxford Unicompartmental Knee replacement surgery in Birmingham, England. His practice also focused on early intervention hip and knee arthroscopy, isolated patellofemoral resurfacing, primary hip and knee replacement, complex and revision hip and knee replacement, mobile-bearing unicompartmental knee replacement, total hip resurfacing, computer-assisted navigated hip resurfacing, and ligament sparing biocompartmental deuce knee replacement. Dr. Seymour was by far the most qualified compared to the other orthopaedic surgeons we had encountered.

Poppa shared with me later that Dr. James had mentioned Mother's health decline over the past two months since her last visit. Although, Dr. James was not sure of how there could be any connection between the metal allergies and Myopathy; he was completely open-minded to learn more. Dr. James encouraged Mother to get a second opinion from Dr. Seymour. She agreed almost immediately and Dr. James asked his office staff to call for a quick appointment.

As a new patient, the soonest time frame was in four weeks. Since Dr. Mullinsworth was already working on Mother's case, but had only continued requested lab work for possible infection, Mother and Poppa were excited about the idea of getting another opinion from Dr. Seymour. We became very anxious to learn about a new orthopaedic surgeon with experience in revisions, and his caliber of professional skills, based on his curriculum vitae.

If Mother chose Dr. Seymour, and he chose to perform her revision surgery, this would keep us from dealing with a lot of overnight trips, which had already accumulated approximately 11,000 miles traveling just for medical attention.

Her health seemed to be continuously slipping with gradual weakness. Her abilities decreased dramatically to dress, care and feed herself, much less any other activities. It was a hard transition to watch as I felt helpless as she struggled.

As a caregiver, I kept the house work going, did the shopping, and became the driver, the helper, and the "whatever." It wasn't always smooth sailing but most days were easy and peaceful. We were not a family who thrives on chaos. Mother, Poppa and I had become a tight threesome, with a growing trust, love and patience. We all wanted what was the best for everyone.

I returned home after owning my house. Living in the same house with my folks, worked out fine. Fortunately, we had a house plan which allowed all of us plenty of privacy. It turned out to be one of the best transitions in my life.

While we were waiting for Mother's appointment date with Dr. Seymour for her first visit, Dr. Mullinsworth's nurse called two weeks after her meeting with Dr. Mullinsworth. The lab report showed abnormal blood work which delayed Mother being seen again for another month with Dr. Mullinsworth. He wanted the infection to be treated first.

At this point, we were glad the appointment was already scheduled with Dr. Seymour since it was only two weeks away. There was an unspoken urgency which loomed as time seem to be more precious for Mother to get immediate attention, should it be her knee replacement.

Mother made the decision to call John, expressing her gratitude locating Dr. Mullinsworth. She also shared the news about her upcoming exam with Dr. Seymour. Since John is originally from our home area, he understood how much better this arrangement would be for the family since Dr. Seymour was located closer.

Mother had dreaded calling John since he took time to properly research a reputable orthopaedic surgeon. She knew he did not want her to experience the previous treatment. John completely understood the logic and timeliness of Mother's unique situation, and believed getting another opinion was a good idea. He later shared with me how much weaker her voice had become over the past few months.

In the meantime, Dr. James placed Mother on strong medications to combat the infection Dr. Mullinsworth lab work revealed. It made me wonder why Dr. Doubter didn't do an x-ray or blood work on our last day. Perhaps he really was afraid we would be correct? That is a decision he has to live with, just as we all make our choices.

A week before meeting with Dr. Seymour, Mother developed pneumonia. Her weakness was really becoming more of a struggle than tolerating her disabilities. It was also very discouraging. I knew surgeries were rarely, if ever, planned with this type of illness.

We had to reschedule and extend Mother's appointment for June 8, 2009. As the antibiotics worked to pull Mother out of her rapidly decreasing slide, her knee was becoming more painful. She was determined to keep moving so the pneumonia would not settle in both lungs.

Finally, the day arrived to meet Dr. Seymour. We arrived presenting a weak patient accompanied by her two devoted live-in caregivers. After we were escorted to the exam room, Mother was assisted onto the exam table. Poppa sat nearby in a guest chair. I was propped in the opposite corner anticipating the meeting, not having any assumptions what this orthopaedic surgeon would, or would not do. We left it in the Lord's hands.

When Dr. Seymour entered the room, he was polite, mannerly, soft-spoken and exhibited compassion. There seemed to be a peaceful aura about this physician. To be honest, I was very surprised. It was as if God was healing a hurt in all three of us, previously experienced by unnecessary rude behavior of Dr. Jiffyluber and an exasperated Dr. Doubter.

Dr. Seymour began asking Mother about her ailments. His calm demeanor immediately placed each of us at ease. Hesitantly, I remained on standby waiting to share anything I had discovered or researched until Mother gave me the "help" look. She often times had difficulty explaining the medical aspects, which apparently was one of my jobs as her caregiver. Mother was able to express specifics in how her physical abilities had changed over the last three years as she summarized her journey.

Slowly and gently, Dr. Seymour examined Mother's left knee while she was sitting on the exam table, facing him with both legs dangling. As he placed his hand on her knee, it was as if he could sense or feel, what was occurring. He did not order x-rays. He had very few questions. And then, Dr. Seymour asked for her previous records and/or films.

I handed over Mother's medical files organized in a thick notebook. Each physician and their specialty were tabbed for easy access. We also had acquired a copy of the bone scan film.

He began reading Dr. Doubter's medical notes, appearing to pick up key words as he flipped through the pages in a matter of minutes. We were as quiet as wide-eyed mice watching his every move. Dr. Seymour picked up the bone scan film results, held it to the light. He immediately commented on the inch of dark space above Mother's top knee implant. He said, he also suspected infection. Dr. Seymour explained that if Mother had an infection in her knee, he would advise the same procedures for caution, as Dr. Mullinsworth had explained.

Mother's exam was on a much more personable approach as Dr. Seymour exerted the kindhearted nature. You could sense an indescribable serenity by the look of total relief on each of our faces. Mother's stress level dropped immensely, as her body was fighting off an infection.

Dr. Seymour shared that he had seen a couple of patient cases, which metal allergies were the root cause of a failed implant. He was also extremely knowledgeable and fluent about metal toxicity as we conversed. As I shared my medical research articles from the United Kingdom, Dr. Seymour was on the same page. A specialist, well aware of everything I was led to research. At last, I knew we were in the right place. Everything seemed to be coming together ... finally!

Even though, this was Dr. Seymour's first time to meet Mother, he was keenly aware that she was not in the best of health due to her skin color, slow reaction and repressed expressions, when trying to elaborate what she had endured and was experiencing. Mother shared she had pneumonia which was almost clear and the type of medication she was taking. Then he said, "Well, when would you like to schedule a revision?" I stood in silence, bowing my head as tears began streaming waiting on Mother's reply.

After several seconds, I never heard an answer. I looked over to see tears streaming down her face. It was if an angel appeared ready to caress her worst pains and hurts, emotionally and physically. By repairing her knee, I sensed she felt as if her soul was about to be repaired as well. Poppa had pulled out his handkerchief, to dry his eyes. Dr. Seymour continued to sit right calmly in front of her on his physician stool comforting her as he offered a tissue, waiting for her reply. I imagined he sensed the relief and peace we so desperately needed to hear when his exam was summed up with ... "when?"

Mother finally was able to speak, "As soon as possible." Dr. Seymour said there was no doubt she had a knee problem based on her previous bone scan.

However, the radiologist's bone scan report dated August 8, 2009, which Dr. Doubter interpreted, gave possible warning signs:

> "The patient is being evaluated for joint pain. She has had a left knee and right hip anthroplasty (implant a.k.a. prosthesis). There is particular pain at the left knee. There is moderately increased uptake around the knee anthroplasty. The right knee appears unremarkable."

I found it remarkable two orthopaedic surgeons from two different medical practices saw the inch of darkness on Mother's bone scan. Yet the PA stated, Dr. Doubter reviewed the same scan and said, "There was no indication that anything was wrong."

We left Dr. Seymour's office excited and elated! We never anticipated walking into his office with our medical reports and walking out with a surgery date. THIS is what we expected by trusting Dr. Doubter referring Mother to Dr. Jiffyluber. It was faith and perseverance that led us to the right specialist, to the right place, at the right time. Now, we were lined up with a compassionate and very knowledgeable subspecialty surgeon with relevant experience.

August 22, 2009, was the set date for surgery. However, Dr. Seymour said there was only one stipulation. If Mother did not recover from pneumonia by her surgery date, the revision would be rescheduled until her lungs were clear. We certainly understood this precaution and requirement.

Over the next few weeks, Mother's health began to stabilize. She returned to Dr. James for an overall medical review so she could be signed off for surgery. Another chest x-ray was required. Two days later, we received a call from Dr. Seymour's nurse who received the latest chest x-ray report. She said Mother's surgery would need to be bumped another week and more antibiotics were prescribed to continue her recovery from pneumonia.

Mother was incredibly disappointed, as fear began to set in. Poppa and I felt her despair. It had been a long wait, but only seven more days for her to remain patient. Since March 2, 2006, Mother had gone from dull pain to severe pain on a gradual scale accompanied by weakness, fatigue, loss of muscle use, yet she endured this "walk" like a trooper.

The next chest x-ray was an "all clear" report. We were all set for August 25, 2009 surgery date. It was a day I will never forget. We arrived at the medical center early. Poppa and I stayed with her while she was being prepped for surgery.

Mother's anesthesiologist, Dr. Bailey[42], was one of the doctors I had known for many years since my health care career began at this medical facility. It was so good to see him and he remembered me. He was refreshingly jovial and friendly which helped alleviate any anxiety Mother might be experiencing.

Ahead of her laid the entire process of going through another knee surgery, once again experiencing a tough rehabilitation work schedule to acquire a 120-degree range of motion with continued pain expected. The revision would be just as intense as the original replacement, but we prayed Mother's pain would be alleviated this time compared to her last knee surgery.

Within a matter of minutes, the nurses completed the Pre-Op and I.V.s were started. Jack arrived shortly before Mother was carted off to surgery to give her a kiss and hug. The four of us joined hands and prayed for her surgery to be successful. Soon it was time for all of us to scatter as the surgical nurses came to retrieve the lady who was struggling much like a "victim" but was about to become a "victor!" I could feel it in my bones!

After several hours, Poppa and I were called to the private family room. Jack and Bridget were on standby at their jobs. We waited anxiously for Dr. Seymour to arrive. As he reverently entered the room, we were all ears to hear how the surgery proceeded. He said Mother was doing extremely well.

Then he said, "There wasn't any infection." I sat there perplexed, as Poppa was just as amazed. In a split second, my thought was "What was her problem?" Before Poppa or I could say a word or ask any questions, Dr. Seymour said, "It was a failed prosthesis. The metal never adhered to her muscle or the bone. The top of the implant fell out in my hand and the bottom portion was very easy to pull out."

I went into a blank stare as I could not believe what I just heard. He continued to say "The revision surgery went smoothly with no complications." We thanked him, as I am sure Poppa and I looked dumbfounded. We were dumbfounded!

As soon as Dr. Seymour left the room, Poppa and I stood up and hugged. Then I said angrily, "How could Dr. Doubter do what he did to Mother? How could he allow her to suffer for 37 months? Why did he not try to do anything to help her?" My questions were rapidly firing, not giving him any time to answer. I had grabbed his shirt as if he were Dr. Doubter. An intense rage overcame my emotions. I said, "How could he have done this to Mother? All this time, she was walking on a failed knee replacement!" Poppa was very relieved Mother was alright, but he was just as angry. He then hugged me as tears came streaming. The battle she had endured was uncalled for.

Just knowing, she could have easily fallen and broken the bones where the implant was supposed to fit securely. Mother walked on a failed prosthesis as the metal implants were slipping up and down inside her bone. The pain had to be agonizing! If Dr. Doubter had been located in the same town that day, I would have found him and personally let him have it. What would I have done? I would have tearfully approached him, grabbing his starched white coat, demanding to know "Why would you not listen and believe my Mother for so long allowing her to be in such excruciating pain?"

No matter what his reply, there was no relevant explanation he could have offered.

Realistically, I knew the metal not adhering to Mother's bone and muscle for over two years was not Dr. Doubter's fault. However, what I did hold him responsible for was not doing anything to further investigate her symptoms. Then he sent us to someone who apparently covered I. M. Doubter's own erroneous footprints.

Both orthopaedic surgeons twisted her knee, creating more pain which she adamantly voiced during both exams. Neither "said" that they believed she had a real problem with her knee replacement which was a failed prosthesis!

I stewed as I called my brother to share the report. Then I called my friend, David. I needed help to release the deep seeded anger I felt throughout my entire being. My hurt for Mother was almost unbearable, as I had witnessed her going through so much unnecessarily.

David was instrumental as we talked about how I should best cope with my emotions having been with Mother through her continued suffering, particularly in the last six months. He reminded me it was okay to be angry because it was a righteous anger, and my anger was validated. He encouraged me to give myself time to recover.

As I refocused, I was so thankful for the relief of Mother's successful surgery. I began to realize the major healing process that was taking place in Mother's journey by God's hands was through Dr. Seymour as His vessel.

Within an hour or so, our family was notified that Mother was on her way to her hospital room from recovery. When I saw her lying on the bed, I reached for her hand. I could not believe the strength from her grip. It was astonishing.

Before surgery, Mother complained while lying on the gurney, that her neck was still bothering her. She had developed a crick several days before the surgery. The muscles in her neck and shoulders were stiff, and at times it seemed she had difficulty holding up her head. After the surgery, she whispered to me that her crick was gone, as a slight smile glazed her face before quickly dozing off again.

It was several long dozes before I could share the news that her knee replacement was a failed prosthesis. She had been heavily dosed with anesthesia for four-plus hours, in addition to a considerable safe amount of pain medicine, administered on a regular basis.

About two hours later, she woke up long enough to fully be aware that Poppa was on one side of her bed, while I was on the other. She grinned as she grabbed Poppa's hand and nearly bruised it from squeezing it! At that point, I shared the news with her. She just looked at me with her wide opened eyes. She appeared to be in almost in disbelief. Then she grinned again, just before her eyes closed, as if she were completely relieved to learn it was indeed a failed prosthesis as we all knew something was very wrong with her knee replacement!

The really odd part after her surgery, was remembering how her once frail arms began a transition almost mysteriously! Now her muscle tone suddenly increased. I wasn't sure I would ever see this transformation, much less, so rapidly! The next time she woke up, Poppa and I were laughing with joy as she began flexing her muscles and almost arm wrestling both of us! It was a sight to behold!

Within a few hours, the nurses sat Mother up in the bed as they placed her knee in a motorized stretching machine for knee bends. Miraculously, she was able to use her arms to lift her upper body to a sitting position. I was totally stunned! This was the woman I had been feeding, dressing, taking care of... whatever because she could not do for herself. God allowed a phenomenal healing as her restoration began.

God has revealed the culprit! He answered my prayer! I was completely grateful in her almost instantaneous recovery. It was just incredible to watch a human body rebound so quickly!

Dr. Seymour made his rounds the next day, and signed her orders for rehab. He asked Mother's permission to write a medical journal about her medical case wanting to use the research I shared. It was an honor to know her rare condition was a medical benchmark to be used profoundly for other medical practitioners and patients to learn more in-depth information about metal allergies.

We then had an unexpected detection brought to our attention in regards to Mother's pacemaker. Dr. Bailey made a special point to bring Mother's EKG strip to with her. This was a rare and unusual gesture on the part of an anesthesiologist. As he pulled the long paper strip out to explain what he thought was very strange, he had circled the places where her heart was having irregular electrical surges, as the pacemaker was forcing Mother's heart to beat when it was not necessary.

We were extremely grateful! We had "strongly" suspected as to why she needed a pacemaker implanted when we were told rather "strongly," it was a "necessity." Dr. Hardheart continued to say, "She could walk out into the parking and have a heart attack and die, if she did not agree to a pacemaker."

So, now we had some credence for another follow-up visit with him, once Mother was better! It certainly warranted a concern requiring further investigation. We appreciated Dr. Bailey making the extra effort to bring the information to our attention and EKG strip.

When it came time for inpatient rehab, we were so very fortunate Mother was going to be transferred to a new facility in our hometown where Poppa is on the board of directors. He has been instrumental in helping our small town develop excellent medical care facilities for our aging population.

Two days later, as Mother continued to gain her strength, she was transferred by ambulance to Centre. She was only 15 miles from the house. I exhaled a sigh of complete relief watching her regain her strength, learn to walk properly again, dress and feed herself, and returning to doing everything else for herself. It was a miracle!

Within a month, she was released to outpatient rehab where she returned to the medical facility's rehabilitation center. Within two weeks, she was mobile without the assistance of a walker. She used a cane for only one week.

During the outpatient recovery, I spoke with the hand therapist sharing Mother's diagnosis of Myopathy. He said her muscles would not be able to regain the flexing and ability she was demonstrating in full usage of her hands and fingers if she truly had Myopathy. Indeed, it appeared her diagnosis was a side effect!

After Mother's recovery, I notified Dr. Doubter in a personal letter stating the discovery, the facts, and a copy of the surgical report. The letter was shared in a tone of sincere forgiveness, wishing the best in his practice as a skillful surgeon.

Forgiveness was the path we chose. Mother was finally on her way to a complete recovery after having "bend" there, done that... with two surgeries on her left knee!

+ + +

Chapter 13
ON MY KNEES

It was imperative to rid my thoughts and mindset of revenge, animosity and deep seeded anger that rushed through me faster than my next heartbeat. The rage I felt for Dr. Doubter grew when I periodically thought about his lack of professional demeanor to seek ways to help Mother. A deeper rescind was required than just forgiveness. A true repentance was essential. I believed when I prayed asking forgiveness towards Dr. Doubter and others, that it was complete. But the memory and issues kept surfacing. The devil wanted me to continue to suffer as Mother's suffering continued to enrage me from time to time. Her issue was treatable with surgery. My suffering continued to exist because I allowed it to linger. It was difficult, but the truth was… it was truly unequivocally over!

It was weeks before I could let go of the mental impressions of Dr. Doubter's laid back medical approach towards the numerous times Mother was in his presence, in his exam room, in his care as she continued to plead for help from him. She knew better than the rest of us exactly the limitations for her threshold of pain. Her body tired needlessly. Dr. Doubter kept the same pace, with the same level of voice inflection when he talked as if she had a "chigger" bite causing her to scratch more often than she desired.

As I reflected on the amount of time she spent, almost begging for his help as her continual hurting was approaching three years since our last visit with Dr. Doubter, my feverish temperament escalated. "He called himself a Christian!" … continued to cross my mind. He said in Mother's presence; he prayed for her as she sat in his office so hopeful that he could assist her.

"But wait a minute…" I thought, and pondered… "Why I was coming back to the same point again, and again?"

I called myself a Christian, yet I continued to carry a tremendous grudge against someone, a proclaimed brother in Christ, who may not have known any other way to practice medicine, without the insight I believed I had received from God.

I was the hypocrite if I could not forgive, no matter what the consequences! Whether Mother lived or died, I was no better than the person I was placing all the blame towards. Mother chose to follow-up with him for her knee replacement surgery and continued exams for years. I could have strongly suggested for her to go to another orthopaedic surgeon for a second opinion, but I didn't. That idea could have crossed her mind as well, but it didn't.

My point: when it came to the blame game, we were ALL responsible, and there was certainly enough to go around!

In the dedication of Steel Standing, I was inspired by the Father to write "forgiveness is not an option."

God began revealing the truth; the real culprit of Mother's health dilemma. But what had I learned besides more educational facts about the science of our human anatomy? What had I grasped in all of the research, my private times of prayer, and my dependence on my devotional depth?

I wholeheartedly continue to give God all the praise and glory for Mother's many miraculous medical treatments! But if I could not forgive in my heart as deeply as I prayed to God to save my Mother's life, what had I learned?

The healing lesson was forgiveness against this, or any other culprit, Mother faced in her quest to find excellent health, again.

My unforgiving ways were just as wrong in my personal walk as a Christian, as the orthopaedic surgeon who refused to go to the next level of learning, or researching in an effort to exhaust all possibilities for Mother's welfare. Dr. Doubter is accountable… but so is each person equally accountable for their own actions and walk in this world.

Who was "I" to blame Dr. Doubter, with a continual revisit on the past? Perhaps the answer was, I could not let go… because I didn't want to let go. Allowing the enemy to deter my thoughts, when I sensed the greatness of God. Praise God! We thank the Great Physician!

The failed prosthesis from March 2006 literally fell out into Dr. Seymour's hands when he performed the knee revision surgery in August 2009. I can still recall his facial expression as he braced Poppa and me with the news, which proved to be equally distressing and delightful.

It was distressing because Mother needlessly suffered and delightful since the information I shared with Dr. Seymour helped in his decision to move ahead with her revision. We earnestly prayed for Mother to be healed. God answered, providing everything needed to accomplish this successful "Masterpiece." It was faith in God that prevailed.

As Christians and believers, we are not all on the same level in our faith. Our level of faith is as unique as our bodies were formed by our Creator. We may be close in our walks of faith, yet we each bring our own life experiences and our personal relationship with God into our decisions.

"Why is that?" I asked time and time, again.

I think the key is "each one."

To have an individual relationship with God is personal. It must be individual in relationship…"one-to-one." A growing relationship with God is the same, as any relationship one has with another living being. If a relationship nurtures healthy growth, it has the potential to become more intimate which makes it all the more extraordinarily special.

A relationship with The Creator is also exceptionally unique. We are all similar creations, yet unique in God's sight. If we each understand this visionary concept, adding unconditional forgiveness… what a world we could live in!

If you can wrap your mind around that realization, which may be so easy for some to comprehend, or too difficult for others, perhaps it's possibly perceived as philosophy versus fact.

When God forgives, He wipes the slate clean. A good example is my failures just as my Mother's knee prosthesis failed.

Faith bonded with forgiveness is the impression of my footprints illustrating my learning steps on this journey. Those are my spiritual prosthetics God provided for me, since I chose to lean on Him… need Him… know Him!

So what if Dr. Doubter panicked… what if he confided in a best friend to figure out what to do if Dr. Doubter reviewed his notes and discovered he could have done more... what if.... What if???

The point is....I could "what if" for the rest of my life, and it would not help Mother's situation which was ultimately orchestrated for success by the Great Physician.

Mother's testimony is an alarm to wake up others whose feet may be asleep... not attempting to step up their own medical mysteries through education and investigation. You may, or may not, find answers. No one will know until they try, ask, seek, and dig.

I was still dragging up the drudgery of the past. It spiritually locked my knees to keep from moving forward towards true spiritual forgiveness.

Instead of investing time and energy in contemplating a lawsuit to prove wrongful action believing both men were highly competent at some level of medical practice to help others... why not pray? If I prayed for their practices to be blessed by God so His healing intervention is practiced in their patients' lives who walk into each of their medical office doorways for better health and hope, isn't that solution far better than trying to make a statement through a court case?

That was exactly why we did NOT choose to litigate. We gave our hurt and deep seeded red-hot anger, burdens, pain - all of what we had experienced towards these men to God... for the Father is the Judge... as He judges and evaluates every individuals' actions, or lack of actions.

If I could not forgive - and I mean truly forgive in my heart, clearing my mind of wrong doing by Dr. Doubter and Dr. Jiffyluber - then how can I call myself a Christian, which translates to being representative of Christ?

God is the One who provided the medical information to me for Mother to be healed. I prayed to be His vessel. The great discovery did not come by way of a medical degree. It came by the great Creator having mercy on me, when I got down on my knees asking him to forgive me, and to bless those who come against me. It's a daily battle, whatever failed in your life... knees or needs.

I realized I had to dig deep within my soul to forgive the hurt being generated, intentionally or unintentionally, by others towards someone I loved deeply and dearly.

Holding grudges holds me to an unforgiving spirit which creates poison just as harmful as the poison my Mother's body experienced in her walk: physically, emotionally, and spiritually.

He made the path clear for others to be educated - not just about the toxicity from metal exposure containments referenced in *Steel Standing* - but from the spiritual toxins we allow and sometimes, even inspire to be created in our hearts through the way we think and live.

On my feet, I thank God for leading me to the next level of intimacy in a personal relationship with Him.

On my knees, I ask for forgiveness, often!

Chapter 14
METAL MENTALITY MIGHTILY EXPOSED

As Mother's health issue was an extremely gradual process working towards a multitude of health crises, seemingly like clockwork, her signs and symptoms evolved as the culprit was revealed to be the metals in her knee replacement.

Previously, I never gave any thought to metals or the different metal ions released by all metal products placed internally. Subsequently, I now have a new "Metal Mentality," literally seeing metal in a different light from its intended use. My eye-opening experience consisted of understanding that we are all exposed to metals, often on a daily basis, through the corrosion of metal alloys which make up prosthetics, dental restorations, heart stents, pacemakers, wires, clips and other implanted metal devices.

External exposure to metals comes through cigarette smoking, jewelry, vaccines, environmental pollution and metal pigments in food, cosmetics and pills, to mention a few. It seemed I had not previously grasped the extent in which metals are used in a number of ways, considered routine by most medical teams and patients, and sometimes potentially lifesaving.

However, the research acutely projected the devices as dually life threatening devices – for those that are sensitive to metals. Why? There is nothing wrong with most metals per se, although some can be damaging to anyone in higher doses, such as mercury and arsenic. The problem is the way some people's immune system reacts to metals.

When I became aware of the possible devastating side-effects which metals can induce, I was led to write Mother's story as a provoking challenge for anyone else experiencing any similar symptoms and had any type of metal implants in their body.

When I first began my research, my hopes were high on finding other published material such as personal stories or testimonies, on this particular subject matter of this medical magnitude. When no other publications were revealed as I searched every possible angle with my attempts, it was laid on my heart to write Mother's true story as a tribute in hope that the massive amounts of information could help and encourage others in similar situations.

Based on the research I conducted, and in talking with many physician specialists, I found out that metals can appear as a silent predator contributing to a toxic situation with the patient being vulnerable and clueless of what triggered their health's failure.

Also, I learned from speaking to many patients we encountered in medical facilities for hospitalization, physician visits, in addition to people directly contacting Mother, that her journey was just one of many. It appeared to a classic example of skepticism, as metals issues were being "swept under the rug."

Metals are essential for life on planet earth. Our own individual body chemistry requires a balance of metals in our system to function; otherwise, we could not exist. However, my focus continued to be on metals, specifically those released from metal implants or prosthetics.

In my non-clinical health career, I never imagined what our human bodies experienced when metal is inserted, whether allergic or not. It was not a headline interest - in 2009. When I began to learn more about the specifics of the metals placed in Mother's body from academic sources, it was alarming to learn the wealth of information available. It was truly an education. All I had to do was research the specifics versus accept or be persuaded by skeptics.

One key which helped tremendously was researching the specific manufacturers of the metal implant products used, or to be used, in my Mother's body.

It was reassuring that all metal implants are federally regulated with strict policies and periodic inspections by the government if located or distributed in the U.S. To ensure each metal part meets strict specifications, the manufacturer's environment is mandated as a sterile environment and the metal implant must remain sterile until it meets its match.

There are also expiration dates and identification numbers on every individual metal implant.

Several manufacturers worldwide produce implants. Our world offers an incredibly fast paced active society, with hoards of opportunities to enjoy a productive and rigorous lifestyle. Due to medical breakthroughs, people are living longer. Time and technology have advanced in so many ways. I doubt my grandparents could ever have comprehended this age of technology. It was difficult for me at times, but I was eager to learn!

As I explained some of this information to my Mother, the details needed to be explicit. She is a sharp thinker, however, to stay on top of today's fast paced life, one must stay within the learning rim. At times it feels as though I am sliding down towards the far edge of technology!

In researching Mother's case, I understood that for an implant to succeed in her body it would have to be made from the right metal combination, which worked best for her body's chemistry - how she is uniquely designed with her own customized "mother-board" by the Creator.

The information my mind absorbed seemed endless, yet pertinent to share with others. I also spent hours reading blogs of so many people's desperate requests to know where to get metal testing, because they never felt the same since receiving their metal implant. Most of these bloggers were able to track back to dental issues as the metal is camouflaged through a brilliant smile, with a new set of teeth inserted into their gums.

Many bloggers were so desperate for any information that they left their email address to receive replies with tidbits or suggestions. People were searching for more information for evidence to support their suspicions with metal implants, which appeared to have ignited a seemingly unrelated health problem.

It baffled me how many people were seeking answers. Perhaps specialty physicians have not yet discovered the metal tsunami heading towards our society as the use of a wide range of implants has increased.

*Please note: Since this chapter was first written in spring 2010, the beginnings of metal murmurings has been highlighted so much more particularly in the past 12 months through the U.S.

media. The New York Times is just one source, with articles revealing more information about metal implants and general concerns. Their investigative journalists are providing vital detailed insights to Americans, about Americans experiencing many facets with metals and joint replacements - whether it's the types of metals or the types of metal devices.

The following titles can be searched on The New York Times' web site for archived articles in the health section; www.nytimes.com

"The Implants Loophole"-Barry Meier, The New York Times, Dec 16, 2010

"Hip Makers Told to Study More Data"-Barry Meier, The New York Times, May 5, 2011 *This article highlights the FDA's unusual move to mandate major producers of metal joint replacements to begin keeping a data registry in the U.S. (The United Kingdom has been doing this protocol for 20-25 years.)

"In Medicine, New Isn't Always Improved"-Barry Meier, The New York Times, June 6, 2011

"Hip Implant Complaints Surge, Even as the Dangers are Studied"- Barry Meier and Janet Roberts, The New York Times Aug 22, 2011

"Metal Hips Failing Fast, Report Says"-Barry Meier, The New York Times, Sept 15, 2011

"The High Cost of Failing Artificial Hips"-Barry Meier, The New York Times, Dec 27, 2011

Other sources:

"Patients Reveal Agony of Toxic Hip Implants"-Quentin McDermott and Karen Michelmore, ABC News (Australian Broadcasting Corporation), Sept 26 2011, www.abc.net.au

"Hip Replacement Poisoning"-Bobby Shuttlewoth, WAFF News, Huntsville, AL, Sept 21, 2011, www.waff.com

"New Hip Implants No Better Than Older Ones,-Not enough data to tell which device is best, researchers say"-Steven Reinburg, HealthDay Reporter, Nov 29, 2011 www.everydayhealth.com

"Faulty Hip Implants May Cause Long-Term Health, Joint Damage" -Janice Lloyd, USA Today, Feb 02, 2012, USAToday.com: http://yourlife. usatoday.com/health/story/2012-02-08/Faulty-hip-implants-may-cause-long-term-health-joint-damage/53002186/1

"Fears Over Hip Replacement Poisoning"-Sky News, Yahoo News, Jan 29 2012, http://uk.news.yahoo.com/fears-over-hip-replacement-poisoning-035637034.html

"Hypersensitivity Reactions to Metallic Implants" -Diagnostic Algorithm and Suggested Patch test Series for Clinical Use. Peter C. Schalock, Torkil Menne, Jeannae D. Johansen, James S. Taylor, Howard I. Maibach, Carola Liden, Magnus Bruze and Jacob P. Thyssen, July 24, 2011

The studies in "Hypersensitivity Reactions to Metallic Implants" were most intriguing, particularly in their reference to Pacemakers/ Defibrillators. In summary; most allergic complications are rare, however there are certain cases in which the patient is allergic to the metal casing of the device, since the outer shell is made from a Titanium "Alloy" versus "Pure" Titanium. Since the exact place on Mother's chest area itched almost all the time with a red rash, I was not at all surprised to read this enlightening report.

The sources are not singled out for any reason. These particular articles caught my attention while keeping up with metal issues regarding joint replacements and implants.

The United States Food and Drug Administration[43] states in their information online www.usda.gov for public access the following: "Talk About Metal Allergies" By: Deborah Yoder, Nurse Consultant and Terrie Reed, MedSun Project Coordinator.

Problem Description:

Many implanted devices are made of, or contain, stainless steel and other metals that can trigger sensitivity or allergic reactions. Stainless-steel medical devices that release nickel and other metal ions can trigger metal contact allergies and result in adverse patient outcomes. The incidence of nickel contact allergies in the overall adult population is estimated at 10% with a higher prevalence in women than men. Metal surgical clamps and coronary stents are examples of implanted devices associated with local or systemic allergic reactions.

Reported Incident:

FDA received a voluntary MedWatch medical device adverse event report describing a potential metal allergy in a patient that recently received an implanted stainless-steel stent to treat a serious heart condition. The surgical team asked if the patient had any allergies during the pre-surgical preparation. The patient did not report her metal allergy. After a successful procedure, the patient reported symptoms consistent with a systemic allergic reaction for which she was successfully treated. The patient did not realize the stent contained metal until she read the product brochure after discharge from the hospital.

Even if patients know they have a metal allergy, they may need to be prompted to communicate this information. Pre-procedure questions to identify potential allergic reactions are often directed toward issues such as drug reactions or sensitivities to latex products. Metal allergies or sensitivities may not be emphasized or discussed during a pre-procedural patient assessment.

Recommended Actions:

Specifically discuss metal allergies as part of your pre-surgical patient assessment. Document metal allergies and sensitivities on the patient's surgical check list, on the cover of the patient's medical record, and on the appropriate page within the patient's medical record. Encourage patients to document and carry an allergy/sensitivity card in their wallets/purses.

The most disturbing article I read revealed how fewer patients are <u>not</u> trying to research their own health concerns! Had we not started trying to figure things out with Mother's medical mystery, I would rather not imagine what would have become of her quality of life.

"Fewer Patients Researching Personal Health Issues" Robert Lowes, www.medscape.com, 11-22-11

My challenge in helping Mother became larger than I could have imagined once I started doing some solid research. As I developed my own metal mentality, it became a project or mission, to share what I learned based on facts, to help others searching for hope in learning more about the effect of metals on the body.

Stepping Back on my Soapbox

What Mother experienced **should not** keep anyone from having metal implants. It should **teach us** to take precaution and if time is allowed, be tested for metal sensitivity, particularly if there is an allergic reaction to non-precious metal jewelry (often containing nickel) or a family history of allergy.

In another article, "Cutaneous and Systemic Hypersensitivity Reactions to Metallic Implants[44]:"it says most skin reactions are eczematous and allergic in nature, although urticarial, bullous, and vasculitic eruptions may occur. Also, more complex immune reactions may develop around the implants, resulting in pain, inflammation, and loosening. Nickel, Cobalt, and Chromium are the three most common metals that elicit both cutaneous and extracutaneous allergic reactions from chronic internal exposure.

As this *Steel Standing* continues to share the latest news up to press, The Journal of Investigative Dermatology[45] recently stated 30 percent of the population is allergic to Nickel and the rate is rising. It's my understanding from a dermatologist, a realistic range is 3-10 percent.

As mentioned in an earlier chapter, I remembered Mother's right ring finger turning green when she wore a certain ring. The band was silver with a large stone seated on top. No one in the medical Pre-Op process ever asked Mother about any known metal allergies before her knee replacement.

Dr. Doubter did not have a choice with her hip replacement. The neck of her femur bone was broken when she fell. That was an emergency surgery. Although her knee replacement was four months later, there was never a question asked "Do you have any allergic reactions to metals?"

Without that question answered, her medical history was incomplete. It was mid October 2009, and time to answer the many questions as to which metals Mother was allergic to, if any. I was extremely anxious to learn the results.

After spending weeks at a nearby inpatient facility, Mother recovered quickly. Next was outpatient therapy sessions. During this time of her healing process, Mother had a follow-up visit with Dr. Seymour. He carefully monitored her recovery process.

Although he previously had two patients with metal allergies, I believe he was astonished with Mother's unique set of circumstances. His plan to write about her clinical case in a medical journal directly reaching to other practicing orthopaedics was placed on hold until she fully recovered and her metal allergy testing was complete.

When Dr. Seymour requested Mother's permission to share her medical facts in an orthopaedic journal in August 2009, it never occurred for me to write Mother's story from a personal perspective until January 2010.

He also asked Mother to have allergy testing since her knee replacement was a failed knee prosthesis. We needed to know the root cause of the failure. I had prayed for the culprit to be revealed. It was indeed Mother's knee, just as the time line had provided the pivotal clue!

We already knew the implant alloy was comprised of Cobalt-Chromium-Nickel. One or more of those metals caused the implant to fail. This information would also be helpful should her hip replacement begin giving her any trouble.

Dr. Seymour recommended Derm A. Titus, M.D.[70], a well respected dermatologist in Georgia.

Within a few days, Mother and I again were on yet another medical related road trip. This time, she was able to endure the ride without muscle aches and pains. When we stopped for a brief shopping trip lasting over an hour, I knew she was on the road to recovery!

We met with Dr. Titus on October 12, 2009. It was refreshing to be referred to another physician with an extremely personable approach and eager to learn more about Mother's medical case. The real draw was her Inflammatory Myopathy diagnosis and if there was any possibility, as I was led to believe, that the two were connected; not only in theory or research, but in actuality.

Dr. Titus developed a recent interest in metal allergies as more patients with a history of costume jewelry or other metal reactions, came from orthopaedic - or self referrals - for pre-operative evaluations. He shared that some researchers believe that systemic metal allergy or toxicity may play a role in some patients presenting with features of Chronic Fatigue Syndrome.

However, he was virtually in the same boat we were actively paddling. Very little information or patient records had been documented to date and there was not a national registry at this time in Fall 2009 to collect vital information on metal implants.

Dr. Titus was impressed by Mother's stamina to endure a failed prosthesis for 37 months and then having a revision within the last six weeks, only to be sitting in his office ready for more testing with bounds of energy!

The first procedure for identifying metal allergy, called patch testing, required taping 27 metal solutions and 6 formed discs to Mother's back with each metal in a specific order for easy identification. After day 3, Mother was to return for Dr. Titus to review the results of the metal on her skin. The universal standard for placing and reading patch tests is day 1, day 3, day 5 or day 7, as advised by Dr. Titus while sharing pertinent information about patch testing. I wanted to learn as much as possible. It was intriguing to see how different types of metals could be tested on the epidermis, or skin of the human body.

If this procedure didn't clearly identify any metal allergy by leaving a rash or red area, the next step was to ship vials of her blood drawn to a specialty lab to identify what metals could cause Mother to have an allergic reaction.

I'm sorry… Did I say "blood work to test for metals allergies?!" Yes, it's called MELISA® or "memory lymphocyte immunostimulation assay." Yes, the informative letter I had mailed to Dr. Doubter after Mother's failed prosthesis also included the name and address of the lab where Mother's blood work was sent. I thought it could be extremely helpful since this area of testing seemed to be severely lacking. In talking with many physicians, I learned the only lab tests available were measuring **levels** of heavy metals, which is a completely different blood work category.

Basically, measuring the level of metals in blood is fairly futile, as metal ions are quickly bound to proteins and enzymes in the body - they do not "float" around.

Having worked in occupational health for a number of years, I found the ongoing issue of exposure to metals, occupational or personal, to be stunning. As a lay person, now advocate since Mother's troubles were identified, I was only scratching the surface.

Mother was instructed by Dr. Titus not to get wet but she could take a sponge bath. She was instructed to not remove the metals at any time, even if they began to burn or itch. During the 3 days, Mother stated that the metal samples did have a tendency to itch, but we did not have a clue which tapes, as they were attached firmly to her back.

In the same follow-up week, we returned to Dr. Titus' office for the metal samples to be removed. He was as eager to see the results as a kid opening up a present. I appreciated being invited to stand beside him, while I imagined the sound of a drum roll as he began the unveiling.

Unless the tapes attached to Mother's back became unbearable, then it would be necessary for them to stay securely affixed. However, she was able to tolerate the metal markers for 3 days. They were still firmly intact attached to the taped apparatus which was placed across her back within her shoulder blades and down to just above the back of her waistline.

One by one, Dr. Titus used a yellow high-lighter to draw off the blocks around each space where a metal marker had been placed. Readings were made based on redness that filled a test square and appeared similar to what might be seen with a poison ivy reaction. During this exam, it was on the second and later readings, Dr. Titus used a black light to check for any rashes, patches or any redness indicating a specific metal allergy in the highlighted area.

The patch test was positive to Nickel and weakly positive to Cobalt. No visual indicators were showing for Chromium. But the Titanium area, fortunately, was clear since it was the metal of choice for her knee revision.

However, since Mother's patch testing for Titanium, I have learned it does not always give a positive reaction even in people who develop health problems after Titanium implants.

The Titanium dioxide salt used in patch testing is not soluble and does not penetrate the skin under the conditions of patch test. Therefore having a Titanium allergy could be unrecognized unless further blood metal allergy testing is performed, or other types of testing.

Dr. Seymour used Titanium in Mother's case basing his decision on Dr. Doubter's medical information. Since Mother did not have problems or complications with a Titanium stem in her hip, Titanium appeared to be the best choice.

Dr. Titus wanted to proceed with blood samples from Mother and then overnight send her blood samples to a MELISA®[47] licensed laboratory.

There was only one major decision Mother and Poppa would have to make before Dr. Titus could go any further. Although Mother had excellent health insurance for primary and secondary, it did not cover the cost of metal allergy blood testing. His office staff said most health insurance carriers did not cover any portion of the test, which totaled $640.00 plus special overnight shipping costs to test for 15 different types of metals. There was no decision. Their reply was an immediate "Yes, we'll gladly pay for it."

In updating this chapter's information, it's my understanding some insurance companies will pay for the MELISA® blood allergy testing.

My opinion: As the increasing awareness about previously unrecognized side effects of metals become a more acute topic, I think more insurances companies should consider paying to keep patients from going through painful and extensive revisions!

Mother's life depended on knowing more about the reaction to metals in her body. Even if she was slightly allergic to Titanium, it was a need-to-know basis. Titanium may not be the very best alternative, especially if it is not pure or is alloyed with hardening metals that one may be allergic to, such as Nickel. (This is referenced further in the chapter.)

However, the idea of going through another revision due to health complications, again was not an option Mother wanted any time in the near or far future. The entire process of trying to get an orthopedic surgeon to consider replacing her knee implants with a revision surgery was very difficult. Not counting the investigative efforts placed in trying to learn the root cause of what was triggering the Inflammatory Myopathy that she was experiencing.

It was like that old saying when asking for directions, "You can't get there from here. You have to start from somewhere else." That sums up all the research. If not for prayer and faith, we would have never figured out the culprit. Out of all the health problems she experienced, not one lead us to think it was due to an allergic reaction to a metal joint replacement in her body.

Before having the blood drawn to send to the MELISA® lab, first we ordered the test kit from our home to have it sent to Dr. Titus' office so they could clinically draw blood for the lab work. Within a week, the test kit was delivered and we were notified by his staff. Once we received the call to let us know it arrived, we headed to Georgia the next day. Within two weeks, Mother's results were shared with us by Dr. Titus. He personally called to explain the report since it confirmed everything in the research I had presented to Dr. Seymour prior to Mother's knee revision surgery.

MELISA® works by putting a type of blood cells, the white blood cells, into contact with various metal salts and measuring the reaction. If the cells divide and enlarge upon contact with a metal, the test is evaluated positive. If no change of the cells is observed, the test is negative. The situation in the laboratory mimics the situation in the body.

A similar blood test, Beryllium specific lymphocyte proliferation test, is used in our country to determine beryllium allergy in beryllium-exposed workers in factories.

Any worker who is found reacting to beryllium is relocated to a beryllium free environment. If this is not done, he or she is likely to develop a serious and chronic lung disease – Berylliosis. This type of testing can therefore avoid unnecessary suffering and large health care costs.

Mother's allergy test confirmed the patch test results: positive to Calcium Titanate and Nickel, and weakly positive to Cobalt. Dr. Seymour confirmed my findings on Calcium Titanate, which is a bone growth enhancer and sealer.

He also said, that the year Mother had her replacement implants in 2006, there were only two types of orthopaedic cements on the market. Calcium Titanate was one of the two which is a complex form of titanium, calcium and oxygen.

However, Mother's MELISA® lab results did NOT show that she had any reactions to Titanium. The blood allergy test was the key factor validating everything I believed God was leading me to understand through medical research as I had earnestly prayed, asking Him, "Please reveal the culprit."

Recent research studies offer new indications when Titanium is used to replace Nickel - which was one of the metals in a previous implant. However, research also reveals that Titanium is not the best alternative.

Dr. Elizabeth Valentine-Thon[46], (Ph.D.), presented her research studies on "Titanium Hypersensitivity: Does it Really Exist?" at the conference *Identifying triggers of inflammation in chronic disease* in Thessaloniki, Greece in October 2011. Dr. Valentine-Thon gave permission to use the information in *Steel Standing*.

Her studies reveal new research illustrating that the pure Titanium available on the surgical market for implant usage, is not 100 percent pure, misleading surgeons.

Supporting Evidence:
Muller and Valentine-Thon, 2006:
- One third of patients who improved after removal of their Titanium implants were Titanium negative in MELISA®, some of them were Nickel positive.

Current Data:
- Of patients with problems after Titanium implants, many more are Nickel positive (46 percent) than Titanium positive (6.6 percent)
- Most all Titanium Alloys contain Nickel
- Presence of Nickel in Titanium Alloys in Nickel-Free Alloys

Predicting Risk of Titanium Hypersensitivity:
- "... persons with previous reactions to metals have a greater risk of developing a hypersensitivity reaction to a metal implant." - *Halleb et al, 2001*
- " ... the total knee arthroplasty -TKA (replacement) failure was fourfold more likely in patients who had symptoms of metal hypersensitivity before TKA. - *Granchi et al, 2008*
- "The risk of an allergy to Titanium is increased in patients who are allergic to other metals."- *Evrard et al, 2010*

Mother's MELISA® report showed no allergies to her Titanium

implants, which continues to be excellent news since she has not had any adverse reactions as the majority of patients based on Dr. Valentine-Thon's research.

However, the MELISA® findings did clarify why Mother had problems from "day one" with her knee replacement, which was comprised of the metals Nickel-Cobalt-Chromium.

Within three months after her revision surgery on August 25, 2009, Mother completely recovered from nearly all of her symptoms including her muscle weakness experienced since July 2006. Her hand therapist at the outpatient rehab center encouraged her to use wrist braces for strengthening the use of her hands, but that was the only evidence of any trace remaining from her tremendous trials.

She was alert, active, enjoying life again as she was pain free with very little soreness remaining in her healing knee revision. Mother was very close to returning to where she was prior to the knee replacement in 2006.

The upcoming holidays were the first in many years since Mother was able to get out and enjoy herself. She began playing the piano again for special occasions. The New Year 2010 officially arrived. In January, Mother's birthday is exactly one week later than mine. Finally, we were able to enjoy and celebrate! Shortly after she turned yet another year older, weakness started in her muscles. It was like déjà vu. Could this be possibly happening again?

I did not say anything to Mother. Nor did Poppa. And neither of us said anything to the other one. About two weeks into February, Mother was obviously having extreme difficulty opening a twist top on her plastic tea bottle. Something only a couple months ago offered no hassle in trying to grip. It seemed like a good time to mention this problem out loud, as much as I dreaded it.

Poppa and I were sitting at the kitchen table for dinner as Mother was beginning to eat. I asked her how long she had problems with her hands again. She said the weakness was repeating a gradual process, however she didn't think it would get any worse. Poppa agreed when I suggested we call Dr. Seymour to make an appointment to discuss his perspective on this "once again" unique situation.

I pulled out her old medical records I had already packed in safe keeping, thinking we would never need these again... certainly not this soon. Yet, I distinctively remember standing at the foot of her hospital bed when she had her knee revision in August 2009 knowing that her hip was next. I just never said anything to anyone, hoping I was perhaps thinking too much. Besides, that was the last thing Mother wanted to hear was any type of predictions from me even if they became valid.

As I began delving into the metal section I had researched, which seemed like only two weeks ago, there was one particular website focusing on the specific types of metals in the head of her hip replacement. It was comprised of Nickel-Cobalt-Chromium. What I learned would make your hair stand on ends!

Chromium causes a dangerously slow toxic build up in the kidneys, which can lead to renal failure[48] and is linked to digestion failure. Why I did not see this vital information before, is beyond me! This time, I highlighted the information so it would not be missed. I made copies for our upcoming visit to Dr. Seymour.

The Wednesday before Valentine's Day on Sunday, Mother decided she wanted to get her hair dolled up for her sweetheart, Poppa. She said mine looked like a ragtop. Hearing those endearing expressions with a slight grin, I knew two things were happening; she was going to get her way and I was getting a haircut, also! Mother scheduled our appointments back-to-back so I could drive her to town.

Mother's "beauty" appointment involved her ritual hair wash-dye-cut-n-dry. So I planned to get my hair cut first. Then I would head off to the store with Mother's grocery list while in Centre. For some reason that day I hung around and talked with our hairstylist, Sharon, the owner of a "trim for her or him" shop. She was also my former high school classmate, so we know a lot of the same people in town. Her shop environment was always fun. Between Mother and Sharon, there was plenty of laughter to go around, even when I didn't think there was a funny bone perky enough to be tickled, at least at that time in our lives!

When Sharon began prepping Mother to put the dye coloring on her hair, we all three were rattling about some catch up topics; who lost a family member recently or who was sick or anything about people we cared about, but it was not gossip. It was a Christ-based hen party. We knew how to share news, yet be genuine as Mother cracked us up with her famous witty one-liners. It's no wonder I was voted "wittiest" in high school, as an acorn does not fall far from the tree, which is a "saying" in our folksy "Mayberry" Centre town.

By the time Sharon finished placing the dye, which has a quick and distinctive aroma, all over Mother's hair, I was still hanging as I leaned back on the counter. For some reason that day, I felt subconsciously drawn to stay close by Mother who moved over to another chair in the side waiting area, for the dye to stay applied on her head for a few minutes. I decided to go over sit with her while she waited.

Within three minutes, Mother said: "I feel strange." She is never one to say something like that or become sick, much less so quickly. So I asked her, "What kind of strange? Is it your head? Is it a migraine?" She replied with a distinctive "No" as she did an east-to-west nod. Then said, "I feel like I need to go to the rest room. I have a queasy feeling all over my body, almost like I can't breathe." I thought it was so peculiar. And then somehow I knew it had to be the hair dye. My only explanation is that God was directing my thinking. Mother had never experienced this type of reaction before. Her hair has been colored for many, many years.

I calmly but hurriedly hunted for Sharon in the back of the shop to come and wash the chemicals out of Mother's hair. In the meantime, I asked Mother to move to the "hair sink" so Sharon could quickly remove the dye to see if that was causing the problem.

After the chemicals were thoroughly washed out of Mother's short hair, she started to feel much better within 10 minutes. She said the sick feeling vanished nearly as quickly as it appeared and had the strangest sensation throughout her entire body, like she was going to pass out. As soon as Mother was better, Sharon proceeded to trim and style her hair for Sunday's Valentine outing. However, Mother was insistent; no more hair coloring for her!

One of the reasons I kept hanging around that day was Mother's debate whether to color her hair or not. She said it was time to see just how gray her hair had become after years of coloring. Sharon and I stood on each side of the chair, with half-baked grins and raised eyebrows, as Mother vocally argued with herself. We just listened to her rattle, wondering if she was going to come to a conclusion anytime soon... or if our hair was going to turn gray waiting on her decision... or if mine would come from me pulling it!

I can't ever remember the last time Mother was so indecisive about whether to do this or that. She was not at all an overly confident lady coming across like a force to be reckoned with. Her easy going and loving charisma would draw stray dogs from miles away; being so extremely personable.

We left Sharon's shop and headed to the house. On the way home, not only was Mother's hair thoroughly washed out, but her physical strength was washed out too. Once we were arrived, she barely moved from her recliner for the next three days. Watching her go through this weak time reminded me so much of what I saw before her knee revision. After a few days, she gradually did get better, but it was a slow climb back to her already weakened state.

For some reason it dawned on me to check on the content of the hair coloring in the dye. I called Sharon at her shop and asked for the name of the color and manufacturer that was used on Mother. It took about an hour of online Internet searching but again, what I learned was fascinating and shocking[49]!

The first interesting information I read was written by Paulose Varkis[50], author and accomplished researcher in alternative medicine, with a Masters degree in psychotherapy and counseling. He had extensively researched the dangers of hair coloring. His published article, October 2009, "Ten Dangerous Effects of Hair Coloring" caught my attention. He stated: "We are not aware that most conventional hair dyes and coloring agents contain the most potent and harmful chemicals compared to any other beauty product... very important to know more about the product that you are going to apply on your hair."

Excellent advice!

What never once entered my thoughts were the use of metal pigments in hair color and now clearly that was a new area of self-education for me. The chemicals I discovered in hair coloring dye were a blatant indicator that they were too harsh for Mother's body to absorb. I wondered what a body's threshold for toxicity might be. Had Mother reached her limit or perhaps was she dangerously close based on her reaction, which happened so quickly?

The article shared some thought-provoking ideas for anyone to consider, whether it's your hair or someone you care about that has a ritual of hair coloring treatments.

Some health hazards Varkis included as a result of exposure to toxic hair dye chemicals included: Hodgkin's disease and multiple myeloma; breast cancer; bladder cancers; and allergic reactions. Some hair coloring contains pesticides, which can disrupt hormones.

Mother's particular hair brand and color used Nickel and Cobalt in their dyes. With Mother being allergic to Nickel, if she used a dark hair color such as dark red, dark brown, or black, then coal tar[51] was one of the ingredients. "Hair color today, health issues tomorrow?"

After three hours on the Internet, I found a host of web sites offering valid and substantiated information. The biggest discovery was that the U.S. Federal Drug and Administration does not require all the ingredients to be listed on hair dyes. As stated on their web site:

"[FDA][52] bears or contains any poisonous or deleterious substance which may render it injurious to users under the conditions of use prescribed in the labeling thereof, or under conditions of use as are customary and usual" [with an exception made for hair dyes 3]; 3, hair dyes reference is a page long, but this is an excerpt: Several coal-tar hair dye ingredients have been found to cause cancer in laboratory animals. In the case of 4-methoxy-m-phenylenediamine (4-MMPD, 2, 4-diaminoanisole) which had also been demonstrated in human and animal studies to penetrate the skin, the agency considered the risk associated with its use in hair dyes a "material fact" which should be made known to consumers.

"The Dangers of Hair Coloring and Safer Alternatives[53]," written by journalist Cathy Sherman:

"Commented European Commission Vice-President Günter

Verheugen, who is responsible for enterprise and industry policy, "Substances for which there is no proof that they are safe will disappear from the market. Our high safety standards do not only protect EU [European] consumers, they also give legal certainty to the European cosmetics industry." The United States, however, has not required manufacturers to file data on ingredients or report cosmetic-related injuries."

Reading this information reminded me of my former hair dresser's unexpected cancer discovery when she went into the hospital for a gallbladder surgery. Karen had been my hair stylist for over 20 years. No matter where I lived, I returned to have her cut my hair. She was that good... as a person and as a professional! Karen was loved by everyone. She showed an exemplary Christian attitude in her work and with family. Her jovial laughter and outgoing personality will always be remembered as unique, special and she always "walked the walk."

She was diagnosed with cancer in her pancreas, liver and part of her intestine, after being admitted to a hospital for a routine gallbladder surgery. At the time I heard about her passing, I never once theorized... which is exactly what I am doing now... that being a hair stylist could place them in a lethal environment. The fumes from the chemicals are used many times a day, many days a week.

This may not have contributed to her death, but the cancer was a complete surprise to her as she shared with me the last time we spoke on the phone from her hospital bed. Shortly thereafter, I learned she had slipped into a coma.

Again, this topic may not relate to Karen's death, but there is great potential in the connection. I grieved knowing I had lost an irreplaceable precious friend. I am blessed to have crossed paths with such an extraordinary person in my life.

It was about the time after I researched the hair dye information when I found notes I scribbled on the back of a long white envelope from our last talk in June 2009. There were details she shared. At the time I wasn't sure why I jotted down the notes. Maybe it was God's way of bringing her information to my attention to share with others about the toxins all around.

In doing more research, I learned the process as to why the chemicals can react rapidly, as they did with Mother. When hair dye is applied to the scalp, chemicals enter into the brain, which is the richest area of our blood. It continuously circulates throughout the body carrying the chemicals to other organs. Although the skull is thick, the skin is thin allowing the body to absorb chemicals faster.

It made perfect sense after witnessing what Mother experienced. Of course, I shared the information with our current hair stylist Sharon. She said, "I do the best I can not to allow the fumes to overcome me when using hair dye." As I stood there for her concern knowing this is how she earns her living, she then calmly said... "And I pray for protection."

Maybe my former hair stylist, Karen, did not have cancer related to her long devoted profession. But finding the notes where I jotted down her medical problems and information, it's difficult for me to think it's not a coincidence. It does correlate with the information I learned.

In reading some articles again from my initial research, I was reminded that a metal allergy can lead to toxicity. If toxins stay in a human body long enough, they become cancer.[71] Again, I do not think all of the information, the eye witness accounts, and crossing paths with so many that had even the smallest influence on Mother's medical mystery was a coincidence.

After almost a year since Mother's muscle biopsy and the "ugh" cart ride, I called Dr. Luke and left a message sharing Mother's update. He returned my call within 40 minutes. To my surprise, he was elated to hear the news.

I went into more details sharing what we learned about Mother's partial hip replacement with Chromium being one of the metals, and how Chromium can cause kidney problems and renal failure based on the United Kingdom medical information.

Dr. Luke confirmed what I had learned about Chromium! He said it can cause renal failure and digestive failure, even if there isn't any allergy to the metal. So no matter what efforts a person tries to do to protect themselves from Chromium being a part of a metal implant, it will have an adverse affect on the human body, sooner or later! Astonishing!

However, to keep from oversimplifying the topic of Chromium, there are different types of Chromium. Some chromium is essential to the human body, other forms will cause cancer.

Wikipedia[54] states: "Although trivalent Chromium (Cr(III)) is required in trace amounts for sugar and lipid metabolism, few cases have been reported where its complete removal from the diet has caused Chromium deficiency. In larger amounts and different forms, Chromium can be toxic and carcinogenic. The most prominent example of toxic chromium is Hexavalent Chromium (Cr(VI)). Abandoned Chromium production sites often require environmental cleanup."

Dr. Luke was enthusiastic and glad we heeded his advice to continue our efforts on the metal allergy/toxicity "hunch," as he referred to it. He was very complimentary of my efforts, which is when we officially learned her diagnosis was "Inflammatory" Myopathy.

We forged ahead. Together as a family we continued to place our faith in God, as we were all "steel standing" … stronger!

+ + +

Chapter 15

HIP, HIP, HOORAY!

Six months to the day after Mother's knee revision, Mother, Poppa and I would find ourselves sitting in Dr. Seymour's examination room. It seemed another cycle with overall physical digression and physical weakness was looming. What we had hoped would be a onetime revision with her knee surgery on August 25, 2009 apparently was only one "leg" of her medical walk.

Dr. Seymour was well educated in everything I had presented to him with scientifically researched medical cases, which set precedents. However, I am emphatic about how I was led to discover the information in the United Kingdom. If not for continuing prayers for Mother to be well in her whole being, I don't know what the outcome could have been. God opened doors and ideas in my mind I never would have thought to investigate. He provided key words placed in my thoughts. It was almost too good to be true at times. But that was the easy part. The difficulty was trying to explain what I learned as skepticism was always a factor with everyone but with Dr. Seymour, Mother, Poppa, and me.

Dr. Seymour was very clear in making sure Mother knew in advance what possibilities could exist in moving ahead with this surgery. The decision to move forward would be hers. But she would have to take many factors into consideration. Based on Dr. Doubter's medical reports, which I acquired in the spring of 2009, Mother was allergic to the head in her hip replacement which consisted of Nickel-Cobalt-Chromium. However, I had documented her stem was Titanium as told in my phone conversation, with Dr. Doubter's PA.

Dr. Doubter's medical reports also stated cement was used for the Titanium stem. But the specific type of cement was not disclosed in the medical documentation. In our meeting with Dr. Seymour, we learned there were only two types of cements used for implants in orthopaedic surgeries during the years Mother had her replacements.

After a long discussion, Dr. Seymour knew Mother needed either the full revision or a portion of her hip metals replaced. He asked Mother to seriously contemplate two alternative routes for her hip revision. He wanted her to grasp the potential surgical outcomes which included:

1. The medical records from Dr. Doubter stated the head in her hip to be Nickel-Cobalt-Chromium, which meant a less stressful surgery by switching the metal implant to a ceramic implant. The shatter resistance was 0.04 percent and proven to be extremely durable.

2. The other possibility (which seemed farfetched at the time) had Dr. Seymour blatantly warning Mother; if the stem had to be removed for any reason, the surgery would be much more complicated with possible additional fragments of bone breaking in the process of removing a cemented stem.

3.) Even though, Dr. Doubter's medical records stated Mother's stem was Titanium, Dr. Seymour had requested a hip x-ray prior to our meeting. The x-ray showed the stem to be intact with no looseness of the implant and it was cemented.

That's when Dr. Seymour shared (as stated earlier) vital information regarding the two types of cement used when implanting stems. The most interesting part of our discussion was that Mother's hip stem was not Titanium. And it became more interesting - Titanium did not require cement! Dr. Seymour could see the surface of the stem and was able to determine that it was not Titanium, as Dr. Doubter's records indicated.

Dr. Seymour wanted to do more research before moving forward. We agreed and believed it was for the best. We were sincerely grateful to his thoroughness before proceeding with Mother's hip revision surgery. I was completely dismayed learning Mother's entire hip replacement was comprised of Nickel-Cobalt-Chromium.

Mother's knee revision in August 2009 proved to be a failed prosthesis with looseness of her top implant based on a bone scan while Mother was under the care of Dr. Doubter. Without a medical degree, I could see an inch of darkness on her bone scan. When Dr. Seymour first viewed the same film, he could clearly see an one inch of space.

After our discussion, I remembered the bone scan Mother had asked Dr. Doubter to schedule, providing a sharper image than could be obtained from x-rays. Maybe a bone scan of Mother's hip could help since she was having increasing pain with her replacement. I called Dr. Seymour's nurse and asked if a bone scan be arranged based on the previous scan results with Mother's knee. Before long, his nurse called to acknowledge that Dr. Seymour agreed.

Before our next appointment date with Dr. Seymour, Mother was diagnosed with another kidney infection. This one had more intense pain on her right side. She had several follow-up visits with her urologist. Even after each dosage of stronger antibiotics, the infection continued to linger week, after week.

Chromium[48] pertaining to implants can cause renal failure, and serious kidney problems, in addition to affecting the digestive system. However, it never occurred to me that the metal in the head of her hip replacement could be creating additional harm to her health, especially learning the stem and head were Nickel-Cobalt-Chromium.

The bone scan procedure was performed on March 17, 2010. Once Mother arrived, she was informed that Dr. Seymour ordered a full body scan from head to toe. This proved to be a much needed benchmark for Mother.

We were scheduled to meet with Dr. Seymour to learn more about his research and the results of her scan. On March 25, we had a triple doc day. Dr. Seymour's appointment was scheduled at the end of the day.

Mother's first appointment was to meet with a cardiovascular surgeon specializing in the removal of unnecessary pacemakers. The midday appointment was with Mother's urologist for a follow-up with her ongoing kidney infections.

Her issues currently ranged from heart to hip streamed with urology concerns. It was a full day with many issues to ensue. It was a bit overwhelming!

I had wondered why three appointments were on the same exact day involving the examination of three major parts of Mother's anatomy. It all made more sense, by late afternoon.

Our first visit was with Dr. Style[59], cardiologist. Once again, with duplicate files in tow to share where Mother had been and why we were sitting in his office, I continued my assignment as her walking diary. Instead of jumping ahead of Dr. Style with our reason for requesting a second opinion, we patiently listened to his questions and then Mother answered.

By this time in the journey, Mother, Poppa and I had been exposed to so many different physicians with Mother's health issues as they were compound and confounded! Yet there wasn't a scientific explanation how everything could be related which explains why so many physicians didn't comprehend what we were witnessing. We simply explained to Dr. Style what we understood, in addition to Mother's MELISA® metal allergy test results, which may or may not have had any bearing on Mother's pacemaker.

However, the issue we were addressing with Dr. Style was the fact that her pacemaker had not been utilized since implanted. Was there something wrong with the pacemaker? Or was the pacemaker never prompted to do its main function, which was to jolt the heart when the lower heart chambers needed stimulation? If it wasn't needed, why keep it in her body? She already had "metal" issues, although the pacemaker was reported to be Titanium, so what would Mother's metal allergy issue have to do with the pacemaker? At the time, we believed nothing, but it had crossed our minds.

He carefully explained the role of a pacemaker, or medically termed as a "generator" or "pacer." He was adamantly clear about the serious cautions when extracting a pacemaker, particularly one that had been implanted for two years as was Mother's. She had received her pacemaker on October 30, 2008. He shared that the longer the pacemaker is in a body, the more likely the chances were that the plastic covered lead wiring would likely attach itself as it lies against the wall of the heart muscle.

Mother understood the warnings. But, she was also adamantly passionate about having it removed since she had proof that it had not helped her heart. Within the depths of Mother's soul, she sensed the pacemaker was not being utilized, since her heart didn't appear to need it. The pacer was dormant. So all of our thinking lead to the one question; "Why leave anything in your body particularly attached to your heart, if it's just sitting there?"

Mother shared that while she was hospitalized in Birmingham, another cardiologist's assessment determined the pacemaker was not only needed, but insisted she have it "installed."

At first, Dr. Style said there was no reason to remove it even though he clearly understood her wishes. Nothing showed any sign to suggest that the pacemaker had been used since it was implanted for a period of 18 months.

He said if "I had the records from the hospital and the former cardiologist, then I could better evaluate this situation." Voila! This is where my role as caregiver, record keeper, and "all other assigned duties" began to kick in.

I had a set ready for Dr. Style. Each page was highlighted with clear marks on the days, tests, and medicine administered in addition to the facility's hospitalist's transcribed summation; "In review of the medications she is on does not reveal any medications other than Trazodone that could be possibly affecting her heart conduction and she has not had any of the Trazodone by the chart on 10/18 or 10/19." Mother's heart rate dropped on October 15 and 17. And it never again raised or caused any concerns.

Two months prior to Mother's hospital admission, she had a nuclear stress test which subjects individuals to a rigorous workout to produce heart problems, if any. Her test results showed no problems with any function of her heart or any prior concerns for future precautions.

Dr. Style read the records as I also showed him, where she was requested to have another nuclear stress test by Dr. Hardheart which showed the same results as Mother's last stress test. As did her EKG test results. Her lab work also had no indications showing potential heart problems.

My questions remained the same. Why did Dr. Hardheart insist on Mother having a pacemaker after she was taken off the medicine? It had been noted it was the apparent cause for the low heart rate problems? And she had passed all the heart tests Dr. Hardheart requested! Why was there any need for Mother to have a pacemaker implanted?

The hospitalist had already documented her condition had improved, once she was no longer on the medicine! There were no signs of heart problems based on the continuous 24 hour heart monitor attached to her at all times for 17 days.

As we discussed these facts, Dr. Style agreed. He began to read the other records I provided and then notified his nurse to take Mother to a testing room to look at her pacemaker attachments, and check the rate which the pacer was set.

At this point Poppa decided to go back into the lobby area to wait. I think he was so anxious over his sweetheart, he wasn't sure what to do at times. But Poppa was a tremendous comfort to both of us, particularly Mother. "Peas and Carrots."

The nurse connected Mother to a large monitor which clearly indicated where the pacer was located in her chest, and where the lead wires were attached to the pacer. The results were astonishing! Mother's pacemaker lead wire was not correctly attached to her heart as documented on her surgery charts! It was attached to the an upper chamber of her heart, and yet Mother experienced low heart rates in her lower chamber, according the medical records.

Dr. Style quickly quipped, "It's coming out. There is no need for her to have a pacemaker!" Mother and I looked at each other as if that was the best news we had heard since the MELISA® test results proved positive for the types of metals Mother was allergic to in her knee replacement and hip replacement metals! It was an incredible "WOW" moment!

Dr. Style asked his nurse to make an appointment in six months to arrange the extraction or "explant" of the pacemaker. Until then, he set the pacemaker at 30 rates per minute versus the 50 rates previously ramped. If the pacemaker was needed in a failed heart A-fib for any reason, and based on her medical records and heart's history, we have no reason to be concerned.

I thought it was a smart idea for Dr. Style to test the pacer, if it truly may be needed if her heart rate lowered. We left his office jubilant! Our first visit had been blessed with success. Mother was elated to rid her body of a pacer, apparently not needed!

In the days to come with no interruptions from her pacemaker affecting her heart, Mother was able to battle her ongoing kidney infection with more resilience. I have no medical proof to back-up what I witnessed as Mother's quality of life beginning to improve once the pacer was set at a lower rate. It just made a significant difference.

Perhaps Dr. Bailey provided the confirmation we needed when he brought us the EKG strips after her knee revision. He had said it clearly indicated the pacemaker was kicking in when it wasn't necessary. He is an anesthesiologist and not a cardiologist, but he was very keen on what he witnessed with Mother's heart rate during the surgery.

The next visit for the day was with Mother's urologist. It wasn't the good news we hoped to hear. Mother still had a kidney infection that was getting worse, even though she had been taking strong antibiotics for weeks. She was prescribed stronger antibiotics, as she was trying to prepare for her hip revision. We communicated with all of Mother's attending physicians so they were aware of what she was going through. Most everyone gave me their email address to keep them posted. But the one physician who made special strides in keeping Mother closely monitored through her entire journey was Dr. James, her primary care physician.

Our third and final physician appointment for the day was at 2:30 p.m. We were all looking forward to hearing what Dr. Seymour had learned from the bone scan results and his research on her current hip implant.

In the meeting, Dr. Seymour told us the research confirmed Mother's stem was Nickel-Cobalt-Chromium, in addition to Molybdenum. Dr. Seymour repeated his overview from our last meeting the month before.

He based his decision to proceed on her MELISA® lab results. He advised Mother, given the circumstances, it would best to remove the head and replace it with the latest technological generated material, which was ceramic. He reemphasized that this orthopaedic product did not include any metal. It was constructed for intense durability with a less than 0.04 percent of shattering. That fact alone removed a great deal of concern if she were to fall, or have any other impact. We believed in the smallest of percentages. Mother's 0.01 percentage of surviving what we were told was Lymphoma in 2007 had been beat, so she made the decision for a ceramic head.

Based on Dr. Doubter's information, as told to me by his PA when I had called over a year ago, he was emphatic and very explicit that Mother's stem was Titanium. He also stated the head was Nickel-Cobalt-Chromium. I had repeated what he said, as I wrote down the information.

I remember wanting to make sure the information was correct.

I had researched Chromium thoroughly as I did with Nickel and Cobalt. That's when I learned Chromium was a direct link to renal failure. Mother shared her latest kidney infection report with Dr. Seymour and the research confirmed by Dr. Luke when we discovered how Chromium affects kidneys. This made sense to Dr. Seymour concerning her continuous kidney problems.

I asked Dr. Seymour if the cement used in Mother's hip replacement was Calcium Titanate which was the number one metal allergy reported on Mother's MELISA® lab results. He said there was no way to know since it was not properly indicated on Dr. Doubter's medical records. But there was a 50-50 chance it was the cement which was her was allergic reaction. Based on her MELISA® lab results, Calcium Titanate was positive, although the test results did not show any allergy to Titanium.

Dr. Seymour took the time to explain the different structure services of metals and which ones required orthopaedic cement. He repeated what he had shared with Mother in her initial hip revision exam, emphasizing Titanium stems do not need cement. Titanium metal adheres to the bone and muscle in a completely different way than other metals, without the need for cement.

Since we had been misinformed about the metal stem in Mother's hip replacement, I wondered if Mother's femur was reconstructed using the cement, Calcium Titanate. It would help to explain her body's obvious rejection of the metals and the extreme burning sensation she had begun to feel in her thigh aligned with her first incision. Major discomfort became increasingly worse in the last three months, but worsened in the past three weeks. However, without Dr. Doubter documenting which cement, we would not know what was used in her hip replacement until the revision.

Dr. Seymour reemphasized how much easier the revision surgery would have been if only the head were to be replaced. However, he also stressed her recovery process, regardless if it only required the head, (or the head and the stem to be replaced) - the same inpatient and outpatient therapies as she had been through with her knee replacement, hip replacement, and knee revision - would be required again.

Mother wasn't too happy about the "dread" of going through another revision or the therapy rehabilitation process. No one would have been!

She also knew, based on the confirmation of Chromium causing long term renal failure, as confirmed by Dr. Luke, she didn't have a choice. Based on everything shared, she chose to move forward with a complete hip revision.

Since Mother was diagnosed with Myopathy, I learned that it is extremely rare for any toxicity to be exhibited from metal implants, as all the case studies and credible medical resources repeatedly state from the research. But for Mother, it did happen. We spoke with many skeptical physicians truly wanting to believe there was a link… and not for scientific data… but for Mother's personal health and well being. And because a medical case, which appears to link metal allergies to a muscle weakness such as Inflammatory Myopathy, had never been reported or documented in the United States.

It appeared Mother's conditions and results could be the first to establish the connection as a medical breakthrough. This was confirmed by Dr. Seymour (orthopaedic), Dr. Luke (neurologist) and Dr. Titus (dermatologist), each specialists in completely different areas of medicine, all highly regarded in their practices and contributions to science.

The biggest drawback in Mother's medical case is being the first and only one that we are all aware of to be true. Research studies must have repeated incidences or could be considered a "fluke" or a onetime deal. If her hip revision repeated the same results, then it would be construed as more believable, or proof, of Mother being allergic to her metal replacements, creating metal allergies and possibly toxicity.

To validate the research, there would need to be at least two people, with the same reactions to metals resulting with Inflammatory Myopathy, as Mother had experienced.

Mother's hip revision surgery was scheduled for April 20, 2010. She continued to have a severe kidney infection. Due to the severity of the infection based on her lab results, she would be required to visit her urologist and submit a specimen before he could give his professional permission for Mother to go through an extensive surgery and recovery process.

Shortly after specimen, the results were obtained. Her urologist said it was the worst infection their medical lab had seen in at least 20 years!

Just as her knee revision surgery was rescheduled once she developed pneumonia in the weeks prior, again, an additional problem would delay her hip revision. The new date surgery was set for April 30, 2010.

Mother was beginning to have serious doubts, just as she did before her knee revision. She was concerned if her body would be healthy enough to even have the surgery before any further damage to her renal system occurred, as her body's weakness continued to prevail. It seemed imperative to Dr. Seymour and her urologist, the revision needed to take precedence. We continued to depend on our faith in God for Mother's health to be sustained before, during and after her surgery.

Based on Mothers' medical records, since March 2006 after Mother's hip replacement, she had 33 Lithotripsy or "basket" stone retrieval surgeries, not counting the numerous, kidney, bladder and urinary tract infections, which she experienced. Between the years of 2008-2009, Mother had 18 of the 33 procedures. With every procedure, Mother had to be administered some form of anesthetic.

Previously, in January 2010, Mother had a kidney stone blocking her right kidney, the same side as her right hip replacement. Her urologist said it had been blocked for two or three weeks, yet Mother never felt any pain. That is another sign of kidney failure. It creeps up without warning and those who succumb to the disease never know it until it is discovered. Her urologist stated when patients lose kidney function after that length of time, they lose their kidney which has to be surgically removed. It was not the case with Mother.

We continued to pray for blessings, thanking God as we knew in His timing everything would come about for Mother to be a living example of how faith and science goes hand-in-hand with His divine and miraculous works. That has been proven, repeatedly in Mother's journey.

As the days passed, Mother became increasingly weaker with muscle soreness, fatigued yet unable to get adequate rest, stating her burning sensation was increasing in her right thigh. She began to have more frequent migraine headaches, almost daily while battling her kidney infection.

After her first round of medication was completed, she returned to her urologist only to learn the antibiotic did not clear the infection. He gave her a stronger dose for another seven days, but her body continued to become weaker with a dull ache on the back of her right side. She was having a more difficult time getting around the house and did very little beyond staying home in her recliner.

Her body was reacting just as it did with her knee before the revision surgery. She has never been one to be cooped up in a house. To keep her strength up, with an obvious weakened immune system, Mother graciously agreed to stay in the house versus trying to get out and about. She has a warrior spirit, she never gives up, she never gives in but she was giving out ... physically!

Her urologist called to Dr. Seymour to discuss her prolonged kidney infection. Dr. Seymour's nurse called Mother for us to meet in his office on April 19, 2010. Mother's concern lingered that she would not be physically able to have surgery. However, the news was quite the opposite. Dr. Seymour decided to go ahead with the surgery due to her rare and most unusual circumstances. His plan was to administer the antibiotics with an I.V. to accelerate the meds for her kidney infection as soon as she was admitted to the hospital for surgery.

It was rare to go to surgery with an infection. An infection increases the seriousness of the operation raising the chance of staph infection or any other germ as the immune system is in a weakened state. Mother didn't have a choice but to go forward with the hip revision surgery with a kidney infection, in spite of the strong medicines being administered for the past few weeks.

Ten days before surgery, Mother received two important phone calls. The urologist's office called to extend her antibiotics until surgery as he continued to consult with Dr. Seymour. The second was Dr. Seymour's nurse. Mother's surgery was again moved, but this time it was closer. April 28, 2010.

It was hard to fathom six months to the day after her knee revision we would be sitting in Dr. Seymour's office discussing a hip revision. The good news: once the metals were removed with her hip revision, her body could begin returning to a healthier status. After the knee revision, the Myopathy seemed to be disappearing. The metal allergies creating the inflammation in her muscles were not nearly as evident due to her ability to use her hands, arms, and upper body.

If the metals causing the allergic reactions had never been removed, the probability of her body phasing from allergy-to-toxicity-to-cancer was already evidenced in a series of proven medical research cases. A 2007 study "Chronic Inflammation, Joint Replacement and Malignant Lymphoma[55]" revealed the links in patient case studies in the United Kingdom.

The hip revision was to be Mother's last needed joint revision, removing the Nickel-Cobalt-Chromium-Molybdenum metals from the stem and head in her right femur and pelvis. Titanium with a ceramic head would replace the previous metals. Dr. Seymour informed us that a stem removal would be a serious operation and may cause her femur bone to chip or crack at the top portion of the bone since the stem seemed was firmly cemented to her femur, based on the x-rays and full body scan.

The morning of April 28, 2010, finally arrived. Being on time has always been important to Mother but that didn't mean she was ever on time! On this particular morning, Mother, Poppa and I were like the "Three Stooges." I wish someone had recorded us trying to get everything together and out the door! We could have used a good laugh!

It was an unexpected crazy morning. Poppa couldn't get his act together. Mother was in a frantic state, and what made it worse was that she had to wake me up because my alarm clock wasn't set correctly. I think we ran into each other about seven or eight times in the kitchen as one was trying to get coffee, another headed to the laundry room, and Mother was the only one focused on making sure she had everything she needed.

Then the fun part: "Where are the car keys?" "I thought you had them." "No, I thought you had them." Ah, the refreshing conversations that get your day started on the right track!

I had planned to drive my own vehicle, so I was glad to be lagging behind.

Mother and Poppa arrived at the medical center about 20 minutes ahead of me. I was allowed back to her Pre-Op unit shortly afterwards. She was in a better frame of mind than I anticipated, without any medications for "calmness" or anxiety related stress. Nurses were in and out checking on her as the I.V.s were being attached to start antibiotics for her kidney infection. She had a terrible migraine which was always a side effect from kidney infections or kidney stones. In another few minutes, the nurses were also making sure the correct hip was marked and her left knee was secure before surgery.

Poppa and I were given a pager, so we could be updated throughout her operation. About an hour into surgery Dr. Seymour's PA notified a nurse by phone to tell us, it was going to take longer than they expected. The stem in her hip would not come out as easily as cemented stems generally do. From that point on, we were updated frequently on her progress.

A little over four hours after Mother's surgery started, Poppa and I were called back to a private family room to meet with Dr. Seymour. He walked in and looked a bit tired. This report was much different than we expected. Dr. Seymour said the stem would not budge when they prepped it to come out. The top portion of her femur chipped as he had predicted with a high probability. He said usually once that part of the bone chips off, it can be advantageous, so the grip on the stem is better when trying to remove it from the femur. However, he said that didn't work either.

Dr. Seymour continued to share how the next step required mitering through her femur on the right exterior side of the bone. He explained the bone was then opened like a book. Once the stem was removed, the cement presented a problem. He said it is usually brittle and can easily be seen as a separate color from the bone. However, in Mother's case, Dr. Seymour said it was difficult to distinguish the cement from the bone.

He continued to explain the next step. Poppa and I both were in pain for Mother before he went any further in sharing the next step. Dr. Seymour said that he wanted to ensure all of the cement was removed. To do this effectively, he used a router to shave away excess cement which cleaned the inside of her bone known as marrow. This was a necessity before inserting her new Titanium stem. Poppa and I just sat there with unimaginable stares at what her body, her leg... what Mother would feel like once she was alert again.

Once the cement was safely removed, the stem was placed and the mitered bone was resealed, just like it had been opened. Small Titanium plates were firmly attached with Titanium screws to close the split femur. To add more protection, three sets of small 2 mm strands of wire were wrapped around the Titanium plates to secure her bone.

Dr. Seymour also shared the amount of time his PA invested calling several manufacturers as he desperately tried to obtain wire that did not have Nickel-Cobalt-Chromium metals. Unfortunately, there's not a manufacturer that makes any other type of orthopaedic surgical wire out of other metals. The Nickel-Cobalt-Chromium metals were the only type of orthopaedic wire considered extremely durable. Dr. Seymour explained if Titanium wires had been available, it would not be strong enough to support the bone in place for it to heal properly.

He felt assured the small amount of those particular metals should not cause any reactive problems for Mother. He believed the larger implants were the main concern for metal allergies. Dr. Seymour was also able to replace the broken chipped bone back to the femur with additional Titanium plates and Titanium screws.

As I continued to listen intently, I began to fully realize the trauma Mother's body had experienced. Her physical recovery weighed on my heart for her, while I imagined the surgical process as Dr. Seymour shared with us. This procedure was a necessity for Mother to return to any quality of life. We prayed this surgery would be successful in matching the improvements she had gained immediately after her knee revision. Poppa and I thanked Dr. Seymour, repeatedly, for the incredibly meticulous manner in which he proceeded with Mother's surgery.

Prior to her surgery, her urine was a brown color with a thick consistency, indicative of possible blood in her urine due to a urinary tract infection.[79] Post surgery, her void slowly became lighter in color. She was responding positively once the harmful metals where no longer wreaking havoc on her distressed body.

Two hours later, Poppa and I were notified Mother was being transported to her assigned hospital room. I walked in the room after the surgical nurse and Dr. Seymour's PA made sure her I.V. and oxygen tubing were flowing properly. At first glance, Mother was a pasty gray. It was horrifying and overpowering to see the obvious affects her body had endured. The four hours of surgery, on a major bone, resulted in traumatic physical and emotional adjustments. It was evident she had lost a lot of blood, which is not uncommon with such an invasive surgery. I sensed this was going to be a longer recovery.

As Poppa and I walked over to the side of her bed, she awakened a bit wanting to know about her hip. I tried to reassure she was going to be fine. A short time later, she again tried to wake up and attempted to lift her leg. She soon discovered she could not feel her leg. She had a frightened look on her face when she asked, "What happened to my leg, I can't feel my leg… Is it alright?"

For a fleeting moment, Mother feared Dr. Seymour had to amputate her leg. I assured her based on the look of desperation she exhibited, that she still had her leg which was still attached and doing remarkably well. I explained her surgery was more complicated than anticipated. She quickly fell asleep as her facial expression showed "tremendous relief!"

Dr. Seymour had previously shared with us in the family room that Mother would be admitted through Monday. This was Wednesday. He also shared Mother would only be on a 50 percent load bearing weight limitation during the initial recovery, stressing for her not to put any full weight on her right leg until the bone healed.

After a few hours of hearing Mother's snoring solo, Poppa decided to head to the house. He was exhausted. He had been through so much since "Peas and Carrots" said "I do." Poppa is a loving, caring, and compassionate gentleman. Mother surely did find her most special mate in this entire world! My love for Poppa grew enormously, as he stayed right by her side, and helped me in any way he could. How blessed we were they "got hitched."

But the tiredness was starting to catch up with Poppa. Neither of them was able to sleep the night before surgery. It was a very long day emotionally and physically. We did have several friends to drop by the hospital to check on her status during her operation, in addition to several phone calls and text messages asking about her process. That Mother of mine is one adored lady who is loved by so many others. But so is her Navy Sailor once kissed by Marilyn Monroe!

I had become a hospital "sleep over" veteran able to snooze through anything and at every angle a 50-year-old body could manage to bend and not break. I was well equipped with a thicker blanket to soften up whatever funky fold out chair used for an excuse to call a bed in Mother's room. As long as I had my own pillow, I knew I could manage to relax and possibly sleep. To my surprise there was a chair in Mother's hospital room that made a soft decent bed! It was a blessing! I had sorely dreaded the contraptions I had faced in her previous hospital rooms, trying to figure out how to catch a few winks, comfortably.

Hours later Mother still looked pale. She also awakened with a serious case of nausea in the middle of the night. I felt helpless as the nurses were extremely attentive in meeting her every need. In spite of her receiving nausea medication, Mother could not throw off the green feeling. I truly dreaded when she was going to have to get out of the bed. Fortunately, that was hours away. For the present, I enjoyed hearing the sounds of her deep sleep. The longer she snored, the more time for me to rest. So, I welcomed the familiar deep unnerving of her blubbering ZZZs as she snoozed, as I put in my ear plugs proceeding to pass out joining her choruses of "Sawing Me Some Logs!"

The next morning started earlier than I anticipated. The 3rd shift nurse came in to tell Mother that she was here to remove her catheter. That news awakened me quickly out of my twilight zone. I knew that meant she would be getting up from her hospital bed to use the bathroom. My thinking was "NO, let her have a day or two to adjust, PLEASE!" Mother had been in excruciating pain and was not aware of all the surgery details since she had been dozing in and out of our conversations.

So I jumped to my feet like a fire alarm sounded and said, "Do you really need to do that today? She's on a 50 percent recovery due to her complicated surgery." The nurse politely informed me that Mother's kidney infection was clear and she needed to have the catheter removed so it would not create any unnecessary infections. I thought "Okay! She doesn't have a kidney infection!"

Even with the elated news of Mother's quick recovery from the prolonged kidney infection, I was still concerned about Mother moving or rolling to use a bed pan. Actually, I was concerned about her moving at all! With the pain medication, Mother continued to be in sheer agony. She never cried, but I would have, long before she did at this point in her seemingly never ending medical journey.

Later that morning, it was time for Mother to attempt to use the bed pan. "Oh my!" ... as my friend, Ellen used to say when trouble appeared on the horizon. My heart was hurting for her as she struggled. Her muscles seemed to be slightly stronger. However, her hands and wrists had recovered quicker with the knee revision.

It was important to keep in mind; this was a complicated hip revision and a much more difficult surgery than any previous ones Mother's body had experienced.

The initial room Mother was assigned, was small for someone recovering from a hip surgery who needed space to maneuver. When I asked if we could be transferred to a larger room, I had been told we could move across the hall. Oddly, it was the same room where Mother stayed during her knee revision. I knew it would give plenty of room to spread out... and at the nurse's suggestion, I rolled the easy chair I enjoyed sleeping in, to the larger room. It pulled out from the seat, making a lounge chair so even a tall person could enjoy this nice sleeper. At last, I would be able to sleep, which had been incredibly difficult for the first three surgeries' post-recovery nights.

The next day, her blood level decreased requiring two units of blood to replace the loss during the surgery. Significant healing was ahead of her before she would be ready for rehabilitation. My desire was to do everything I could to help her, but at that moment, I felt completely helpless. It was role reversal, once again.

As I watched Mother's muscles slowly regain strength, I remembered Dr. Luke reminding me the last time we spoke before this revision surgery, her rebound rate from metal toxicity would likely be slower than with a metal allergy. He was correct.

Also, the fact her strength returned was a testament to this medical case of metal allergy/toxicity creating a façade which masqueraded as Inflammatory Myopathy. Mother's medical records confirmed the connection. We were so thankful Mother's health issues may very well serve as an alarm to others with possible metal allergies.

Mother struggled as she began transferring from the bed to a chair.

The nurses required her to sit up for at least four hours if possible. Her pain was excruciating and each tiny move was extremely difficult. Flexing her thigh muscles sent her into a pain cycle that surpassed any of her previous pain levels. We were hopeful that her hip was on its way towards finally recovering.

She looked up at me with a pitiful childlike expression, which was a first. She just wanted to cry the pain away so desperately. I said, "As much as I want to make sure you are okay, and pamper you, I can't. You are going to have to reach deep within yourself, spiritually and emotionally, to find your inner strength that comes from your faith in God to make it. And I know you can. I have seen you do it!"

It was not easy to tell Mother to grip her own determination and grit, but I knew she required strong encouragement with the long recovery ahead. She said, "I'm not going to make it." I firmly reassured her that we were taking this journey one step at a time, together, again. This difficult surgery truly pulled her physical, emotional, and spiritual strengths to an all time low.

I encouraged Mother to look past this present situation and see the smoother road ahead back to a healthy, productive and active lifestyle. I reminded her that she had a chance at life many did not, and we need to be thankful to God for having a chance to learn what caused her problem. If He showed us how to fix it, then He will surely bless her.

Mother looked up at me and nodded north to south. It resonated as her facial expression showed a sign of spiritedness ready to forge ahead with resilience. The irony of this "telling her like it is" moment: she was always the one who encouraged me, many times! She had the strength to make it. She just needed a "tough love" reminder.

At that moment, a flash from earlier in the summer came to mind. Without Mother being fully aware of the toil her unfortunate and heart breaking situation was taking on others trying to assist, I discovered I was also in desperate need of a few words of inspiration.

Only the day Brenda Brewer and I crossed paths, she had crossed my mind so strongly. She was an old friend and baby-sitter for Jack and me when I was ten years old. She was the greatest baby-sitter two kids really loved! We lived in the same neighborhood and attended the same church. She had a special way with children, and she was very creative in keeping particularly, Jack, a three year old into all mischief, out of trouble and entertained with fun adventures.

It had been 30 years or longer since the last time I could recall seeing her. Yet, she was so heavily in my thoughts, I began rummaging through some of my old photo albums I had taken of her when I began an interest in photography.

The next day, I later realized God had indeed placed her in my path to offer thought provoking words of encouragement. We "happen" to see one another at a small restaurant in Centre. We only had a brief few minutes to catch up. She had married a wonderful man many moons ago. They had been living in the north part of the U.S. Their three children were adult aged. I remember thinking how fortunate her kids were to have a mom like Brenda!

For some reason, I shared my heavy heart with her. Soon, our parents began calling us from separate directions. They were ready to go and it was a hot July 2010 day as we had exited from the small restaurant. The last thing Brenda said to me before giving me a goodbye hug - "He's gotten you this far, hasn't He?" I didn't sense any need to reply. She had concisely confirmed a greatly needed reminder. I simply nodded "yes." Enough had been said.

When Mother and I returned home, God's words through Brenda were written on a note and placed in a small frame eye level near my desk. That one quote continued to be a frequent reminder to no have doubts are fear or question Who is in control. Everything I needed reassurance from this point forward, that one quotable question popped came to mind!

So, I understand Mother needing tender compassionate encouragement! Although, it didn't matter what I said to Mother, it was up to her to make the willful decision to reach deep within to desire each and every step of her rehabilitation and recovery.

She did prevail! Her determination was ignited to keep going by taking as many steps as necessary to fully recover. This was her goal. The choice was her call.

My influence to persuade her to drink fluids or eat crackers fell on deaf ears. She was nauseated. Until she could eat and nourish her body, which were baby steps, she would not have the physical strength to start inpatient rehab. As time progressed she gained her internal composure. Her goal was to walk without any support. But it had been the worst uphill climb yet!

Mother's first revision from an initial knee replacement was a failed prosthesis due to loosened implants from metal toxicity. Her second revision from an initial hip replacement failed because it cemented tightly to her femur. In life, finding balance is so important. If you are too loose, things slip away. If you are too tight, your grip may be overbearing. Finding one's balance helps when focusing on God. Not too loose, nor holding on too tight.

I've been on both ends of the spectrum in my life. Mother's failed implants were a perfect analogy of my walk with God. In time, it helped me to be a better caregiver as our roles had reversed. Mother needed to find her balance, and I needed to allow that process to transpire through her struggles and successes.

We looked at closure on this leg of the journey.

+ + +

Chapter 16

WIRE AM I HERE, AGAIN?

For the first time, since Mother's fall March 2006 resulting in a broken hip, she felt completely saturated in vulnerability and insecurity. Her outgoing personality took an inward turn. Witnessing her disposition, almost giving up instead of trying to bounce back, I knew something needed to change and quickly!

The demands on her body were great. She had been a fighting tiger through every rough and emotional step of this long enduring and painful walk. It would be the first time she required more than rehab for her body and mind to re-instill her hope. Discouraged and tired in every aspect of her life, Mother had shared, "I don't think I will make it." It had been a long almost three-and-a half-years.

As our days turned to weeks, we never stopped to realize how much time had passed. My journey home in 2007 seemed like a glimpse of yesterdays gone by in a flash once I became involved in Mother's health issues. Again, it was confirmation I was where I needed to be.

The core issue of Inflammatory Myopathy diagnosis was unknown until all the research finally revealed the silent culprit. We had learned many things from Mother's experiences. One of the most prevalent was learning her medical case appeared to be the first in the United States to link the types of metals to metal allergies in her implants, which were severely damaging the muscle fibers in her body.

The toxins came from metal-on-metal friction which released microscopic metal ions which were poisonous, were circulating within Mother's bloodstream and destroying her healthy muscle fibers. The overabundance of the metal ions flowing in her blood became stored in Mother's fatty tissue and muscle cells, causing obvious damage to her muscles and affected some area of her human anatomy system. As Mother absorbed what has been stated by her attending physicians as "toxicity,"... it was a hard battle against her weakened immune system. Thus, she became extremely worn down.

After Dr. Luke confirmed the research findings I had gathered about the specific characteristics of each metal, Chromium[80] raised a huge warning flag when I read that it's number one negative effect to the human body was attacking the digestive (stomach, gallbladder, liver, colons, esophagus, mouth, etc.) and renal (kidney, bladder, urinary tract) systems. The metal used in any body implants causes damage to the human body, whether a person is allergic to Chromium or not!

The old saying "A chain is only as strong as its weakest link," was tried and true in Mother's medical case. Her gallbladder could have been diseased and "happened" to become inflamed, after the hip and knee replacements. She had a history of minor problems with kidney stones and kidney infection. She also had a known recurrence with migraine headaches. All of these were her weakest links as her strongest internal organs were beginning to face trouble, not yet evidenced. Also the numerous surgeries placed her body in a weakened state.

It's no wonder Mother was struggling! Now she was facing six weeks of therapy on a 50 percent weight bearing load. Her medical case set a new precedent for the therapists working with her because the Inflammatory Myopathy had worn down Mother's body, which was in a state of sheer exhaustion!

The day she was released from the hospital and transported by ambulance to the inpatient facility, she was as weak as a newborn kitten. I felt so sorry for her. She was trying with all her might to improve, but it seemed a daunting task as health issues kept hitting her. She began having more difficulties with her digestive system, including swallowing which was also due to muscle weakness.

Previously, Mother's gastrointestinal specialist had dropped by to check with her while she was hospitalized. Again, it was a gesture of goodwill as he was not requested by Mother. He shared that no matter how healthy your body is; surgery, anesthesia, and medicines will cause constipation. He said the sooner you address this issue by eating and drinking to get the digestive system going regular again, the sooner your body will react normally. It was good to learn the information and explained many "flush-strated" times Mother did not experience.

That was always one of the problems Mother had previously struggled with after every surgery. Making matters worse, metals were not the only substance to create an allergic reaction for Mother's body. Some medications, such as codeine, morphine, and others made her extremely nauseated; other medications made her deathly ill. So, I was careful to keep a detailed list of what she could, and could not, tolerate.

After her hip revision, we were not aware that one particular medication was causing a lingering effect creating a great deal of nausea, serious enough to keep her from bouncing back as she did in her previous surgeries. By the time she was scheduled to leave the hospital for an inpatient rehabilitation facility, Mother was dreadfully sick.

I knew she could not leave the hospital in this shape. But without a fever or another complication, Medicare would not pay for another night of care, according to a patient representative. In my search for the physician liaison, Joseph, I asked what could be done. He came to our rescue! A wonderful compassionate individual who made sure the patient's needs were met, with additional medical issues.

When we met with him, I shared Mother's out of the ordinary predicament. He quickly made arrangements to communicate with her doctors, obtaining permission for one more night's stay due to her sickness and vomiting, which continued most of the day. In 24 hours, Mother needed to become well enough to manage an ambulance ride to her rehab destination.

God's abundance of mercy was evident!

The next day she was much better, but extremely weak. We asked for all unnecessary medicines to be stopped so her body could have a reprieve to recover from the excessive vomiting. It was imperative for her to consume small amounts of food and not lose it! Once the nausea medicine was stopped, she began to feel better. Ironically, it was the trouble-maker causing the nausea.

She was able to make the trip to the facility. After staying with her for a few nights to assist with her immediate needs, I knew she was going to be okay. Her strength and personality began to return!

Once again, one of the many instrumental healing tools for Mother's hands and arms was playing the piano. It was conveniently located in a large nearby dining and recreational room. Her former hand therapist encouraged her to play every day. He said it was one of the best exercises she could do to help improve her hands, wrists, and arms. As Mother played, it began strengthening and retraining her muscles for better coordination. Through her struggles, her special gift for playing never left. Patients and staff members gathered to listen as her tranquil music therapy seemed to touch their souls with peacefulness, as expressed on their faces. It was also a way Mother could feel like her old self, which was difficult at times.

Four weeks passed rather quickly. Mother was scheduled to visit Dr. Seymour for a follow-up. She was able to make the trip to his office in a vehicle. Getting out for a ride seemed to help her tremendously. Again, the "ugh" cart was the choice apparatus since she had far surpassed the use of her "Walker" buddy, still sporting the tennis gear for quieter maneuvering!

Dr. Seymour's progress report was good although he continued her physical therapy at 50-percent load bearing. She was now more alert and able to understand exactly the complexities of her hip revision. Dr. Seymour shared that it was the most complicated surgery in all his years of surgical practice.

When Mother was well enough to come home, she was still on 50-percent load bearing weight. While in the care of the medical center's outpatient physical therapy, the staff and Mother were particularly cautious due to the extenuating circumstances of the tedious surgical procedure. About three weeks into outpatient therapy, Mother was moving around the house when she noticed a slight sticking pain inside the upper right part of her leg. I felt it needed to be examined by Dr. Seymour before the upcoming 4th of July Holiday. Within a day, we were sitting in his exam room. We really should have asked for a personalized plaque on the door, "Trish's Hip and Repair Room."

Dr. Seymour entered and he asked how she was doing. He pulled out a copy of her x-ray taken prior to her being escorted to the exam room.

It revealed two of three wires placed around the upper plate on Mother's revision had broken loose. He emphasized how crucial these wires were in keeping the Titanium plates stabilized. I sensed Mother's distress and dread without even looking her way. He stated he was going to have to go back into the upper femur of her leg and hip area to repair the wires.

She had accomplished the amazing feat of regaining her strength on a 50-percent weight bearing. Now she had to think of starting all over again. It was almost more than she could bear. As her tears began streaming immediately, Dr. Seymour compassionately hugged her. He explained, this repair surgery should be much easier than her previous hip revision.

The surgical plan, as he explained, would include a three or four inch incision to access and repair the wires. He stated there was no reason this repair surgery should create any setback. This news was a huge relief compared to what we could have learned! Dr. Seymour further believed this surgery would only require one overnight stay; then in a week she could return to outpatient therapy. The thought of another surgery so soon after her last one, and the additional time for more healing, recovery and rehab, was yet another huge dread for her. At the time, I am not sure any of us comprehended the importance of Mother's role, as she was truly on the frontier, as we all learned more about types of metals which caused allergies from implants!

The surgery was scheduled for July 2010. That was only nine weeks since her last four-hour hip revision surgery in April. But once again, we knew there was a reason it was all happening. It was not evident by the x-rays exactly when or what caused the wires to snap. She had been so careful. Whether it was faulty wiring not soundly constructed or any one particular physical activity; the exact cause could not be determined.

Dr. Seymour shared that had happened with another patient from a state much further away. It was also a complicated case. He did not elaborate due to patient privacy. It helped for Mother to hear just enough to know that it was obvious others were experiencing similar problems.

There were factors to be considered since her femur had to be mitered then repaired with additional hardware. Like a billboard across Mother's forehead, reading her concern, "Will I ever be healed and just walk, again?"

As Mother's track record had demonstrated, this re-revision surgery was not as anyone expected it to be. He felt it was best to reopen the same 18-inch incision that had just recently been cut. The harsh part of hearing the details that made me nauseous was that, before severing, the wires frayed due to a continuous rubbing against the metal plate and her bone! All I could do was think of the pain she endured when I have learned of others and their specific issues dealing with the bone, broken or otherwise.

Again, another four-hour surgery with an extensive hospital stay was needed. Mother was awakened after recovery while being transported into her hospital room. She was in more pain than I anticipated. Dr. Seymour and his PA accompanied Mother to the room. He explained his decision to reopen the same incision to check the lower wires while in surgery since the upper wires were frayed instead of breaking or snapping, as previously thought from her x-rays.

Dr. Seymour later told us that he wasn't sure if it was a manufacturer's defect, based on the way the wires had frayed, versus the wires appearing to have snapped, for some reason. He decided to change all of the wiring, wanting assurance they were intact in case of faulty material. To his surprise, the lower plate was healed and rapidly adhering to her bone. Although the lower wires were intact, Dr. Seymour removed them since they were no longer needed. That was a very good sign of her health restoring itself!

However, Mother's pain was overwhelmingly intense as she became more alert coming out of anesthesia. This proved to be Mother's most difficult lap in her recovery race. In what little long distance running I did in my college recreational courses, the final lap was always the most difficult.

This was to be her final lap and the most difficult time in overcoming the incredible endurance of inescapable pain. There is just no other way to describe what she was experiencing. It was evident at the time based on her moaning and groaning. She could barely endure the rush of agony, as her muscles were already tender and sore from the last surgery, which began signaling to her brain as "PAIN!"

Each time she opened her eyes, it was clear that she was struggling with great distress. The pain medication did not alleviate any of the discomfort as in her previous surgeries. I went to the nearest prayer closet - her bathroom. As I grabbed a towel to place over my face and mouth, I wept as I prayed for God to please stop her intense bone aching pain from surgery.

Major muscles had been cut within the short time span of just nine weeks only to be severed again in the same areas. She was at a threshold of what probably felt like sheer torture. This time, it was going to take grit, determination and will power to overcome the weakness of "I can do this!" Mother had to reach profoundly into her mind to grasp and visualize the next step in reaching towards her final goal of walking.

Step one, with "Walker" then next the "ugh" cart which leads to a cane and finally the ability to stand on her own two feet. This required a deeper reach within her spiritual strength and dependence on God. Mother had to stay focused on her goal - the return to a better quality of life.

Toxicity had overcome her fragile bloodstream for more than three years. Lots and lots of fluids would need to be consumed and more pain medicine would still be needed. Healthy food was a must. To withstand the test of endurance, recuperating, and re-establishing her physical stature, focusing on the journey ahead and the necessary provisions to be successful in her life's new walk was mandatory.

Due to the unexpected circumstances, Mother requested a slower rehabilitation approach and process. Instead of returning to an inpatient facility, she chose the advantages of a home health agency. It was one of the best decisions Mother could have made realizing there is no rush in recovery. It takes time to heal all types of wounds.

I also asked if Dr. Seymour would approve a powered hospital bed to be brought into our home for comfort and ease of getting in and out of a bed, until she was more stable. He agreed with the idea of a slow, but steady recovery at home.

Again, Mother experienced some severe blistering on the sides of the incision where the tape was placed. Even using latex-free paper tape did not stop the painful sores as I changed her bandages often and applied antibiotic creams. However, she still suffered with those small annoying wounds. The main concern was infection. We began keeping a much more sterilized environment during this time. Hand washing and using latex free gloves were essential. Mother and Poppa's bedroom and bathroom had been renovated in the previous months. There is no way we could have known she would need additional room for a hospital bed and easier mobility for six weeks. The remodeling was another God-send, timed perfectly.

Everything Mother experienced was a blessing, sometimes in disguise. Later, I realized the "whys" of things that appeared to be hurtful or perhaps misunderstood with family issues, or friends staying at a distance. Mother needed time to heal, and quiet time to rest her very tired and weary body, in order to move closer to a complete recovery. There's no place like home, when home is like no place you'd rather be.

As her recovery progressed, so did her confidence. It was difficult for her to adapt since she had always been a very active lady. Mother was almost too cautious. I imagine anyone would experience the same precautions to keep from going to surgery and recovery, after a hip replacement, hip revision and now another revision-repair.

The home health physical therapist came three times a week for five weeks. The care Mother received taught her to adapt in her home environment with the added bonus of her family being able to stay with her all the time. That it was a huge help being able to take care of Mother at home. It also allowed me to sleep in my own bed!

Her previous need and dependence on me to stay close by her side becoming less frequent, while she was home. In time, she again not only gained a tremendous amount of confidence in walking with an apparatus but was ready to deal with her return to outpatient rehab therapy sessions. Her uncanny wit which had been sorely missed during this surgery-recovery, was finally beginning to emerge. The world seemed more "normal" to Mother for the first time in months; if not, probably since March 2006, when she had her first hip surgery.

Because of her rare circumstances, this stretch of rehab was scheduled over a longer period of several months, as she continued to make incredible progress. The strength in her hands, wrists, and arms were returning. It was a slow but consistent process.

It was important to not only work on her right leg coordination; but her hands, wrists, and arms during her rehab sessions. Her hand therapist, in addition to Dr. Luke, had already stated that they believed Mother's muscles would not have returned as quickly if she had an initial case of Inflammatory Myopathy that was induced by another source, versus the types of metal implants creating her metal allergies.

After months of outpatient therapy, she was striving towards 100-percent recovery. In her last updated visit with Dr. Seymour, she was placed on 100 percent load bearing with her right hip. She continued rehabilitation with a dedicated and wonderful therapist named Scooter Dunne. When Mother becomes completely healed and walks away without any further need for outpatient rehab… she will be "Dunne!"

Mother continued to beat the odds. Time-after-time we each faced individual adversities challenging us to remain close as a family. The times of spiritual highs with enormous accomplishments made the journey worthwhile outweighing our tribulations, with some mighty low points.

Both legs of our mother-daughter journey are healthier and sewn up as Mother moved closer to a well balanced walk!

Just when we were "wired" to celebrate… her journey began a new change of pace.

+ + +

Chapter 17

CHANGE OF PACE

Everything in our lives started showing signs of being on an upswing, providing a better outlook for Mother's once dire complex health issues. In her bleakest times, she continued to show a determined attitude, which was improving, especially over the past few months.

The one aspect of this entire journey that kept me inspired so that I could be her exhorter and motivator was actually Mother's willpower, not to feel sorry for her own circumstances. Only in times of daunting pain did anyone ever see her illustrate a need for heartfelt encouragement. She was emerging with an emotional vibrancy, especially when she saw others struggling with far greater health care dilemmas than she had faced.

Her determination, perseverance and faith in God, became a resounding testimony of courage for Him, as she continued to touch numerous lives. However, she is an inspiring exemplar to her family - especially her children and grandchildren!

Mother's phenomenal gift for compassion was evidenced in approaching others with simple words of encouragement, especially to those waiting in medical facilities appearing to need a caring support.

Pity is not a word you will find in this journal, not for her own situation or any situation she confronted. It's hard to believe someone could be "that" nice, good, sweet, and wonderful. I witnessed it. I lived it. And I have seen the beauty of God within her soul. She is relentless in keeping a positive outlook!

So how could anyone who has been through so much in almost four years, make it through this final lap to prevail? Her medical troubles were not as critical as some patients, as I shared in the introduction of *Steel Standing*. But, she certainly experienced a lot of twists and turns and ups and downs… only through her undeniable strong faith in God which kept her focused.

As she again returned to the medical center's rehab, it was evident the prime deterrent in her body was reversing. Diminishing effects from her metal allergy were no longer annihilating her muscles. Slowly she regained her strength and built her endurance, with a remarkable comeback when her muscles began developing. It was as if they were "waking up" as she used them more, reclaiming her walking posture, as she placed her feet straight ahead, learning to sit correctly versus "plopping" in a chair!

Once all the revision and repair surgeries seemed to be completed. Mother asked me never again to "boast" about her high tolerance for pain to medical practitioners.

With her pain management under control, she never complained. Mother was not one to take pain pills unless she absolutely needed them. An important lesson is to regulate your pain by staying ahead of it. Mother was a slow learner. When the worst passed, the healing process became bearable. She preferred to take the over-the-counter green gel tablets which worked great.

Also, we learned pain medicines generally create irregular bowel problems. When a "body" is put to sleep or anesthetized, it creates a time for your bowels to stop as does your entire body, thus making it more difficult for the small and large intestines' natural ripple effect to initiate. A high fiber menu was part of Mother's nutritional diet helping to regulate the situation, plus an over-the-counter powdered laxative to jump start the flow again.

With so many health issues behind, we believed this round of physical therapy was the last "professional" assistance she would need in retraining her muscles to return to an improved and independent life.

My role during her physical therapy sessions was to observe her exercises so I could help Mother at home. It was also helpful to Scooter when I was able to share Mother's current status with her improvements and/or troublesome areas.

Scooter could then adapt Mother's exercises to incremental needs for strength, endurance, balance, and range of motion. Mother was never one to be able to describe necessary details. Scooter and I learned rather quickly to keep an open line of communication so the rehab exercises could be better facilitated for Mother's specific needs and limitations.

Mother had been going to rehab for several weeks when I noticed after one session - September 10, 2010 - she was tiring easily. With the combination of professional health care experience and now personal firsthand experiences, I knew the signs of what appeared to be possible heart-related problems. She didn't appear to be having a heart attack, but she was really struggling during the more aggressive and active therapy workouts.

Her face turned pale. She began weak quickly and noticeably perspiring. We had to leave early that day due to her low stamina, which was not like Mother to give out, or give in. As we exited the building heading towards the vehicle, I was asking if she was okay. She said she was extremely tired, but she didn't feel sick. I kept a watch for any signs that could be an indication for a possible heart problem. I remembered Mother was scheduled to visit with Dr. Style on September 23, which was in a few days. Mother's skin became red around her scar where the pacemaker implant was located just slightly left above her heart, approximately three inches below her collar bone. She began itching as if she had poison oak on that area of her chest. It had always itched, but this was vastly different.

I suggested she call Dr. Style's office on Monday to see if there were any cancellations. Somehow, some way, I knew it was her pacemaker. It was another "gut feeling." Saturday, she pretty much napped and rested as if she had no energy to do even the slightest things around the house. Sunday afternoon, I researched the components in her pacemaker on the manufacturer's web site. Astonishingly, the facts were in contrast to the information regarding the metals in her pacer. We were told Mother's pacer was "pure" Titanium by the manufacturer's representative and Dr. Hardheart.

Within a couple of hours, I began reading every bit of information pertaining to her inserted pacemaker. I located the specific components used based on the manufacture's web site and cross referenced the exact pacemaker with the serial numbers listed on her medical ID provided for pacemaker recipients. To my surprise, the lead wires were made of metal alloy coated in silicon. Mother and I were told since the wires were coated, there was no possibility the metal alloy could be a factor in creating any type of rash or irritation.

I reviewed the details of how a pacemaker is made and how it works. The lead wires had open ends connecting to the pacer with a platinum end, which attached to the heart with a hook or a clasp using a tiny metal screw to fasten the attachment for conduction. Then I learned her pacer was not made of "pure" Titanium, but Titanium Alloy which often includes Nickel… which was her second most allergic metal reaction based on her MELISA® lab results.

Now we were getting to the heart of the matter!

Once again, we were given incorrect or less than thorough information about all the metal components surgically placed in Mother's body. Normally, I would not think twice about the integral details of what makes something work, or what it's made of when a trusted physician implants anything into your body. If a body needs a man-made part, then thank the Good Lord, we have those parts available to help retain our quality of life.

Mother's situation was unique as evidenced throughout her true experiences. At this early stage on the frontier of her metal allergy discoveries and reactions, it was rare to say the least! On our last visit in the fall of 2009 when I was told by Dr. Hardheart that her pacemaker was "pure" Titanium, the information was also confirmed by his manufacturer's representative.

In my opinion, their objective was to answer my question so they could move on. They had not witnessed Mother's orthopaedic encounters, even though we were explicit. We shared information providing printed test results from MELISA®. Therefore, it was more than just an idea that metal might be causing her skin to almost continuously itch since implanted on October 30, 2008. During the past two years, she experienced sporadic itching and an obvious red rash on the skin above her pacemaker. These were classic signs of a metal allergy!

When Mother, Poppa and I first met with Dr. Style for a second opinion, on our "three docs in a day," on March 25, 2010, her next appointment for the extraction of an apparently unnecessary pacemaker was in September. In my opinion, the timing could not be more perfect since her last hip revision surgery was in July 2010.

Previously based on a technical evaluation in his office, Dr. Style had programmed her pacer to 30 rpm from 50 rpm. Mother's medical records, learning more details from researching the manufacturer's web site, in addition to seeing visible signs of irritation since implanted, my "gut feeling" led me to believe once the pacemaker and wires were extracted, Mother would regain a healthier life.

It seemed curious that Mother's timing of feeling so low and having no energy was within days for the pacer to be removed. On Monday morning, Mother made the call to Dr. Style's office but there were not any cancellations before September 23. Mother decided to go to rehab that day. She was eager to continue improving so she could drive and become independent, again. For over three years, she had very little privacy, requiring someone close by her side pretty much 24/7. We were all anxious for her to have her own space, again.

Like the previous therapy sessions I had attended, I sat nearby like a parent watching their child become stronger so she could go out and play with the other kids. It made me smile inside out. Our role reversal had been going on for quite some time. Naturally, I was very protective of her, and very proud of her accomplishments from "square zero," as I heard on a sitcom. "Square one" was above Mother's starting point.

After her therapy session, she began panting, turning pale, and then broke out into a serious sweat more so than on the past Friday. As we headed to the vehicle, she was exhausted instead of tired. Her exercises were much lighter that day compared to the ones in the previous sessions when her odd symptoms first became evident. Mother shared with Scooter about her weakness, so extra precautions beyond the already set precautions, were placed in all her different types of exercises.

Mother decided it would be best to head home so she could rest after we went to a local restaurant to grab an early dinner. I offered to carry her to an ER to be checked. She was still looking pasty pale, but she said she'd be fine. By the time we arrived home, she really needed to kick back and rest.

Her energy level had been increasing until the past four days. She had slowly began to transition into cooking, along with doing some light chores around the house. Naps were no longer a regular past-time as they had been for so long. Her world had begun to change. But not in the direction we had hoped!

The next morning, I woke up early to check on Mother. She had slept in her recliner after getting up during the night with a headache. It wasn't a migraine, she said. Her symptoms appeared worse. Her color was extremely pale, with little to no energy to sit up.

I called Dr. Style's office, and asked to speak to his nurse. I was transferred, thinking "I hate to leave a message because it could be later in the day before they call back." Instead his nurse, answered! I explained Mother's condition. She completely understood the situation, but was not sure Mother could be seen that day. As I headed to the sun room where Mother was reclining, I prayed asking for guidance. With so much medical madness, I didn't know what to expect next.

Within three minutes or less, the nurse called back, "Bring her now, if you can. Our patient load is currently light." I thanked her emphatically. She replied, "Hey, I would be doing the same for my Mother." I thanked God I was able to speak to Dr. Style's nurse, and for the receptionist who transferred the call so quickly. This was a miracle in the busy world of physician specialists, especially with surgeons in trying to arrange a same day visit when calling for assistance!

It took several minutes to get Mother dressed due to her lagging physical state. She was literally washed out. I could barely get her out of the recliner. "Trish the Dish" was like a "wet paper plate!"

While in the process of helping her get dressed, I called Poppa. He was at his store but would meet us at the Dr. Style's office. When we arrived, once again I had to use the "ugh" cart to push Mother into the doctor's office. She was not able to put one foot in front of the other. After a tremendous comeback, once again, I hoped this would not be a major setback. I still had the lingering hunch that it was her pacemaker.

Shortly after arriving, we were escorted to the exam room by the nurse I had spoken to on the phone. She checked Mother's stats and in a flash, Dr. Style entered the room. Mother had to lay down due to her extreme weakness. About that time, Poppa came to meet with us.

I shared what had occurred since our last visit. He reviewed her documented notes on her charts about the pacemaker and it not being a necessary device. Based on her physical limitations in addition to her metal allergies, he proceeded to explain thoroughly the possible impending dangers when removing a pacer. Poppa and I said we understood. Mother spoke a soft but empathic "yes."

He felt removing the device would most likely not have anything to do with her physical condition, but he agreed to proceed since the "metal" sensitivity was acknowledged by Dr. Seymour and her urologist. He noted she was not pacemaker dependent, since her last visit with him in March 2010.

Mother, Poppa and I were more than confident with Dr. Style's reputation and skills as a gifted surgeon. He is one of a few cardiologists certified to remove pacemakers. Once again, we were led by prayers to the right physician who was more than capable of handling any difficulties that might occur during the extraction.

Mother loaded onto the "ugh" cart and we headed a short distance down the hall to the surgery scheduler. The first opening was two weeks away. We hoped it would be sooner. About that time Dr. Style strolled into the room and discussed his next week's agenda with the scheduler. He had one conflict earlier on Friday, September 17, but told her to go ahead and schedule Mother's surgery that day. A very lifeless Patricia perked up a wee bit when hearing the news. It was only three days away, after nearly two years of learning it was not a necessary implant.

Since Mother was not feeling well, the surgery scheduler called the medical center where the pacemaker extraction surgery was to be performed. She wanted to arrange an early pre-admission, while in town to save us a trip. Blessed again, there was an opening!

On that note, Poppa decided to head back to the store since he learned Mother was not going to be admitted that day. Mother and I headed to the hospital to do all the necessary paperwork.

Upon arriving, we had a very short wait before being called back to a private office where a nurse assessed Mother. All of her medical information was discussed in preparation for her procedure. Mother continued to sit in the "ugh" cart due to its height providing an angle which put less stress on her healing hip.

There are many changes once a hip replacement or revision, becomes a permanent part of your body, as I have become acutely aware in working with Mother. As much as I feel for her new life and the changes she has to adapt in learning to do for herself, I am thankful for each step I can take... each time I bend over... able to put on my long pants... socks... shoes... and tie them or slip into them without having to use a 24" shoe horn. I am not sure how many people take their health for granted if they can do everything I just named that I can do... but I am much more careful, and extremely grateful.

Within five minutes or less, Mother became so sick she could barely hold her head up. The nurse worked as fast as possible entering her data. She was extremely compassionate about Mother's condition as it appeared to be deteriorating rapidly. About then, Mother said, "I'm going to throw up." The thought crossed my mind that she could have a virus; but, an inner knowing was the pacemaker was the problem.

As Mother started to vomit, I felt so sorry for her as the nurse quickly grabbed a plastic hospital pan. I grabbed some tissues and began holding up Mother's head as I wiped her with a cool cloth, the nurse provided. Within a couple of minutes, Mother was able to take some sips of a Sprite˙ as she began to improve slightly. There had been so many times I had seen her this way; I prayed these kinds of days would soon only be in the past. The nurse and I suggested she go to the ER, but Mother believed she was going to get better so she decided against that choice.

Our next designation before leaving the medical center was to head to the lab for Pre-Op blood work. Mother said she was well enough to do this one last requirement. As we left the nurse, we thanked her for her compassion and genuine care. She really did everything possible to keep Mother from feeling embarrassed, and she also hated to see her in such an ill state of health.

As we arrived at the lab, Mother seemed to be getting a little better. However, by this time, it was about 4:00 p.m. The day was long, so we headed home. Within an hour after we finally arrived, Mother, Poppa and I caught up with all the details. Then we all took a break in our designated recliners to rest. The phone rang. Poppa answered and brought it to me in the den. He said it was Dr. Style's assistant at the lab. Turns out, the caller was a pathologist calling from the hospital.

Mother's lab work had been checked twice on two calibrated machines resulting in her Calcium level at 17. He said it was the highest level their lab ever recorded. He instructed me to bring her back to the ER, ASAP. This was totally unexpected. I had no idea what her normal Calcium level should be, much less the high and low ranges.

While explaining the news to Mother and Poppa, we immediately prepared to leave. Since she had signs of possible heart problems, although previously no pain existed or any serious signs were evident, I thought we needed to move "rapidly." Mother could not move rapidly due to her weakness. It was like trying to get a turtle to run a road race. It wasn't happening!

In the meantime, I grabbed my cell, which was almost like an implant on my hip for the past three years. More information was needed about the Calcium levels, so I called John in Texas. It was about 5:30 p.m. He answered… yet another miracle to get John on the first attempt at that time of day, since he sees patients into the early evening hours. I quickly and concisely explained the situation sharing Mother's Calcium level was reported to be 17…and asked "What does the high rate indicate?"

John said 17 was extremely high and said the average high was around 10 or 11. In his very calm doctor voice demeanor he said, "Christa, there is no need to rush in getting to the ER to create any dangerous driving, but you do need to proceed directly."

In sharing that John resides in Texas, one might get the idea of a country doctor who wears cowboy boots, with horses in his barn, talks slow enough for others not to misunderstand, and is in no "all out" hurry to get anywhere. Yep, you've got the right vision! That's our John. And his wife, well she is an amazing lady - smart as a whip, fun loving, and caring as the day is long. Quite the pair saddled together.

Meanwhile back at our farm…Poppa helped me load Mother in the vehicle. Poppa had decided to drive his truck since we might have to stay overnight, which meant he could return home. To be better prepared, I grabbed my stay over hospital gear, pillow, and laptop… again! Then I contacted my brother to inform him of the change of plans after I had just texted Jack, "We're home."

When we arrived at the ER, I proceeded to get Mother out of the vehicle and into a wheel chair. As soon as we registered, she was immediately escorted back to a room in the ER. Dr. Jackson[56] was our attending ER physician. I explained why we were there, as one of the nurses pulled her medical records on the computer to confirm the Calcium level. He was a physician I worked with indirectly, and remembered as being very compassionate with his patients and their families.

He explained a high Calcium level is called "hypercalcemia" - a condition which requires medication. Another possibility was that her thyroid and parathyroid were not functioning properly. The last option: the high level meant an indicator for cancer. Not to sound like a "medical expert" or give the impression I am a "know it all," my thoughts kept leading to her existing pacemaker… that somehow, some way it was creating the problem.

I shared with Dr. Jackson that Mother was scheduled to have her pacemaker extracted on Friday. I then asked if there could be any correlation between a high calcium rate and her pacemaker not functioning properly. Dr. Jackson replied he didn't know how there could be. I explained the metal allergies to him. Without any hesitation or "scowl look of wonder" in facial expression, he shared his understanding of metal allergy issues and revisions. A huge relief!

Mother shared with Dr. Jackson about John, our family MD. She also was relieved to know Dr. Jackson understood her metal allergies, and what she had been through. It seemed to be a great relief to her. We knew how rare it was for a physician to accept metal allergies. We had to repeatedly explain the situation more times than our name, address and phone number, it seemed! Dr. Jackson offered to call and speak directly with John, once the lab work returned. We were grateful for his offer.

After a couple of hours, the lab work came back with the same high Calcium level at 17. The ER nurses administered fluids as Dr. Jackson announced he was admitting her until her Calcium rate came down because it was dangerously high. Again within a short time, she became nauseated and began vomiting. It was a grim reminder of the long 17-day hospital stay when in the Fall of 2008 when she was admitted to a hospital from their ER.

If only I could tell him I believed it was the pacemaker, but I felt it was best for the test results to show the evidence, because quite honestly... I didn't know how to explain. It was just something I knew.

The blood work from her parathyroid and thyroid were normal. That was a huge relief. The medical treatment plan was to get her Calcium lowered and find out what was causing it. About midnight, when we learned Mother was going to be admitted, Poppa decided to go back to the farm, and we were escorted to a room on the cardiac floor. "Peas" went one way, and "Carrots" went another.

The medical center's on-call hospitalist came by shortly after Mother arrived. Yet again, I had to explain Mother's medical journey. I shared that she was scheduled for a pacemaker extract on Friday at their facility. He said it might have to be postponed if the Calcium continued to be high. More fluids were ordered along with Sodium Potassium and Magnesium throughout the night, and other meds for her ongoing nausea and vomiting. Due to her severe weakness and Mother being a "fall risk," a catheter was ordered so Mother would not have to get up from the bed.

Once again, I fixed my temporary sleeping contraption which was a hide-a-bed in a chair - and the bed was well hid! I moved the less than fluffy resting pad close to the side of her hospital bed. If she needed me during the night, I wanted to be able to get up at a moment's notice to help, if she became more nauseated.

Mother finally began to sleep. Then with little warning every couple of hours, she began a round of violent vomiting spells. I'd been with her a great deal during times like these, but never witnessed so much fluid being expelled when it appeared she had very little in her stomach.

It was a long night for her with little rest as the vomiting continued. I was so grateful with the physician's decision to put in a catheter because what fluids she dispensed from vomiting, she expelled equal amounts from her kidneys. We had our own Niagara Falls flushing through Mother's distressed and weakened body.

Prayerful thoughts were repeated for her to improve quickly. When prayers don't get answered when I ask, I've come to understand God has a reason. It may not be the answer I want, but I've learned to trust in His ways, His will and His timing.

The next morning, Mother continued to have no appetite. There was little chance in trying to persuade her to take a sip or two of a Sprite, or try eating a tiny bite of a cracker. She was beyond miserable continuing to vomit but a little less than the previous night.

The hospitalist assigned to Mother's case came in to check on her. He was a personable and friendly physician who made her feel better, uplifting her spirits with his wonderful bedside manners. For all the physicians we encountered since 2006, those qualities appeared to be extremely rare, as we had crossed paths with many in a wide array of specialties. This special doc was an internist.

Dr. Sadar[57] told us he and his wife moved to the United States from India about five years ago. He explained the high expectations he experienced in his country while attending medical school, sharing that if a student was caught going to a movie by a professor instead of studying, the student was either placed on probation, or kicked out. That is serious schooling!

Dr. Sadar asked how Mother was doing. I said, "She is trying to make sense but is making less sense than she did last night, but somehow we still understand what she is trying to share." He laughed, which made Mother feel better even though she really didn't have a lot to say. She was exactly opposite from her personality.

He said Mother's confusion was a prime symptom from the high Calcium rate which had dropped to 14. That reduction was a huge relief and welcomed news. Once again, I explained Mother's metal allergies, surgeries and everything else that applied to her health situation, as he asked many questions. Dr. Sadar was very inquisitive, completely absorbed in learning more about Mother's medical mysteries and how they had been approached and solved.

He said "I am always open-minded as there's no way for a physician to know everything about science. You really have to see how a patient responds and that is often how you know what could be the problem by process of elimination." Dr. Sadar's view was music to my ears! God was paving the way.

While he was all ears, I mentioned the idea of the pacemaker and the Calcium rate being so high and if there was any connection he might be aware of from his previous medical studies or any correlation. He jovially said "No, but your Mother is that one percent, and anything could be going on with the medical history she has had!" How strange he would make that remark. Mother had faced the less than one percent odds in the very beginning of our journey; we were gaining against the odds!

I gave a copy of the medical research from the United Kingdom I located on the Internet the day before when I went home to shower and change clothes. He was very eager to read it, and learn what I discovered. But again, it was a "gut feeling" and not because I was trying to be medical expert or clinician, by any means. My answers came as a direct result of praying.

The report entitled "Specific Pharmacology of Calcium in Myocardium, Cardiac Pacemaker, and Vascular Smooth Muscle[58]," stated pacemakers can create a high calcium rate in older patients. I had no idea if this article was valid in Mother's case. However, I was led to search the two elements placed heavily on my heart for "Pacemakers and High Calcium levels." It was the only article linking the two separate issues with any possibility of making sense. It was a well documented article, with several medical researchers contributing.

The other suggestion John made in a conversation with me later that day, was dehydration. Lack of physical activity and too much rest, in addition, to not being able to get adequate amounts of exercise, also made sense.

Her pacemaker continued to weigh heavily in my weary thought process. It was only a slight pain to Mother since its implant with sporadic itching and redness. The worst part was the irritation of placing her seat belt across the same spot on her chest to fasten her driver's side seat belt. It had always created a pain or hindrance with her.

The process of elimination began as soon as we entered the ER with her lab work results. The physicians were absolutely mystified as to what could be causing her Calcium rate to soar from nowhere. It was only two weeks prior to her hospital admission that her primary care physician, Dr. James, had performed a complete blood work analysis during her regular check up. It was a good report with no abnormalities.

Just two weeks later, she's admitted to a hospital with an elevated Calcium rate. "Was it the lack of exercise creating dehydration or somehow the pacemaker creating a hindrance by pulling her body down, due to any metals comprising her healing body?" I wondered.

During her hip revision, the marrow in her femur had to be reamed out due to the cement being unidentifiable from the interior of her thigh bone. Dr. Seymour shared this information with us after her last major hip surgery, which was only 90 days earlier. Now, she was back in a hospital with a high Calcium rate.

It was one of many questions on my mind; but again, I believed it to be a metal allergy related issue with the pacer or the lead wires. I had the "metal mentality" going on. It seems since that's all that was wrong every time, time-after-time through her medical mystery.

Her body appeared to demonstrate a pattern to the metal allergy discoveries. The same things previously happened, seemed to be a repeat process. Although the size of the metal implant was smaller, I still continued to believe the pacemaker was the instigator in what appeared to be an isolated incident. Somehow, I continued to believe it was more of the same reactions to the types of metals implanted in Mother's body.

Mother's pre-hip surgical revision issue is a good example. For eight weeks she had a nasty kidney infection antibiotics could not touch. Within "eight hours" after the metal was changed to Titanium from Nickel-Cobalt-Chromium-Molybdenum, the nasty infection was gone.

Dr. Sadar had made an excellent point. How the patient responds is worth reviewing on a case-by-case basis, even if the human body is made the same. As I thought about his point, it reminded me of different personalities in people. In other words, should human bodies be stereotyped like we do with people's personalities?

As the medical process of elimination began, the first test arranged was a CAT scan. The results showed no indication of any problems. The next day was Thursday. Her Calcium level dropped to 11.8. Dr. Sadar ordered a full body scan.

Again, the report was negative. Nothing suspicious was reported or linked to explain her high Calcium rate. The only mark questionable was a scar on her right lower lung from when a biopsy was performed with a 99.9 percent diagnosis of Lymphoma in 2006. Once again, cancer was ruled out based on the full body scan!

This had been Mother's second full body scan within approximately the last six months. In the spring of 2010, before Mother's hip revision, Dr. Seymour ordered a full body scan. It did not reveal anything suspicious, or the radiologist would have alerted him, hip related or any other area of her body. It provided as an excellent bench mark, as did the blood work Dr. James completed only two weeks prior to her high calcium rate. There were no indications of anything significantly abnormal.

When Dr. Sadar came in to Mother's room later that morning, I asked if the pacemaker extraction was still scheduled. He said that would be Dr. Style's call, but he would advise him based on Mother's condition when the time came, if her Calcium was within the acceptable normal range.

Mother was feeling better, but she said she was starting to see colors on the wall with weird spots like yellow, red and green. Honestly, I was hesitant to mention anything to the nurse. With Mother's confusion still evident based on her unusual and humorous conversation, I also sensed we needed to make sure this was another symptom she was experiencing due to a high Calcium level.

The catheter was removed and she became stronger. She was able to get up and walk down the hall. She had been flat on her back for three days without any exercise. It was a huge relief to see her get better!

Poppa was with us every day, all day, since she was being admitted. "Peas and Carrots." He arrived in time to hear Dr. Sadar's medical summation of Mother's results on Thursday afternoon. He said there was no cancer. Her Calcium was 8.4, and he had no explanation as to why it became so high. So the Potassium Sulfur and Magnesium fluids were stopped. Once the I.V.s were removed and she was off the fluids, Mother's nausea was gone.

Dr. Sadar recommended to have her lab work checked by her primary care physician again, to make certain her Calcium was stabilizing within a lower range. I asked him if the pacemaker extract was still a "go." He said "I am going to call Dr. Style[59] right now. I will advise him to proceed, based on her results and Calcium levels in the normal range. Again, it will be Dr. Style's decision but I don't see any reason for her not to go ahead based on our reports." We were elated, but assuredly relieved the pacemaker was going to finally be removed.

Friday morning, we didn't have a clue if the procedure was still planned, or had been cancelled. Around mid-morning, nurses and techs from Dr. Style's team arrived ready to cart Mother to surgery. Mother was thrilled! I still believed, once the pacemaker was out, everything was going to be fine. Mother was still seeing spots, but she was so glad to be getting the pacer out.

While Mother was heading to surgery, I called Poppa on his cell phone. He had already left the house, on his way to the medical center. He was obviously disappointed not being there to see Mother before the procedure. When he learned the day before that Mother did not have cancer, I have never seen such a relieved man! What a blessing he is for Mother and Mother is for him. "Just like Peas and Carrots!"

As I sat in Mother's hospital room, intertwined with my thoughts, the phone rang. It was Dr. Style. He said, "She's fine. No laser needed (for the lead wire was thought to be attached to her heart muscle in removing it). The implant pulled out fine." I later was told by the nurses, Dr. Style used a local anesthetic and anesthesia was not administered. That was great news! No nausea or irregular bouts for Mother to deal with. Sheer delight captured my soul as I grinned like a possum.

Mother was placed in CCU for overnight observation, where she was pampered and spoiled continuously, until she was discharged later the next day. I called Mother earlier Saturday morning at 8:00 a.m. She said, "I had the best night's sleep I've had in my entire life!" Her voice was chipper and spunky. She laughed with tremendous relief. After a moment or two, she continued, "I can't remember the last time I was headache free." Her appetite returned with no signs of nausea. She was alert, and her chest where the pacer was formerly implanted, no longer itched!

At approximately 11:00 a.m., Dr. Sadar called me at home to personally update Mother's results, and her discharge orders. We talked about her pattern being consistent with her other positive responses when metal was removed. He said, "All indicators demonstrate she rebounds upon the removal of metal which seems to trigger negative results in her body." The pacemaker was now a fact, which coincided with Dr. Sadar's statement.

I remembered Dr. Style saying in his office when Mother was laid back on the exam table before we headed to pre-admission, "It would be a miracle if removing the pacemaker made her feel better." I knew a miracle would be seen as soon as the words hit the airways! With Mother's Calcium level running high … there was not one doubt, even in her lowest times, God was showing us… He is the Great Physician. Miracles happen all the time, but there are some which seem more significant to those who need reassurance, which He displays at the oddest times in the most peculiar ways!

There was no explanation based on Dr. Sadar's thorough examination and testing as to why Mother's Calcium level rapidly shot up to 17, dropping to 14 then 10.3 and down to 8.7. I believe God's hand was all over this situation to prove a point. I may never know the details, but somehow God will use Mother's medical case some way in the medical clinicians' lives as a reminder, or possibly a link, or connection should they see this situation again.

Steel Standing's original draft was thought to be near completion May 2010. Many new revelations have been made in the past 22 months. In 2011, a medical research case study did prove it was most likely the pacemaker's metal casing which was Titanium Alloy with Nickel, in addition to the lead wires and a screw being Stainless Steel, that were causing the allergic reactions[68].

In thinking back before I resigned from my previous employer, one of my coworkers had asked me, "Are you willing to do whatever it takes?" I answered "Yes!" ... without any hesitation in a definitive tone. From time-to-time, her question comes to mind, enduring what seemed like incredible hardships, wondering if this medical mystery would ever evolve into to a happy, healthy closure. I believe God was asking me through another believer, "Are you willing to do what it takes?"

Every job I've ever worked, I've always had a job description. I think every human being needs one for their own life... "Go the extra mile, be cheerful, be positive, give others the benefit of doubt, be kinder than necessary, and accept ALL other duties as assigned!"

Until you have walked in another soul's shoes, there's no way to know how an individual is affected, or what changes in their life's happenings affect their thinking or attitude. I have questioned in my heart why some people do not go the extra mile, but choose to stay secluded in their social circles. Social circles run 360 degrees bringing you right back to where you were before. I was sure of one fact; we were going not going in circles. We had a dedicated alignment to break what appeared as circular motion.

Mother had three metal implants requiring removal as her health deteriorated, quickly. Before each of the three revision surgeries, she had three serious health issues to become complications working against her goal to gain better health. Yet, the circumstances changed each time for Mother to move forward. It was her deep-seeded faith in God. Mother continued to do exceptionally well as her muscles began rebounding, gaining strength and her piano tune-ups are right on key!

Her next appointment with Dr. Luke was May 27, 2011, which seemed like an eternity as a follow-up with a possibility of reverting the diagnosis of Mother's Inflammatory Myopathy, as a side effect from the metal inducing her muscle weakness.

Dr. Luke said Mother's case was the first metal allergies linked to muscle debilitation, he had seen in all his years of practice and research.

He is a renowned medical researcher.

With her change of pace without a "pacer," we believed with all our hearts Mother's medical mystery was finally seeing conclusion. However, a destination can appear closer while eagerly glazing at the path ahead.

Her journey's path was about to be challenged. Would she be able to grasp deeper faith and resilience with her new pace in this journey?

+ + +

"He's gotten you this far, hasn't He?"

~ Brenda Brewer Hoyt

The Mystery. The Journey. The Miracle.

Chapter 18

THE HEART OF THE JOURNEY

What?!? I am thinking! "Mother, did you say what I think I heard?" But indeed she did! Somehow, once again, her right hip seemed to hurt as if a wire was sticking into her leg when she walked, or sat.

This newly discovered pain recently began to bother her about midway through a therapy session. It was beyond me how she could tolerate even the mildest forms of suffering, again.

The last hip repair surgery was supposed to "fix" the wires stabilizing her mitered femur and Titanium stem securely intact with Titanium metal plates. She was very hesitant to share the news with Poppa and me…and for good reason! No one, more than Mother, wanted to have any additional surgeries or anything else, requiring a visit to the doctor, much less the far-fetched thought of hospitalization, in addition to more therapy!

As soon as she shared the news, I believed she needed to share this discovery with Dr. Seymour to have her hip checked for possible problems. Within a few days, Mother was quickly worked into his busy appointments. She had become a "regular" after nearly two years, as his patient. When one of us called, his staff knew we were not calling to just say hello, but due to more serious issues. In this case, it was the newly implanted wires.

After Mother's routine x-ray of her hip, we were escorted to what felt like a "home away from home" type exam room! As we waited for Dr. Seymour to enter, Mother was extremely apprehensive about what he would share with her x-ray. She was acutely aware that something was not right with her hip, stating it felt like the first time the wires snapped creating a sensation as if they were sticking her from the inside of her upper right thigh.

The moment arrived as the exam door slowly opened. Dr. Seymour entered the room trying to be jovial, but he looked as disappointed as Mother was already feeling. He showed us the x-ray where the two upper wires had snapped, again. Basically the wires were not strong enough to stabilize the range of motion Mother was placing on her hip during therapy while in a compromised situation. She was trying to exercise a healed area of muscle, previously cut three separate times. The first incision was during her original hip replacement after her fall. The second and third times were under Dr. Seymour's incredible attempts to correct her metal implant revisions which called for innovative expertise.

The third surgical revision we called "repair" to keep surgical procedures separate when referencing. In reflection, Dr. Seymour had removed the lower wires where the bone had grown back together but he felt the upper part of the femur needed continued support so he replaced the upper wires again with Nickel-Cobalt-Chromium 2 mm metal wiring to enforce the healing process. Again, these were the strongest and most durable metal wires available on the market, based on Dr. Seymour's extensive research. For Mother to have any possibility of mobility in her right hip for range of motion, she was literally put back together like Humpty-Dumpty®, again.

Mother was looking at yet a fourth orthopaedic revision surgery on the same hip, while looking at a surgeon who hated to break the news, while looking at his patient who was looking incredibly crushed. And I wasn't looking!

Dr. Seymour explained how he believed the wires had unfortunately snapped. Due to the floating bone which is anatomically located in the highest area above the human's large bones in each hip, someway it had shifted upward several inches from where the floating should be stationary. He was basing this report on her previous x-rays compared to the current film he had to explain his understanding to Mother.

For every word he said, I bet you could count the tears that began dropping as Mother held her head down, while most likely listening with a numbness ignited by dread. It was all I could do not to get up from the guest chair and hug her. I felt for her in so many ways, having witnessed the many struggles and attempts to literally get back on her feet versus feeling defeated!

Overwhelmed, and never believing the surgeries on her hip were going to stop so she could heal and walk forward with a quality life, she wanted to know if there were any other options. Dr. Seymour explained that he would have to surgically repair the wires. He also shared that she would be facing a longer recovery rate since the muscle had two previous cuts in the same area within the last year.

It was not the news Mother wanted to hear. Quite honestly, it was not the news I cared to learn for her. I wanted Mother to be well from her broken hip. And if she were well, then I might be allowed to move forward versus appearing to shuffle my feet with limitations as I have tried repeatedly to enter the working world, and have an independent life, again. Yet, deeper within, I knew I was on a mission from God… and no, I was not one of the Blues Brothers!

Dr. Seymour said she would need to stop her physical therapy to give him time to investigate other surgical device options hoping she would not continue having any surgery repairs. The difficulty in her femur healing so her hip would again gain strength and stability was the necessary cut Dr. Seymour had to previously cut to make due to the cement not loosening for the original stem to be removed. Therefore, Dr. Seymour did the only thing he could by mitering the bone. This has created more unexpected problems but it was the only option to remove what was thought to be Titanium, but was Nickel-Cobalt-Chromium-Molybdenum metals.

Once a bone is broken or split, it is never as solid, even with very secure metal reinforcements. That is why Dr. Seymour made it a priority to secure her mitered femur with a Titanium system to offer a more secure reinforcement for her femur and hip. Her body could no longer tolerate Nickel-Cobalt-Chromium metals.

Mother was faced with going through another hip surgery repair or quite possibly losing her limb, or life, due to the toxicity obviously induced on her entire body. Her battle seemed endless.

Without any further options to consider, Mother finally agreed to do whatever was necessary. Dr. Seymour was a God-sent physician for

Mother. His compassion for her had become deeply entrenched because they had been through so much in the effort to save her life. They were both strong believers in how God works. He adamantly encouraged her to keep her faith.

His gentle approach, with his incredible demeanor was emotionally healing as she was facing yet another setback with the same leg. There could not have been a better physician to take care of Mother, as far as I was concerned, in watching how compassionately he was in sharing, caring, and consoling his very special patient!

"He's gotten you this far, hasn't He?" Stated through another faithful follower, Brenda Brewer Hoyt's quote would again provide a surge in helping me to keep Mother's spirits uplifted. How simply stated, yet a powerful reminder - why doubt? Our journey was evident of God's abundant grace!

Within two weeks, Mother and I were again waiting in the same exam room for Dr. Seymour. He walked in with a grin and good news to share. He had researched a new customized device for rare patient situations such as Mother's femur, which needed to be stabilized for healing with tremendous support to allow her bone and muscles to heal. The desperate permanence was needed for Mother to regain her posture, agility and strength through physical therapy sessions.

It was imperative in our thinking for Mother to able to walk without a cane, if at all possible. We all became her much needed cheerleaders, encouraging her to move forward and "Just Do It." Dr. Seymour had spent a great deal of time in trying to accomplish that single goal by researching the latest newly designed customized Titanium braces.

The one he believed would be best suited for Mother's situation involved using monofilament, or fishing line, to secure the plate. The sturdy thin line would harness the brace, as it intertwined through the device but never touching her bone anchored exactly over the previously mitered femur. The brace was made with claws at the further end which would be embedded into her bone. Titanium screws would be attached to her bone through the device keeping it motionless.

Additionally, the customized brace allowed for Dr. Seymour to secure the floating bone with the monofilament in a way that would pull it back towards its natural origin. Stabilizing her float bone was a key factor to assist in Mother regaining her balance.

It all sounded great, but then again, it was not my leg or hip. I asked, "How long would it take for a customized device to be made?" Dr. Seymour said it was already on order, with specific measurements of Mother's femur to make sure the fit is secure. It was truly a customized Titanium brace made for Mother's new implant device. The surgery for "reconstruction" was set for February 11, 2011.

Another additional surgery required so much more than I believe most anyone could fathom that's never had a surgery, much less complicated surgeries so close together, which affected her livelihood. A multitude of other individuals have extraordinary medical cases that are probably way beyond anything Mother, or I could comprehend. Based on the origin of Mother's case, it was going to require more determination, deeper faith, and a great deal of mental preparedness. To be successful in what we believed would be the last "hip, hip, hip HOORAY" revisions!

We continued to seek God for all things needed, and things we never anticipated we would need. The first thing that came to mind was to pray for Mother's pain not to be as harsh as the previous surgeries, particularly the last surgery which broke my heart in watching her struggle and suffer. Previously, it never entered my thoughts to pray specifically for all of her surgeries to not to be so painful.

The day for surgery arrived. We anticipated a minimum four hour surgery since the others were about the same duration. We had an abundance of supporters to drop by the hospital, which was comforting.

By this time, Mother had experienced so much difficulty, word was finally spreading in our hometown about her metal allergies to her metal implants. Many phone calls were from those who had metal with health problems as they began asking Mother about her surgeries, experiences, and symptoms. People finally began comprehending Mother's rare medical situation. Others appeared curious and doubtful. But the skeptics are the ones I believe will see the truth!

Another factor that helped to educate the public which also was beginning to make more sense to the average person who was remotely interested in metal implants, was the 2011 Johnson & Johnson's DePuy's metal hip replacement recall[60]. It seemed to be reported on every channel, and was also the main attraction of many law firms advertising to seek patients with this exact implant device. Ironically, we were already educated with specific details three years before this news made news! How interesting to hear others talk about this topic, as if it were a new discovery, when we had first began to experience it since 2006.

That's when Mother's closest friends began to comprehend her problem was very real. It wasn't as if they ever doubted her metal allergies, but so little has been publicly disclosed, I suppose I would be skeptical, at first. Since the entire ordeal, we have also learned to be very open-minded to what may appear impossible from a physician-patient standpoint.

Finally the four-hour mark had passed. About that time we were notified to meet Dr. Seymour in the family room. Once again, he delivered great news! Prior to making his incision, he decided to change the location on her leg. The new incision was in the middle of her thigh facing frontwards versus to the side of her thigh. He believed cutting into the same healed incision area would create additional scar tissue, making the healing process much more difficult. It was a brilliant decision.

Another huge relief that came about from this revision was Dr. Seymour deciding to remove all the 2 mm Nickel-Cobalt-Chromium wires previously left in place from her last hip revision. He said there was a pocket of yellow fluid[80] where the wires had frayed. Speculation of the fluid coloring made us wonder if she had some infection from where the wires were rubbing against her muscle.

When Mother arrived in her hospital room, she was not in as much pain, as she had been. She was not nearly as nauseated. I believe my specific prayers were answered! Within hours, she began to move around because her new incision was not nearly as painful. This hospital stay was better for both of us.

On Valentine's Day, three days after surgery, she was getting ready to be transported by ambulance to an area hospital where an inpatient rehabilitation service had been added to their 60 swing-bed facility. I had already packed our belongings anxious to move forward.

Once again, Mother would go through a severe nauseating spell just before the EMS crew was to arrive for transport. The nausea began shortly after she ate breakfast. With no additional signs of a headache, or any other symptoms she experienced with her other Post-Ops, I called the nurse so Mother could be given meds. She was sitting in a recliner, preparing to get dressed when her nausea worsened.

The nurse entered the room and began administering a shot through her I.V. About 10 minutes had passed while the nurse and I were talking over how odd this was for Mother, considering she did not have any nausea prior to that morning. The nurse was making sure she was feeling better when Mother said, "I feel a strange light sensation up and over the back of my left shoulder." For someone who could not seem to be descriptive in her discussions with physicians or therapists, she could not have been more clear.

I had worked in medical centers for several years. Heart attack signs and symptoms were probably the most educated material I had repeatedly promoted year after year! Based on that information, Mother appeared to be having a mild heart attack, if it was her heart.

Calmly, I turned to the nurse and said, "Please notify Dr. Seymour and her primary care physician, Dr. James." Nothing else was said. We were on the same wave length of what "might" be going on. There was no time to wonder, worry, or fret…we responded accordingly. I sent Jack a text message. He came instantly as he "happened" to be in the medical facility, which is a rarity since his administration duties are just about anywhere but in the hospital.

While the nurse notified the physicians, the charge nurse came to the room and checked her vitals. An EKG was ordered, stat. Within the hour, a very young personable but highly concerned cardiologist came into Mother's room as Jack and I stayed with her. Dr. Booster[61] shared some astonishing information.

Mother did have a very mild heart attack. My knees locked as quickly as my thoughts. I immediately thanked God! We were within 20 minutes or less from leaving the medical center. We could have been on the road.

The heart attack could have been worse! But everything was happening in the right place, for the right reasons. I felt a peace amidst my confusion while trying to translate the information as I continued to hear "heart attack" talk. This was yet another new area completely different from the pacemaker exploits. Or... could it be related?

As I stood near my brother, he sat while quietly listening, though obviously stunned even as his professional demeanor kicked in versus the child whom shared a unique and close relationship with his Mother. Dr. Booster continued, "There are two choices based on the lab results which show within a short amount of time that she did experience a mild heart attack. One is a test that is noninvasive but does not always give clear results based on the heart's reaction to the test. The other alternative is a Cath lab (cardiac catheterization procedure) which is invasive, allowing us to see the damage or blockage in the heart."

Mother sat quietly listening to Dr. Booster. She then looked over to Jack and me, and asked what we thought she needed to do. I asked more questions. My concern was the fact that she just had a major orthopaedic reconstructive revision surgery on her right leg. She had been through so many surgical procedures requiring long doses of anesthesia. There were concerns of what to do, and it seemed we had very little time to decide. Exhausted, as we had been, we were in the mindset to leave for the rehab facility. It was a total 180-degree spin for me. Mother's mild heart attack changed everything, and not just the days' agenda, but everything in every aspect of her life and within our small-knit family.

Jack and I had to get into a quick mode of thinking to make the best decisions for Mother's well being.

To my astonishment, Mother handled this new health issue with great calmness. She was incredible, accepting the news with a peacefulness. I think she knew in her heart, God was in control and could have already taken her last breath many times before now. I just felt for her to have yet another invasion into her already weakened body.

Then I asked THE question that really brought on concern, "If you find a blockage, you will place a stent in her heart, correct?" Dr. Booster confirmed. My next questions came quickly to mind..."What is the stent made of? What metals are used?"

After spending as many days researching metals used in the body for knee and hip replacements - not once did it cross my mind the wide range of many types of metals used for repair in any surgery!

My metal mentality was kicking in, as I became highly sensitive to what would be placed in Mother's body from this point forward! Dr. Booster said, "I don't know, but I'll check and get back with you." Then, as I had done umpteen times before, I explained Mother's rare and unheard of story about her metal allergies.

Thankfully, our young astute cardiologist was open-minded and understood her metal sensitivity, which was well charted from Dr. Seymour's medical records. Also, Dr. Seymour could have substantiated the medical information verbally versus her medical charts, but he was out of town attending an orthopaedic seminar in California for the remainder of the week.

Dr. Booster said we needed to schedule the Cath lab first thing tomorrow morning. We all agreed this procedure needed to be done, but I still didn't know the type of metals that were to be used if stents were a necessity. Poppa was upset when he learned the news. He had heart procedures previously and knew what she might be facing. He was so sweet to observe, as I saw how comforting Poppa was for Mother. What an incredible Valentine's Day this would be for Mother! The Harton's Heart Day. "Just like Peas and Carrots."

The next morning, Mother was wheeled away before Poppa could arrive to see her. Jack was in a meeting. Once again, I was the point person with my cell phone ready to contact our immediate family, which included John, our family M.D. I wanted all the best and most reliable professional resources available to help make an educated decision.

John's oldest son is a vascular surgeon and we may have needed to seek his medical opinion. His work was becoming recognized by his colleagues on a national level.

While Mother was being prepped for the procedure, Dr. Booster came to her bedside and shared the types of metal that were used in the stents. At that particular medical facility, the choices included Stainless

Steel and Nickel-Cobalt-Chromium! My response was firm, as I stated to Dr. Booster, "Neither of those stents will work due to her metal allergies and how Mother's body has reacted from their adverse reaction."

I asked if we could step aside for privacy to explain in more detail why, and what I had learned from well researched data, regarding the two optional stent choices and the types of metals in the stents he might of needed to use. He was piqued by Mother's most unusual medical case, and wide open to learn more about what we had experienced.

For Mother's quality of life, much less longevity of life; neither of the metal stents he stated were options! I requested Titanium stents. He said that could take time and he didn't want to compromise Mother's heart if she did have a blockage, which could trigger a fatal or severe heart attack. I completely understood his concerns, as I had the same. But I knew this was either going to be a quick death, or a slow death for Mother. Based on her previous history of metal allergies to certain types of metals, her muscle tissue had deteriorated, thus she was diagnosed with Inflammatory Myopathy. Any additional metals she was allergic to, being placed back into her body, would place her health in great danger, again.

As we stood just a short ways into a private hallway area, my heart began to sink - thinking she may have metals placed in her after we had prayed for the culprit to be removed.

What I have previously learned about stents; once a stent is placed in a vessel of the heart, it cannot be removed. It's a permanent fixture due to the way a stent expands and is attached by the cardiologist to adhere to the vessel, where it is inserted.

Dr. Booster in fact, understood my concerns. I asked him if it was possible to go forward with the Cath lab and share the results "if" or "before" the stents were to be placed. He agreed.

As we concluded our conversation, I remained in the hallway for a few moments before returning to Mother's bedside. Praying to the Great Physician was all I could think to do, asking for Him to take care of Mother's needs. I never felt the need to cry or become overly anxious. This was just another step in Mother's ability to move forward in her healing journey. What appeared to be a setback, was in reality another learning curve, for us and many others.

Once Mother was rolled away for the procedure, I waited near the Cath lab. At best, I was in a dazed fog. My thoughts seemed to be flat-lined. I suppose, the stunned numbness of this on-going journey was starting to become a tad overwhelming. Approximately 30 minutes had passed. I was summoned to a family room in the Cath lab area to meet with Dr. Booster. As I walked in, I noticed educational material was readily available. There were two guest chairs and a couch. There wasn't a magazine or brochure I carried to read to just pass the time. Nothing seemed to interest me... at least of... sitting.

When Dr. Booster entered the room, he said. "Why don't you sit down?" I said, "I'm fine standing." He proceeded to tell me Mother did have a mild heart attack, but they could not use stents. A huge relief came over me! Then he informed me, "She has three severe blockages. Two are 90 and 99 percent. The other was an overflow artery with 70 percent. She is going to need open heart surgery."

My tad of being overwhelmed just sky-rocketed to a height so far in my mental capacity, my brain waves must have gone into shock! As I attempted to sit down hearing the totally unanticipated news, all I had to do was move two steps and sit down on the couch. Short walk. No problem! My right foot would not move! I couldn't move. I actually remember looking down, and thinking, "move." It was like it was not attached to me somehow.

At that point, I literally took my right hand, placed it on my right thigh, picking up my pants' leg to jump-start my right foot. My synapses seemed to be temporarily "snapped" like a rubber band had been stretched too far... and WHACK, its broken - only to snap-back and sting like a bee!

The words coming from Dr. Booster were incomprehensible and stunning as I continued to hear, "She is going to need open heart surgery."

While thoughts and physical motions seemed to be completely obliterated, my brain and leg began communicating after I had to help it move... and I thought "How is Mother going to take the news?" I thought he was telling me to be supportive when he shared the shocking news to Mother. But, it was if Dr. Booster read my first thought. He said, "I've already told your Mother the news." Oh my! There goes the other leg! I stood in a paralyzed state of mind that had captivated my entire being, which was in complete astonishment. My mind was reeling in everything she had been through prior to this news! Now open heart surgery. Whoa.

My horrified concern for her went into complete disarray. Finally, I was able to get the words out of my thankfully working mouth and ask, "How did she take it?" Dr. Booster said, "She seems okay, under the circumstances."

Why did I think I needed to be with her when news like that was delivered? Except for a very few physician patient follow-ups, I had been in every physician-patient consultation prior to a major surgery, or procedure. This issue was a true heart organ/muscle matter we were discussing… not another orthopaedic modus operandi for a revision or replacement, gallbladder removal or kidney stone procedure… it was open heart surgery! It doesn't get any more real, unless it's brain surgery in my opinion!

From nowhere, tears began streaming. Fear was trying to grip me; I was determined not give in to it. In my thoughts, I solemnly gave my heartfelt thanks and praise to Him for saving her life, again. Quickly, I recomposed myself, as I felt an inner spiritual strength emerge.

Dr. Booster asked which surgeon we would be requesting. I told him I needed to consult with my brother, Jack. As Dr. Booster left the family room, I continued to pray within my thoughts asking God to give each of us strength and courage, particularly for Mother.

I sent Jack a text message… "Call me." That was all I could think to type. Within five seconds, he called. I said, "Mother is going to need open heart surgery. Which surgeon?" He suggested any of the cardiologists. All were excellent. We decided on Dr. Goodheart[62]. Jack said he was on his way, and would contact Bridget.

I had the chore of calling Poppa to share the latest information. Needless to say, Poppa was really upset. He was almost to the medical center. I imagine he had to pull over to compose his emotions as well. We were all living on the grace of God, as our exhaustive states reached further into our psychological understanding as humans.

When I asked the nurse to notify Dr. Booster, I informed him our choice was Dr. Goodheart. He said Dr. Goodheart was currently on call down the hall in the Cath lab! In my relief when I heard the news, I knew God was in control as a unspoken peacefulness came over me. Dr. Goodheart being in the Cath lab gave me tremendous confirmation Mother was going to be fine. As I have shared, we no longer believe in coincidences.

Within two minutes or less Jack arrived. Bridget arrived within 10 minutes or less. We were all gathered beside a drowsy "Valentine Sweetheart[63]" while she was lying in a hospital bed. A fabric divider curtain became our private barrier from the world. Mother was doing great, but was still a bit drowsy and slightly in shock from the news. Every annual check-up, which included extensive heart testing, showed no signs of any problems. How could this be?

Dr. Goodheart entered our private fabric of drawn walls. Jack, Bridget, and I stood like ducks in a row on one side of her bed, while Dr. Goodheart stood across on the other side. He began to explain the Cath lab report, the blockages, the locations of the blockages, the procedures he would be doing for open-heart surgery, and that she would be transferred to another medical center equipped for open-heart surgeries. That was a lot of information to absorb rather quickly. Again, another surreal moment in this unbelievable journey!

He said, "Friday, February 18 would be the earliest I could perform the operation." But, he also reiterated that he believed she was okay for now. If any of her vitals changed, Dr. Goodheart said he was available to do an emergency surgery within a short amount of time, since it was his week to be on call.

Once again, I am the metal conscious kid, having studied the medical research, learning surgical metals come in all shapes and sizes for all types of surgical implants. I asked what he would use to close the chest. He answered "Stainless Steel wires."

Here I go again - explaining very concisely the path; the metal implants associated with metal allergies which Dr. Seymour or Dr. Luke could easily verify what I was sharing. Dr. Goodheart stood across from me, looking boldface. I felt I was going to be up against another force of a "naysayer," after we had been through so much to clear up any types of metals causing Mother's severe allergic reaction creating some level of toxicity.

Before I had to find the courage, I asked for an alternative choice of metal, preferably pure Titanium. It was as if I had no idea how that information just rolled off my tongue and presented itself in a articulate translation. Yet, I was very aware of the Comforter, as I was not nervous or intimidated by speaking up on Mother's behalf. He said, I only use "Stainless Steel."

What part of the medical madness had Mother been through for the last four years that he did not understand? It had been concisely explained, her medical records were clearly documented with a trail of tears, known as surgeries to rid metals causing her health issues! Why was the subject so difficult for physicians, the ultimate human caregivers for patients, to comprehend what happens when metals create problems inside a human body? These thoughts just rolled in my mind.

Now, my heart was racing! I expressed calmly that Stainless Steel was not an option in her rare and unique medical case, primarily due to Nickel. Bridget suggested, "We need to take Patricia's condition into consideration and whatever would save her life." I understood her view.

In an instance, I quickly replied as I looked directly into Dr. Goodheart's eyes, "Take your pick; she either dies a slow death or a quick death. Either way, if you close her chest with Stainless Steel, which is a combination of Metal Alloys including Nickel, you will not be helping the health issues we have been battling for over four years."

Jack stood silently between his wife and his sister. Mother continued to be in and out of her sleep-induced Post-Cath procedure.

Dr. Goodheart said we should decide what we wanted to do and he would get back with us the next day on his rounds. He was not disturbed by my request and explanation, as he appeared to be on an agenda. Perhaps he was one of many skeptics regarding Mother's metal allergies. Maybe his patients did not have the same seemingly rare issues.

It's difficult to witness the oddities of Mother's case, knowing you know, what you know… yet trying to get everyone onboard. But at least my brother and sister-in-law appeared closer to the reality Mother had been facing.

Moments before Bridget and Dr. Goodheart had previously arrived, Jack and I were alone with Mother. Jack shared a news story stating, "Metal implants can cause serious health problems."

The night before, Bridget had shared with Jack, that she watched Diane Sawyer on ABC News reporting a story on metal implants and the many adverse affects on the human body. The news network focused on Johnson & Johnson's DuPuy hip implant devices, more than the types of reactions certain metals can create in the human body. Finally, it seemed the metal message was heard. Hopefully, this was just the beginning of more people learning about metal implants and metal allergies in this country! Maybe others were going to be educated with the same major facts we had learned.

It was indeed tiring, trying to convince anyone of anything any longer. So, I kept a lot of my research which God revealed through studying, to myself. My priority remained focused on Mother and taking care of her, to the best of my ability. That was the mission I believed God had sent me home to do.

While Mother was becoming more awake from the anesthesia, Jack and Bridget graciously moved all of our packed belongings from the orthopaedic floor to the cardiac floor. We were again facing another new medical staff to share Mother's rare medical-metal story. That's a major reason I believe Mother's case is to be exposed to the public to share what most until 2011, believed was rare. Remember, the discovery was linked in spring 2009 before anyone in the mass media thought twice about metal joint replacements, or what type of metals are used in the body which could create an adverse reaction.

In a short time, Mother was transported to the cardiac floor, shortly after I arrived in her room. Dr. Goodheart made his rounds later that night. He was well aware of our stance on metal. To our surprise, he tried to contact Dr. Seymour to learn more and already researched Mother's thick volume of medical procedures and physician notes, along with the

MELISA® test results. He still appeared a bit doubtful and remained steadfastly adamant about closing with Stainless Steel.

Long before it was time for Dr. Goodheart to visit with Mother, we already gave this to the Great Physician in prayer. We specifically prayed for him to have a good change of heart in understanding our fight to keep certain types of metal, which she is allergic to, out of her body.

Our discussion was extremely civilized when Dr. Goodheart said his standard closing procedure was to use Stainless Steel wires. His routine had a great deal to do with his decision.

Mother had been inclined to have me be her spokesperson for most of this journey due to a number of circumstances:

1.) She was heavily medicated;

2.) As shared earlier, she found it difficult to share specifics; and

3.) She wore her hearing aids only when she thought she needed to hear. I SAID, SHE ONLY WORE HER HEARING AIDS WHEN SHE THOUGHT SHE NEEDED TO HEAR.

This was one time Mother was clearly thinking, without being heavily medicated, and she was wearing her hearing aids! I thought I needed to sit down for this rare interactive conversation. It was refreshing to listen as she spoke directly from her heart. Mother was explicit about her concerns in a way I could never have conveyed. She emphasized the intense trauma situations, which seemed endless to not only her, but her entire family since March 2006.

Dr. Goodheart listened attentively, never once attempting to interrupt. As he turned to leave Mother's hospital room, Dr. Goodheart was calling a representative from a company which made Titanium plates with Titanium screws. He said "There is a manufacturer's rep that's been wanting me to try Titanium for closure. If the rep can be here on Friday for the surgery, then we will try the plates." I asked him if they would be "pure" Titanium without Nickel. He said he'd check. He and Mother were on the same medical chart. He seemed to understand her dire need to stay with the metals which did not have any allergies.

Within an hour, two very excited nurses came to deliver the good news. We had previously shared Mother's medical mystery. Hearing the

Titanium plates and screws were "Pure" versus "Alloy" plus the rep being available on Friday, was great news! Again, our prayers were answered when we believed we were up against a mighty force.

During a later time when Mother was fast asleep, Dr. Goodheart came by to check on her. That's when I learned he was a believer. He and I had a wonderful conversation about our beliefs in God intertwined with creation and science.

The next day, we were transported to another medical center. Everything had to be repacked and moved to the vehicle. Our initial maximum five-day stay was quickly expanding to a possible three-weeks excursion. I felt a little bit like I had been aboard the S.S. Minnow when it was swept up in a storm, landing abruptly on what was known as, Gilliland's Island. It seemed to be taking forever for Mother and her crew to be rescued from one adventure to another before going home!

Later that day, Mother was transported to yet another newly assigned hospital room. It was time to set up housekeeping ... once again. I've never felt so much like I had been living in small dorm rooms since college. The "ugh" cart came in handy to transport more than two bags, which is about all I was able to carry at this point. What we didn't need - stayed in the vehicle! I was getting plenty of cardiovascular exercise shifting things back and forth from here-to-there.

February 18, 2011

Exactly seven days after Mother's last orthopaedic reconstructive revision surgery, she was scheduled for open heart surgery. It was stunning to witness what she endured. It saved her life; however, we prayed this was her victory lap. I never doubted Mother's fate. Somehow, I knew God had a mighty purpose for her story to be told as she experienced many things needing to be shared.

John Adams, M.D., said, "Patricia is on the frontier of a medical discovery linking metal allergies to muscle issues." Those of us dealing with Mother's case very closely, knew she was a real soldier as she forged ahead with little to no complaining in her battles.

When the OR tech came to transport Mother to surgery, Jack,

Bridget, Poppa and I surrounded her bed when she requested to have prayer with a visiting minister and his wife.

In February 1992 Mother's Daddy had open heart surgery for a valve replacement at the age of 89. She would find herself in a similar situation 19 years later. She was currently 73 years old.

Granddaddy was healthy as a horse throughout his entire life. He just waited too late when his body became weaker, before he finally went to a physician. He thought it was heart burn. He was a farmer, plumber, electrician, carpenter, church music leader, and deacon as a faithful believer in the Almighty and Great Physician. He never liked anyone referring to "God," as "the man upstairs." Granddaddy said "He is not a man. He is Mightier than anyone I know."

It was a surreal moment for Mother to be facing open heart surgery. Even with today's mentality due to so many people having open heart surgery, it appears to have fallen into a routine medical procedure, which is a life threatening surgery and very serious procedure. Anytime blood is extracted from the body while being recycled through a "heart machine" to keep a person alive... that is a huge step of faith in human hands and equipment. Not to mention your chest and rib cage cracked wide open while both patient's arms are pulled back and strapped down. Once the heart is repaired, the rib cage is reattached using metal. Mother requested pure Titanium plates and screws, but the majority of patients are wired with Stainless Steel, according to Dr. Goodheart.

Mother's surgery was a huge success! The three blockages were repaired with no complications. We were told by Dr. Goodheart and the inpatient cardiac physical therapist, Mother would experience a general weakness, which would be difficult for her to believe she would be able to overcome. She had already experienced a great deal of weakness throughout her latest hip revision's repair surgery only seven days, prior to this major surgery. So, Mother was dually setback in more physical ways that probably most people could comprehend. We were also cautioned that her cardiac surgery would also affect her emotionally.

Mother's healing process was expeditious. We were elated that she was released to a room less than 24 hours when we were told it would be 72 hours! We were elated when we learned that her breathing tube was removed after 7 hours and we were told it would be 72 hours! She was meeting and exceeding, previous set records in an open heart surgery-recovery. Those facts alone caught my attention.

When the cardiac educational nurse brought a heart template showing where her blockages were previously located and the percentages of each, I had a "gut feeling" this was not an ordinary heart surgery. How or why I sensed Mother's heart problem was related to metal allergies, I can not begin to explain. It just kept staying with me. It was a very strong thought.

Ironically, the 90 percent blockage was where the pacemaker was located. The 99 percent blockage was located exactly where the lead wire screw (Stainless Steel) was placed before being removed.

The 70 percent blockage was located in a very small artery about an inch north from the main artery where the two blockages had existed... at the top and bottom of her heart. The 70 percent appeared to be an "overflow" from the bottom 99 percent blockage. Interesting? Yes. Most definitely there had to be a connection with her pacemaker even though it had been previously removed five months prior to her heart issues. I certainly could not begin to explain, nor try.

Since Mother had two huge surgeries back-to-back within seven days, she was not able to have "regular" orthopaedic therapy for her newly revised right hip, until she was released from the hospital. As a matter of fact, she was also released early from the medical center due to her unexpected quick recovery! In less than a week, Mother was on her way to our original destination.

When patients are closed with Stainless Steel wires, their weight limitations are only 5 lbs. Because of the Titanium plates, Mother was allowed to lift 20 lbs! The Titanium plates and screws cost twice as much as Stainless Steel, but the recovery time is much quicker, in addition to the medical cost. In the long run, Titanium plates are much less expensive, and in most cases may be less harmful to an individual's body. Imagine helping to cut costs and time in health care!

The "ugh" cart seat had been used as a desk for my laptop. Dr. Goodheart was trying to figure out what type of apparatus would help with Mother's recent orthopaedic recovery and open heart recovery. A walker was too strenuous due to her overall physical weakness. About the time he walked in her hospital room, I had just removed the "ugh" cart from the bathroom. Considering the small room, the shower was the only place I could think to place it. When Dr. Goodheart saw the "ugh" cart, he said "That would be perfect for her to use in therapy!" All I could think; "In God's timing... **even** the 'ugh' cart had a multi-purpose beyond what we could have ever imagined!"

We were finally shipping out to Centre. Mother was released to an inpatient facility in our nearby hometown. In less than three weeks, yet another record breaker, Mother was released to come home!

One week after Mother arrived, we understood the emotional aspects we had been emphatically warned would happen. However, Mother was not the only one who experienced tremendous grief. We are animal lovers, critter caregivers, and think of our pets as family members to an extent.

Samson. Our Samson. He was a puppy literally left at our barn's entrance one week before Christmas in 2009. We were experiencing financial hardships. Christmas gifts were to be hugs that year, until an incredible healthy, beautifully marked thoroughbred puppy was to become our gift! We didn't know who brought him, his breed, or his age based on weeks or months. He was black and tan with a double-coated fur, with distinctive lines, which created the most handsome face with big brown eyes - intelligent and quick to learn commands. He had huge feet we knew he would grow into! It was obvious he was going to be a large dog, so he was named Samson. What joy Samson gave us for as long as we had him in our lives!

When Mother arrived home after being away longer than she would have ever desired, much less anticipated, Samson greeted her like she had been lost from home! It was quite a reunion. I think she was more anxious to see our pets, than anything or anyone else! The entire first week after Mother arrived home, she was finally able to sleep in her own bed. Samson laid beside her on the floor rug. He literally did not want to leave her side.

One afternoon, he gently placed his paws on Mother's lap while she was in her recliner. He looked into her eyes as she patted him. Samson never jumped on anyone. He was very mild mannered. But Mother remembered how special it was for him that particular day to almost hug her.

Samson was protective of the kids nearby. He was standing near the side of the road that same day, watching the children play when a pickup truck aimed at Samson and killed him. My nephew witnessed the accident and ran into the house to get me. Quickly, I grabbed my car keys and told Poppa what had happened. We drove to the road where he was still alive! Without thinking, I picked up a 90 lb. dog out of the ditch and placed him on a blanket in the back of my Honda Pilot. I called our Vet on my cell phone, and asked him to meet us at his office.

My nephew, Poppa and I sped as safely as possible to Centre. Within three miles of the Vet's office, Samson passed away. When my nephew told me he had stopped breathing. I pulled off to the side of the road so I could get out and check Samson. He had indeed passed away.

It broke my heart, as I began to weep over losing him. Poppa and my nephew were just as upset. This was a Friday afternoon. Only one week since Mother had returned and one of the things she wanted the most to come home to, was Samson. We were all emotionally drained, and why did we have to lose Samson - a joy and delight, greatly needed in our lives right then.

My own sorrow quickly turned to immediate concerns, as reality hit me in an instant. It occurred to me, Mother was going to have to be told. "Had she already not been through enough?"... I repeated. My heart was hurting for Samson, but oh, how I hurt for Mother, and for Poppa.

By the time we got back to the house, we drove in slowly. She was aware. Poppa and I told her and she lost it. Mother had been through so much and come so far. One of the most precious joys in her life, was gone. As we had been told, her emotions were fragile. She become deeply saddened, almost instantly depressed.

I called one of my best friends. Tina, was working as a psychiatric nurse, again. She had been with us every step of the way since I had resigned from the nuclear plant. She knew all too well, how caring and compassionate Mother was to others. And how she felt about Samson!

Tina gave me great counseling advice to console Mother, but nothing seemed to help. Mother cried more than I had seen her cry in a very long. It was if she had lost a parent or a child. She was absolutely pitiful. I also knew, it was also a release of her emotions associated with everything she had experienced in a relatively short amount of time.

Instead of allowing my anger to get the best of me by telling God how upset I was that He allowed this to happen... I got on my knees, and asked for his mercy and comfort for Mother... for all of us. The kids, Poppa; we were all upset. But Mother was battling a more serious emotional phase in her recovery, now added with the loss of Samson.

On Sunday, I got in my Pilot and drove off. I didn't tell Mother or Poppa where I was going as I headed to a nearby animal control shelter. There were plenty of big dogs that needed good homes, but this time I was led to the puppy area. We already had one inside dog named Skippy. We rescued him in 2007. Maybe another inside dog was the answer? I didn't know; only that I was led to get another pet for Mother.

So, I came home with a 12 week old mixed puppy, completely opposite from Samson in gender, color, stature, and size. Yet, they have the same odd habits, and same features! Their mannerisms were uniquely similar. Poppa named her "Katie." I was totally amazed at how our new little one was so much like our Samson. Again, I believed God answered our prayers providing a loving dog - not to take Samson's place - but to fill a major void in all of our exhausted hearts!

Samson was 14 months old at the time of his death. We later learned he was a Tibetan Mastiff - a very rare and very expensive dog. It was odd for his breed to be located in this area of the South. To this day, we still don't know where he came from, or how he arrived in our barn. But Samson will always be remembered. Forgiveness, again, became a repeated lesson when the driver didn't stop to check on an obvious large dog, no one could have missed!

Mother and Katie quickly became gal-pals. Katie comes into my room every night, as Mother and Poppa retire, to tell me good-night. I was the one who brought her home, yet she is Mother's light shadow. Samson was Mother's dark shadow. Maybe there was symbolism in the story - large dark issues became small lighter issues.

We experienced the emotional upheavals after Mother's open heart surgery. She began to rebound remarkably! Katie has certainly been a huge part of her recovery process, for which I am eternally grateful! During the next four weeks, Mother returned to outpatient rehab but the process was very slow based on her extensive dual surgeries and recoveries from her hip and heart.

In Mother's first cardiothoracic exam, Dr. Goodheart explained her weakness, "You have been hit by a proverbial Mack truck! Two surgeries in seven days, four surgeries in the last 16 months, and you really think you should be back to business as usual?" Yes, Mother did!

Within four weeks, she was released from his care. Her recovery was incredibly fast! Within eight weeks, her meds were being dropped slowly due to her excellent chemistry levels revealed in lab reports. Within 12 weeks, Mother was no longer taking any meds!

Dr. Goodheart said she did not have any valve problems, no other pending artery blockages, and her heart muscle was not damaged nor did she have any signs of progressive cardiac stress. Also, she only had blockages on one side of her heart. I was told by a heart specialist, that is very odd. Usually, if there are blockages, it affects both sides of the heart.

Was it the metal allergy from the pacemaker and wires that created the problem? In my humble caregiver opinion, most definitely! The heart of her journey continues to be centered on God.

Chapter 19

KEEPING IN STEP

Mother handled her physical recovery exceptionally well. However, her emotions did have several intervals of change. She seemed extremely vulnerable at a moment's notice after the loss of Samson as she tried to readapt to her worldly environment. She was always a super out-going person. All the health issues, surgeries....everything, shifted in Mother's own personality. She became more reserved. She had to learn who she was again, where her strength had gone and cope, with a more devout understanding to pace herself. That was her most difficult learning curve.

Having cardiac surgery affected her sentiments more than any of us expected, especially her. My best guess as to why: the human heart is touched by human hands protected with a structural rib cage, not easily accessible for surgical procedures. Every component of the body experiences a traumatic seizing and sensing. Mother has always been emotionally strong. I suspect that's the very reason no one expected a season of turmoil stirring in her life. Mother had always been able to cope by hiding her feelings extremely well; it was disturbing to witness her loss of composure.

A couple of months before Mother's open heart surgery, I had recorded an ABC Special. Barbara Walters narrated her own personal open heart surgery experience in conjunction with other celebrities giving details of their circumstances. Ms. Walters described her feelings as a very emotional healing process, with an almost overpowering weakness. As I listened, I could relate. I understood exactly what she was sharing with the world, and those of us close to this touching subject.

The special was hosted with her cardiothoracic surgeon and other cardiologists. Ms. Walters asked questions about her own heart surgery and the recovery process. It was an exceptional dialogue as each phase was recounted, sharing the entire process. When she interviewed three other celebrities who had open heart surgeries, their experiences also brought more meaning to the subject. Each of those individuals, including Barbara Walters, made exceptional comebacks... in time.

After Mother's surgery, I felt as if I needed to watch the recording again, to learn what I might have missed. Perhaps something to reassure me since I didn't know at the time while recording it, Mother would be experiencing open heart surgery on February 18, 2011.

Mother never knew what to expect with her emotions, as she was living through it for the first time. She recalled Granddaddy's open heart surgery and how weak he was once he was returned from Post-Op and placed in ICU. In 1992, she said "I wish Daddy could just say one or two words." Now, she understood how incredibly weak he was before the surgery, and knew he tried so hard to hang on, afterwards.

Mother was able to share with our family what we witnessed with his results after the surgery, not realizing how much he might have wanted to say on some level. Or how frustrated he must have been in not being able to express anything, except with his eyes.

We could see the heart of a gentle humble man through his soft blue eyes which transcended love without needing to say a word, or lift a finger. Nineteen years later, Mother would come to understand just how much strength it takes to overcome a heart's healing hurdle. His surgery was due to a worn out heart at 87 years young.

Edgar Pennington Williamon, the grandest Granddaddy two grandchildren could have ever adored, survived 19 days after his open heart surgery. Now based on what we know, it is probably incredible he lived so many days afterwards, as weakness overcame him. Our "E. P." (Jack and I called him respectfully and fondly) had a full life! He was alert and was with us until he drew his last breath. We knew his beliefs, and Who had control of his heart.

Keeping in step with everyone to share the latest of Mother's triumphant health wins, remained vitally important and greatly needed support. Through email letters, I kept family and friends informed on

Mother's progress and status. The email replies and countless cards, from so many wonderful people on a daily basis, kept Mother going in the most dreadful of times!

Prayers continued to lift her up, as she struggled with fewer days than most from the devastating weakness she endured having two major surgeries, within seven days. The wonderful news: Mother is able to drive by herself, and works out in rehab on a regular basis. She is currently in the follow-up care of Dr. Luke for neurological observation. And recently began follow-up cardiac therapy to strengthen her upper body muscles.

Our prayers were answered when the public became more informed. As noted earlier, May 10, 2011, The New York Times released an article "Hip Makers Told to Study More Data." It was the first time, the United States Federal Drug and Food Administration mandated orthopaedic manufacturers to execute follow up research plans on how the orthopaedic producers would study patients' using their metal implants, which have been linked to early failure rates reported to the FDA.

Severe health effects in some patients warrant the research, as the same issues were clearly stated in the research I gathered from the University of Bristol, Bristol Implant Research Centre, Avon Orthopaedic Centre, Southmead Hospital, United Kingdom[64].

Metals release microscopic ions into the patient's bloodstream. The metal ions can create havoc to a seemingly healthy body with no direct path to the joint replacement or metal insertion of dental, or spinal rods, or whatever metal components are used. Metals can appear as a silent culprit decimating a healthy human body, no matter the age or previous health issues unrelated to metal allergies.

A recent written article by John Gever, Senior Editor, MedPage, Today, February 10, 2012 "Confusion Reigns in MoM Hip Implant Debacle[65]," states metal ion levels have become an indicator for device failure due to excessive wear of metal on metal (MoM) devices increasing microscopic metallic ions to be streamed through patients' blood flow, presenting symptoms which correlate with tissue damage. The article was recently posted from studies presented at the Academy of Orthopedic Surgeons' annual meeting. Although, there is a tremendous amount of skepticism even among orthopedists, metal ions have been a proven factor in my Mother's case which began as a medical mystery.

In 2009 when I began my research to learn more, it was easy to comprehend the U.S. hosting a society where millions of active baby boomers desire to stay mobile and fit. Another extreme in this sector of society falls into the obese category, pounding extra wear and tear on their joints. Add to the escalating statistics the average human is living longer; it's no wonder knee and hip replacements are mounting, or being mounted.

I became more acutely aware of how many individuals would more than likely have joint replacements, or revisions, in the years to come. Since starting to gather more information to substantiate *Steel Standing*, not as a theory, but based on medical research and vital information linking the awareness of metal implants, new data on the number of patients with implants - or will have them in the near future, has been provided.

The Associated Press released a new and alarming news article on February 10, 2012 reported by Lindsey Tanner, "Nearly 1 in 20 Adults over 50 have Fake Knees[66]." Based on the release, there are more than 4 million people with knee replacements!

This was the first national estimate which indicates the number of people seeking replacements, as a common surgery. The American Academy of Orthopedic Surgeons and chairman of orthopedic surgery at the Mayo Clinic in Rochester, MN, Dr. Daniel Berry, stated he was not involved in the research. He elaborated that the estimate is important because it shows a large portion of the population might need knee-related care. Dr. Berry's comments are very similar to my prior observations in 2009. Again, due to many factors in our society because people are living longer, potential threat of increased obesity, and as a nation, and a world, we are more active.

The article also quotes Elena Losina, led author of the analysis and codirector of the Orthopedics and Arthritis Center for Outcomes Research at Harvard's Brigham and Women's Hospital, "These data are sobering because we didn't know what an array of people we've created over the last decade."[66] The new analysis was presented at the academy's annual meeting in San Francisco.

When I began collecting information, it was to help my Mother when her journey began in March 2006. Without realizing it, the more information I began gathering, the more crucial it became to share with the public. I have given my best effort to compile valid credible resources in addition to a true story with facts to support the very fragile issue, many physicians and people are skeptical of believing - based on my personal experience and interaction. My advice based on my Mother's case: Educate yourselves! Most of the research or articles were recent when I started this chapter, but the facts are still quite exceptional.

In May 2010 by Huffington Post, entitled "Joint Replacements for Baby Boomers[67]" shared vital information: "The numbers tell the story. There were 288,471 total hip replacements in 2009, nearly half of them in people under 65, according to the Federal Agency for Healthcare Research and Quality, which tracks hospitalization."

In Mother's neurological examination with Dr. Luke on May 27, 2011, he told us after performing a follow-up muscle and nerve conduction study, "It appears her Inflammatory Myopathy was induced by the metal allergies from the metal implants." He said it was a process of elimination. I like to call it a process of illumination – shedding Light on the dark silent culprit, I prayed for God to reveal.

We spent Mother's exam time sharing with Dr. Luke the latest she had been through with another hip surgery for repairs and open heart. However, he was kept well informed during the two year span through my email updates. Since Mother's case "appeared" rare, he was kind enough to take her as one of the few patients under his care. Dr. Luke's primary role as associate professor and medical researcher is for patients who have Lou Gehrig's disease.

We knew this was a medical breakthrough IF the Inflammatory Myopathy was indeed induced or caused by metal implants creating allergies from the metals. He is all about his patients' needs as he wants each one to have the best quality of life possible.

However, in sharing with Dr. Luke about Mother's cardiac surgery and where the blockages were located in addition to her body's ability to properly function with a pacemaker, I asked if there was a farfetched chance the metals could have somehow affected her heart. Dr. Luke said from a neurological standpoint, "Absolutely. The metal alloy contributed to her light heart attack she experienced because Patricia's heart muscle was not able to function healthy thus allowing the blockages which created abrupt circumstances inducing a heart attack."

As far as her muscles regaining strength, he said "It appears her condition is induced by severe allergies to certain metals, and even with the metals removed which caused the allergies and toxicities, I am currently uncertain of her long term outcomes." This was a first for his renowned research to witness a patient with metal allergies causing deterioration of muscle tissue due to metal implants creating the culprit.

*As *Steel Standing* remains committed to update research right up to press time; February 2012 I have been extremely blessed to add some incredible resources as major contributors to support this book's content. Metal allergies are no longer considered rare as suggested in 2009. When I could not find any stories, and only small amounts of research to help link the connection of Inflammatory Myopathy to the type of metals in Mother's body, I was led to write *Steel Standing*, and share the research.

The New York Times article published August 22, 2011 "Hip Implant Complaints Surge, Even as the Dangers Are Studied[69]" discussed hip implants and the side effects metal implants are having on the human tissues. It was an excellent article by Barry Meier. The information revealed was the beginning of what we witnessed in Mother's not-so "rare" medical case.

If an implant device fails, why not investigate the possibility of the types of metals creating an allergic reaction?

Maybe it is, or is not, the device.

The article shares, the number of complaints many experts have feared – that all-metal replacement hips will become the biggest and most costly medical implant in years.

"Prone to Failure, some All-Metal Hip Implants Need To Be Removed Early[80]" by Robert Knox, National Public Radio

News, March 19, 2012 supports *Steel Standing's* findings and research. Although the article states most patients are doing fine based on their research, it also states high levels of Cobalt and Chromium have been found in the blood and organs of patients with all metal hip implants. However, one quote in the article prompted an apparent rhetorical query regarding "the uncertainty of what risks are posed."

Perhaps copies of *Steel Standing* will be sent directly to several sources to enlighten their "posed" thought after reading what Patricia Davis Harton experienced! I do not believe Mother's case to be rare!

Why doesn't the news broadcast the damaging facts about Chromium in metal implants? Whether anyone is allergic or not to Chromium, it causes renal and digestive failure! That was linked to Mother's renal system due to the type of metals used in her hip and knee replacements.

Mother's last hip surgery continued to heal once the metals were changed or revised.

Dr. Seymour released her from his orthopaedic care at the same time he was offered a promotion, relocating him to another state.

It seemed to be perfect timing. Mother was making an incredible comeback. Dr. Seymour had witnessed the joy and the sadness she felt in their parting ways. His compassion, his Christian fellowship and support, had most definitely made the worst of times so much better!

Mother's dermatologist, Dr. Titus, was also an incredible encourager. When I updated him with the news, he was elated. He shared that her potential medical breakthrough, could possibly help certain patients that have metal implants and meet the criteria of Chronic Fatigue Syndrome.

He further explained that if those patients demonstrated metal allergies, particularly in the setting of metal joint prosthesis or dental implants, or any metals in their bodies, it could provide a medical link.

That's one area of medicine or research I never dreamt could be helped through what has been discovered in Mother's medical case!

As John Adams, MD, said, "Patricia is on the frontier." Who knows what may come from one woman willing to go the distance?

Dr. Luke was instrumental when he told me to go with my "hunch." He believed in the theory, encouraging me to contact every physician Mother visited as a patient, to share the vital news about the metal allergies and outcomes thus far.

Another issue I eagerly wanted to understand was how Mother had been diagnosed with Lymphoma in her lungs in 2007. Dr. Luke explained "Granulous cells are often times mistaken for cancer cells."

When I carried Mother's lung biopsy samples for him to exam, he said they were identical to her arm biopsy. The cause was due to metal allergies creating the toxicity from the metal ions released in her tissues which, if not alleviated through diet, exercise and a continuous healthy eagerness to live, could still stall out her ascension back to a healthier Trish!

I believe God changed Mother's outcome at the moment when we first believed and we prayed for Him to please heal her. I will always believe God rearranged her life for His purpose, perhaps to tell her story in *Steel Standing*. Some people believe their lives are already planned and destined.

I agree with that - to an extent. I believe if we pray "specifically" and "fervently" God hears our pleas, providing miraculous and mysterious solutions. One may never know, until one simply asks Him!

Mother did all the right things, yet allergies to certain types metals from her implants turned her world upside down, inside out!

Dr. Luke also stated in her May 2011 visit that Mother's muscle and nerve conduction studies showed she still had some degree of Inflammatory Myopathy.

The visit was three months after her last hip repair and open heart surgery. He ordered physical therapy for three months for her legs, arms, hands, and wrists.

Mother and I returned for her second follow-up exam with Dr. Luke on August 12, 2011. We were fully expecting a decrease in the Myopathy. Dr. Luke believed her condition to be about the same but maybe somewhat stabilized. That was far better than hearing possibly ALS almost three years ago, or that her Inflammatory Myopathy would, or could, become worse than it was currently.

───── Medical Breakthrough! ─────

February 17, 2012: Mother returned to Dr. Luke. It was her four month follow-up exam. *Steel Standing* was already headed to the presses for print. We were elated Mother's health was no longer considered in dire circumstances, which was a huge recovery. Then God steps in, and takes her recovery further than we could have imagined. Amazing!!!

Since her last visit, Dr. Luke placed Mother on 20 mg. of prednisone, once a day for three months. It was a very low dosage. The objective was completely different from Dr. Young's (previous neurologist) best advice. Dr. Luke wanted to give Mother's nerves a chance to heal. If the nerves are not irritated, then the muscles have a far greater chance of healing and growing.

During those three months, a difference came about slowly in her energy and eating habits. If taken in smaller doses, that is one way the medicine usually helps the human body's natural steroids which sometimes are screaming for help! The harm from steroids is from "over" using the medication. Sometimes there's not another alternative to give a patient some level of quality of life. With Mother absorbing a very low dose, she became increasing better, as we had hoped.

In her recent visit Mother passed Dr. Luke's strenuous muscle exam with flying colors! It was an incredible scientific and spiritual confirmation!

Imagine for a moment, you are in a clinical setting. The specialist has an intensified job, day in-day out. He is very focused on trying to learn or discover how he can help his patients overcome their illnesses, terminal or otherwise - primarily related to a muscle disease. The majority of the time, I imagine, all Dr. Luke is able to do, is tell the dreaded news - offering comfort through medication or other alternative treatments. That's a devoted human being: to live in his medical world everyday for others!

Now, try to visualize this brilliant doctor with an incredibly passionate heart for his patients. He doesn't allow you to see how much it hurts him to face his days, yet he hangs on with a glimmer of hope, thinking - "Tomorrow we may find a cure, a link, a closer solution to helping patients suffering!" That's how I see Dr. Luke from the outside in, having talked and been with him on a fairly regular basis for almost three years.

Friday was an outstanding day! I like to call it a "WOW" day, which is "MOM" turned upside down - just as Mother's world has been! Dr. Luke was beside himself with Mother's recovery, and he stated it was a "medical breakthrough!" To have a scientific medical breakthrough, there must be two patients responding in the same way.

In Mother's previous visit, there was no mention of her left upper arm muscles returning to a healthy status, where Dr. Luke removed a large sample of muscle tissue for a biopsy in Spring 2009. He had never given us any hope it would grow, again. Friday, Mother was given new exercise instructions to help her arm renew its strength! What an incredible report! We were ecstatic with to hear the news!

The graph I created on the following page, illustrates a more detailed overview of how Mother's body was impacted from the metal allergies from the specific types of metals which triggered the Inflammatory Myopathy.

February 20, 2012, was a glorious follow-up from Friday's new report. The headlines read: "Allergy Tests Needed Before New Knee or Hip,[72]" by MedPage Today. The article enlightens discussions on the increasing importance of metal allergies before joint replacements. Two other articles report the information, from the Archives of Dermatology[74], and the Daily Rx[75].

Our mission was to share what we learned about metal allergies caused by culprits. What we learned was to beware of many types of culprits.

We are elated to help expose Patricia's true accounts to help another so they may not have to suffer mysteriously as she did.

My Mother never gave up, she never gave in and she never gave out in her journey. She's keeping in step… as God keeps her *Steel Standing*!

+ + +

"O Lord my God,
I called to You
for help
and
You healed me."

Psalm 30:2

The Mystery. The Journey. The Miracle.

The Path of Patricia's Medical Mystery

Replacements:

Hip Replacement:
March 3, 2006
Head/Ball
Cobalt-Nickel-Chromium (Co-Ni-Cr)
Stem: Cobalt-Nickel-Chromium-Molybdenum

Knee Replacement:
July 12, 2006
Nickel-Cobalt-Chromium

Revisions:

Knee Revision:
August 25, 2009
Titanium

Hip Revision:
April 28, 2010
Femur mitered with Titanium stem, closed with Titanium plates, secured with Ni-Co-Cr wires

Hip Repair:
July 29, 2010
Replaced broken wires with Ni-Co-Cr wires

Hip Reconstruction:
February 11, 2011
Customized Titanium plate placed over length of mitered area from revision with monofilament vs previous metal wires (Ni-Co-Cr). Titanium wiring inadequate for secure femur positioning.

Diagram by:
C. C. Davis
Steel Standing, LLC

Metal Allergies → Metallic Ions in Patricia's Physiology

Renal: July 2006-Feb 2011
Issues continuous for years until all Cobalt-Nickel-Chromium implants and wires, which fueled metal allergies, were replaced. She had 33 lithotripsies from July 2006-January 2010
*Data does not include: kidney, bladder, or urinary tract infections, or basket retrievals

Respiratory: Jan 21, 2007
Lymphoma diagnosed. Sarcodosis cells were mistakenly identified as cancer cells based on similar mutation from tests prior to surgery. Biopsy revealed granulous nodules in right lung. Same granulous nodules found in left arm biopsy in March 2009.

Heart: Oct 27/30, 2008
Temporary and permanent pacemaker implant. No history of heart problems. Titanium Alloy with silicon Stainless Steel wire attached with a Metal Alloy screw.

Digestive: Oct 28, 2008
Gallbladder extracted after abrupt pain and fever for 7 days, creating imminent danger unless removed.

Muscle Biopsy: April 21, 2009
Biopsy upper left arm. Diagnosis: Sarcoidosis a.k.a. Inflammatory Myopathy destroying muscle tissues as her body became weaker. The muscle inflammation was likely to be caused by metal allergies, as revealed by patch test and the MELISA® blood test. All the metals were revised to Titanium or removed. Patricia is the first patient appearing to have muscle deterioration due to metal allergies.

Pacemaker Explant: Sept 17, 2010
Surgical removal revealed original pacer implant was not wired as cardiac medical records stated.

Heart Attack: Feb 14, 2011
Cath lab revealed 3 blockages in one main coronary artery.

Open Heart Surgery: Feb 18, 2011
Blockages were located at site of the pacemaker and where Stainless Steel lead wire was attached with a Metal Alloy screw. Blockages only one side of heart. No damage to heart muscle, valves, or other arteries. Titanium plates and screws used for chest closure instead of Stainless Steel Alloy metals with Nickel.

Neurology: Microscopic metal ions were being released in Patricia's blood stream attacking various body organs as a silent culprit. Sarcoidosis/Inflammatory Myopathy developed from toxins formulating granulous nodules in organs slowing down function, appearing as cancerous cells in her lungs.

Chapter 20

PUTTING YOUR BEST FOOT FORWARD

Replacement. Rejection. Revision.
Reconstruction. Repair.
Recovery. Rehab.
Rejoice!

Adversity came against us in waves…each crashing harder trying to knock us off our physical and proverbial feet. There were greater difficulties, which we endured than I have shared in *Steel Standing*.

To get to a point to disclose an abundance of information, mysteries, miracles, and yes … even the madness … took greater faith than what I knew to be of God. He certainly showed me otherwise!

He directed my path to return home and then placed the vital information before me to expose Mother's health culprit, just as I prayed and asked! His Spirit is the only way we could have survived going through this journey and gain greater faith versus allowing our weaknesses to overcome our outcomes.

The joy I have come to experience in completing this last chapter pertaining to my Mother's new walk in better health is true jubilation! The harder the mission, the harder the adversity comes against anything that is good for others to learn and be educated. The lesson is not just about getting to the finish line; it's how one accepts or rejects any and all lessons during the times while striving for a particular finish line.

"He's gotten you this far, hasn't He?"

A few simple words prevailed as a reminder of how great God provided for our every need. When the last edits of *Steel Standing* needed sharper proofing eyes than mine could possibly continue to provide, I began floundering due to an exhaustive transition from caregiver to full time creative writer in my humble attempt to share an incredible journey. It didn't matter that my professional aptitude and experience had been in publication for decades. I was emotionally rooted to *Steel Standing* in ways words could not convey. My prayer was for one more gust of wind to taunt my sagging sails onward towards our publishing goal. I asked for His help. After all, He had gotten me this far!

Every member of the book's team had contributed greatly, and then some! It was time to go to print. I sent it! However, I stopped the presses when Mother's neurologist stated her medical mystery was a "medical breakthrough!" It was an unbelievable miracle ending to an incredible, almost unfathomable mystery and journey!

While I attempted the last overview of edits, which can be an endless task, I felt my work was not at its best with additional changes and new information added to be prepared for print. Once again, Brenda Brewer Hoyt came to mind! She was one of the few, outside of our small book's team, whose encouragement had been continual since the announcement of *Steel Standing*. The idea came to my thoughts to send her a copy of the final draft to read. When I contacted Brenda, she was overjoyed and couldn't wait to start reading her sneak preview. I was honored she was so excited!

Within a short time after receiving my email attachment of the draft, she was kind enough to send me a gently worded email. Brenda said that I must have sent her an old file. So, I checked. No, she had the original! Brenda humbly and graciously offered her skills as a proofreader. She acquired her ability over the years while assisting her husband's published research works. It was an enormous gust of wind blowing from my true North!

How would I have ever known that our baby-sitter when I was 10 years old, would become a skilled proofreader to check my work, I had been blessed to write decades later - yet we lived states away!?! Although, our meeting in Centre during the Summer 2010 appeared to be a coincidence, it was not! Mother and I had already come to understand - coincidences don't happen! It is circumstances or accidents that happen - often times it seems people can bring it on themselves - but God can intervene at times;

at other times He has a different way.[82] (Isaiah 55:8-9)

The quote "He's gotten you this far, hasn't He?" remained instrumental in the last phase, which was the most difficult, of our endearing journey. The quote was His words of inspiration said through another believer. Neither of us could have ever imagined how God would link our lives 43 years later! Brenda was the best person to do the final edit checks. We were from the same hometown. We knew one another's families. We had the same beliefs in God. And both loved Auburn (she's a grad!). All-in-all, it just didn't get any better than that!

When it was time for the e-book and print books to be prepared for publishing, Brenda spent a very few days doing a remarkable job! God made it possible! He knew "eons" ago, when I was a naive kid with a big idea I could write a book one day, that I would need someone that had entered my life long ago, equipped with excellent skills to help in my time of need! Imagine for a moment, the illustration of "Plaid," as I have referred to God, weaving in and out through each others' lives.

I rejoiced when Brenda shared her abilities! Immediately I grasped how God had orchestrated for her to care for Jack and me as a baby-sitter - spend a few minutes one recent summer as she shared His inspiring words laid on her heart - and continue to cheer my writing efforts as a part of Steel Standing's story! It was another wonderful example of how God works all around each of us, if we watch and listen.

The really mysterious part of our "memory lane to manuscript lines," was when I decided after 23 months to go pull my old photos of Brenda, which were in one of my early 1970s brightly colored flowery designed "hip" photo album. Interestingly, the date on the side of the Kodak prints was "March" 1969. Exactly 43 years later to the month, she continued to be a part of my creative existence adding to my life's sensational adventures just as she did when I was kid! That's was indeed a "WOW" moment to realize it was the same month she made the edits to Steel Standing! Incredible!

You never know how you will touch one another's life. The dynamics of God are phenomenal. God is awesome! He does similar interactions in so many peoples' lives every day. Some people get it. Some people don't.

I immediately recognized this gift - a gift of friendship and love through Christ - and Yes, "He HAS gotten me this far," and will take us all further!

Whatever mistakes you find in *Steel Standing*, place the blame on the typographer because I am not perfect! There's only is only One that is perfect. His Name is Jesus Christ!

The information shared throughout *Steel Standing* is to help enlighten others from our experiences. The potential dangers are lurking, carelessly and carefully crafted then deployed, such as metal implants into the human body, which can pose serious harm.

Some implant recipients may never experience the ill-fated dangers crucial to their health. Then others are victims, struggling and wondering why they don't feel well, after a metal implant has been inserted into their body. Their attitudes, personalities, or daily habits may change but it is so gradual that a family member, spouse, friend or neighbor may never be able to place their finger on the exact cause of their slow declining health process. Maybe it is a metal allergy. Maybe it's not related to metal, or caused by metal. But for those who do suffer a silent metal allergy agony, we pray this story helps you.

We are not against metal implants used in human bodies. We just learned the hard way how to test for types of metals which create allergies. Metal implants are not bad. But anything overly used in an unsafe way can lead to corruption. Our bodies must exist with metal quantities, as part of our anatomical and chemical existence.

However, there are metals placed in people's bodies that are causing impending dangers. Based on our highly credible medical research specialists, which we are indeed grateful, *Steel Standing* is disclosing the first known case recorded demonstrating the inducement of muscle weakness to metal allergies with relevant medical proof. Hopefully, many others will see this information as a nudge to examine your health options and physician care.

I don't believe Mother's case is the only one, or that it is rare! Every day, the awareness is growing to prove otherwise! In time, I believe this issue will surface with far greater numbers, as many seek answers to questionable health problems which are associated with metal implants.

Remember: it's not always the device. If your body absorbs the metal ions released from certain types of metals which cause an allergy in your body, it can be a difficult recovery.

One of the many lessons we learned during our tremendous tribulations, was to turn to God. Often times, the hardships were just the "ump" needed to give a dose of "spunk" to complete this mission. Whatever the reason, or reasons, for our incredible journey...we endured but only because of Him

It started with a prayer and greater faith which requires believing from your heart... all of your heart, with no doubt! You may ask... "Was it worth the hell on earth?" Ab"soul"utley! I ask you... "Are you more aware... more educated... learned new information that might help save another's life from a possible health mystery? If so, that's what made this mission wonderful and successful!

The same principles apply. Ask and educate. Beware and be attentive to your own health. During the past five years while at my Mother's side, there are countless times I could have physically or emotionally collapsed. Collapsing was never an option. Even when I felt I deserved an out, God's strength kept me going - kept me seeking!

The research I was led to do was easy compared to the frank and civil "toe-to-toe" talks with many physicians. The majority of physicians placed in our path, were open-minded and listened to the theory based on medical research from the United Kingdom.

It was difficult, but the only consistency through the entire journey was her ability to continue to play the piano! That IS what gave me a sign of deep seeded hope - not to give up when I started studying as I was able to watch her daily interactions. I began to see her struggle, then trying to survive. Her music helped me became more in tune with, what was offbeat in her body's timing. As I previously mentioned, when her hand therapists learned she was a pianist, they told her playing was the best therapy in exercising her arm muscles to regain strength. A bit of self-confidence was lost for a few months due to her weakened arms and hands.

Mother is again playing robustly on a regular daily basis, and with sheer joy in her heart! What a comeback! She plays beautifully. It is a thrill to hear and watch her play all across the keyboard in her unique style, so many folks in our area know when they hear her notes, then say, "That's Patricia!"

In writing *Steel Standing*, my keyboard was a little different as I did my best to convey what has transpired. It was not an easy task. I learned to train and discipline myself every day when I sat down at my computer to compose the trials, tribulations, and triumphs through this journey.

Some days didn't go well, for either of our keyboards! Other days delivered huge accomplishments! A friend once told me, "When it comes to writing a book or dissertation, or anything of great length or a great accomplishment that needs to be done for whatever reason, you have to make yourself "JUST DO IT.®""

Above my desk, I have one of the famous black and white Nike® "Just Do It." posters I purchased in 1992 from the Chicago Nike® store. Preserved in a black frame, I have always hung it above my work space. It continues to be a bold reminder throughout my career and day-to-day tasks... just keep moving forward... do what needs to be done.

I learned adversity is a measurement tool of growth in our individual spirits. I believe that's why God allows us to come against just enough! Otherwise, how would a Christian know he is defeating the enemy's attempts to subdue our individual missions, ministries, and work for God? It's a way we can measure our individual growth. So, I try to accept adversity as a compliment.

God knows you can take it, as He teaches you to make it! Whether it's being a caregiver, writing a book, or doing what's next in life, know the "Keeper" of your soul, and do your best... put your best foot forward.

God does the rest.

God gives the rest.

The rest I learned to give to God.

Mother is living proof; never give up, never give out, and never give in to anything except your individual exaltation to the Father! May God bless you, as we hope *Steel Standing* will inspire your life, as it did and does, in our lives!

+ + +

"What
is impossible
with man, is
possible with
God."

Luke 18:27

Steel Standing!

Patricia and Christa

The Mystery. The Journey. The Miracle.

STEEL STANDING SUMMATION

ONWARD!

D avid and Goliath. What a story! What a vision! Think of a small framed young man, whose heart was bigger than most. Whose determination was a path where he saw nothing he could not overcome. Whose power was his complete faith in, and consuming love for, God.

He used five stones the day he met Goliath in the battlefield. David chose not to wear a heavy suit of metal to weigh down his body. Instead, David chose to face his giant with the Armor of God, which is the mindset of God.

He used one stone and knocked out something he could visually see larger than him. Realistically, it would have been true, if you'd placed them man-to-man. But David went with his Spirit. David sensed the forces of God giving him impeccable courage to carry through to victory! Should David live or die, he had already won the battle, because he loved God with all his heart.

My Mother's struggles against the pitted forces, was also a "Goliath." She has won her battle! Patricia exudes the same Spirit within her, as did David!

In 2010, there were five small stones perfectly aligned in her left kidney. She was scheduled to have those removed before her last two surgeries in February 2011; a major hip repair/revision, followed by an unexpected open heart surgery.

In February 2012, at the close of *Steel Standing*'s written journey... just before going to print, those five small stones created yet another kidney infection. When x-rayed, the five had formed into one large stone. It would be the last kidney procedure needed to rid the remaining toxins from her body.

She faced the battle and won! The last traces of her fearless battle in this journey were scattered and voided. Her suit of armor was the Spirit of God. Her slingshot was her determination in His faith, which directed her path. Her victory knocked out one of the largest giants, she and her prayer warriors had ever witnessed!

Her Goliath was slain, as was her pain. Always a victor! Never a victim... not in God's eyes, nor the crowd watching as her story unfolds. Gasping at times, we were all encouraged by her powerful faith in God.

Patricia knocked her giant out, within a stone's throw! Her Goliath battle was down for the count... of five small stones into one. The battle was victorious, as she fought the good fight. "Well done, my child," as I imagine hearing the Master's words for her ... "Well done, my good and faithful servant!"

Steel moving forward, Patricia's body rebounds as she journeys onward.

Humbleness. Courageousness. Faithfulness. Willingness. God.

Five stones. We know which One knocked down the giant.

+ + +

LESSONS LEARNED
FROM
STEEL STANDING'S JOURNEY

1. Show kindness to others at all times.

2. The saying is true - you never know what someone else is experiencing until you have walked in their shoes.

3. Respect your medical doctor. If you don't believe you are receiving good medical advice, seek a second opinion.

4. Don't presume you know more than the doctor - but learn to ask questions, become more educated about your own health.

5. Live each hour as it could be your last. As hard as it can be, enjoy the moments.

6. Never regret the things you do for others. You may never hear how grateful they are to you. Everyone deserves to be loved, liked, and given attention.

7. Know your limitations with your own emotional, mental and physical health. Respect your own body's limit.

8. Exercise "you" - if not physical workouts - then mental workouts.

9. Be thankful. And learn to say "I am sorry."

10. Be open to alternative ideas even if you know you're right. You may be "right"- But someone could be more "righter" that will expand your ideas.

11. Learn to pace your day, your rest, your quiet time, eating, reading, working - In other words don't allow other things or people to manipulate your time.

12. Don't assume anything. Ever!

13. If you don't understand, then ask!

More Lessons Learned

14. Learn from one another and be open to learning whether reading or listening or watching.
15. Learning in this life doesn't stop when school is out.

16. Be willing to be challenged to think outside of your set ways of thinking, traditions and habits. Another perspective may be a good one for you.

17. Listening to others will teach you how to hear what they're saying.

18. Show respect at all times, especially to those who can't do for themselves.

19. People older have lived longer. There is value in remembering wisdom comes from age and experience. Learn to appreciate the wise. Learn to adapt to the aged. And learn from both - because not every person older is wise.

20. Open doors for others. Show courtesy which is the better side of you.

22. Never allow your bad day to dictate your mood.

23. Forgive! No matter what, who, when, where, why or how - go deeper inside your heart and forgive others who hurt you.

24. Whether you live to see it or not, what goes around comes around.

25. You are accountable for every word and action, even in private isolated moments. If those times were recounted and shown to others, imagine how much we would truly learn in seeing ourselves through their eyes.

26. Never lie or cheat. You only hurt yourself.

27. Even when times become difficult, learn to adapt and adjust to make the most of the difficulties so you can learn how to do it better... if there is a next time.

+ + +

CHRISTA CARMELL DAVIS
STEEL STANDING
TESTAMENT OF FAITH

I asked.
He answered.

"Call to Me and I will answer you,
and I will tell you great and mighty things,
which you do not know."

Jeremiah 33:3

The Mystery. The Journey. The Miracle.

SOUL ACKNOWLEDGEMENTS

There is so much more to a book than just being a story to read or information to share. The tale, creation, work, advisors, and encouragers... It takes a team for a book come alive, to convey through words so life is seen while it's being read; heard through each sound; emotions emphasized create visual images as the story unfolds. The following is only a partial listing of the individuals who devoted their time, support and ongoing encouragement!

OUR HEARTFELT THANK YOU!

William R. Brannon, O.D., John Adams, M.D., Rebecca Adams, Tina Gossett, R.N., B.S.N., Tim Gossett, Denise M. Martin, Linda Stejskal Nelson, Vera Stejskal, Ph.D., James Collins, M.D., Kenneth Sands, M.D., Dr. Kenneth Sands' staff during Patricia's care, Dr. L, Dr. C, John Thomas Apgar, M.D., Richard Hull, Ph.D., Elaine Hull, Ph.D., Brenda Brewer Hoyt, My friend, David, Nellie Lowery, Patti J. Ford, Dana Gibby (In Memory), Deborah "Boo" Morrow, Robert "Uncle Bob" Morrow, Susan Livingston, Senator Gerald Dial (AL), Pam, Diane, Ellen, Big Kahuna and Family, Arlette Harrell, Emily Ward, Gail R. Hayes, Joan Mosley, Sharon Ollis, Gaines Adams, Linda G. Peachy, Rosa Betancourt, Aileen Finley, Katherine W. C., Emma C. Barnes, Hobart Barnes (In Memory), Bill Barnes, Rebecca Huntington, The "Sisters," Ernestine and Rufus "Red" Byrd, Nancy Mattingly, Slamdot.com Crew, Elizabeth Christman, Barbara M. Lee, Red Horseshoe Books, Gail Livingston Mills, India Vincent, Carrie H. Phillips, Phyllis H. Casey, Judy Espy, Connie Swafford, Ellen Graves, Remonda W. Shepard, Russ & Julie Harton and family, Tim & Rita Harton, Jeff Browning, Chad Browning, Lonnie and Anita Dorcey

Most Importantly - Trish's Prayer Team!

You know who you are, and your prayers made the difference in Patricia's life!

Trish's Beloved Pets

Shannon, Sammi, Skippy, Katie
In Memory - Samson, and her buddy, Clem

Samson

Soul Resources ~ End Notes

1) Not real name.
2) Not real name.
3) Not real name.
4) Not real name.
5) Not real name.
6) Not real name.
7) Not real name.
8) Not real name.
9) Not real name.
10) Nor real name
11) Alabama Environmental Management Commission
12) Amy Grant Musical CD "Rock of Ages...Hymns &Faith, 2005. Word entertainment, LLC 25 Music Square West, Nashville, TN.
13) The Holy Bible: Matthew 11:28-30 "Come to Me, all who are weary and heavy-laden, and I will give you rest. Take My yoke upon you and learn from Me, for I am gentle and humble in heart, and you will find rest for your souls, for My yoke is easy and My burden is light." (www.Biblegateway.com)
14) Not real name.
15) "Gumpisms: The Wit and Wisdom of Forrest Gump" Winston F. Groom, Jr., author.
16) Not real name.
17) Not real name.
18) Not real name.
19) Mayo Clinic Definition -www.mayoclinic.com/health/hida-scan/MY00320
20) Not real name.
21) Not real name.
22. Not real name.
23) Not real name.
24) www.webmd.com/brain/electromyogram-emg-and-nerve-conduction-studies
25) www.ninds.nih.gov/disorders/inflammatory_myopathies/detail_inflammatory_myopathies.htm
26) www.neurologychannel.com
27) www.jigsawhealth.com
28.) www.jigsawhealth.com
29) www.jigsawhealth.com
30. The Holy Bible: Genesis 1:1"In the beginning God created the heavens and the earth" (www.BibleGateway.com)
31) "Allergy to Metals as a Cause of Orthopedic Implant Failure," by Kreciz B. Kiec-Swierczynska M. Bakowicz-Mitura K., Source: Int.Occup Med Environ Health, 2006;19(3):178-80
32) The Journal of Bone & Joint Surgery (Br) by: G.M. Keegan, M.D.; I.D. Learmouth, M.D.; and C.P. Case Case, M.D. Volume 89-B, No. %, May 2007, From Southmead Hospital, Bristol, England
33) Chromium-Induced Kidney Disease – Richard P. Wedeen1 and Lifen Qian2: 1VA Medical Center, East Orange, NJ; 2 University of Medicine and Dentistry of New Jersey, the New Medical School, Newark, NJ
34) The Journal of Bone & Joint Surgery (Br) by: G.M. Keegan, M.D.; I.D. Learmouth, M.D.; and C.P. Case Case, M.D. Volume 89-B, No. %, May 2007, From Southmead Hospital, Bristol, England
35) Not real name.
36) Not real name.
37) Not real name.
38) Orthopaedic Metals and Their Potential Toxicity in the Anthroplasty Patient – G.M. Keegan, BSc, Research Assistant1; I.D. Lermouth, FRCSEd, FRCS, FCS(SA)Orth, Professor

Soul Resources ~ End Notes

of Orthopaedic Surgery1; and C.P. Case, DPhil, FRCPath, Consultant Senior Lecturer in Orthopaedics with Pathology1: University of Bristol, Bristol Implant Research Centre, Avon Orthopaedic Centre, Southmead Hospital, Westbury-on-Trym, Bristol, BS10 5NB, UK

39) Chronic Inflammation, Joint Replacement and Malignant Lymphoma- L. Lidgren, MD, PhD, Honorary FRCS, Professor, Department of Orthopaedics and Clinical Sciences, Lund University Hospital, SE-221 85 Lund, Sweden

40) Not real name.

41) Not real name.

42) Not real name.

43) www.fda.gov

44) "Confusion Reigns in MoM Hip Implant Debacle," by John Gever, Senior Editor, MedPage Today, February 10, 2012

45) The Journal of Investigative Dermatology http://en.wikipedia.org/wiki/Journal_of_Investigative_Dermatology

46) "Titanium hypersensitivity: does it really exist?: Identifying triggers of inflammation in chronic disease: The key to successful treatment" by Elizabeth Valentine-Thon, Ph.D., Health Diagnostics and Research Institute, South Amboy Medical Center, South Amboy, NJ Dr. Valentine-Thon is the General Manager of Health Diagnostics and Research Institute in New Jersey. Her research work has spanned the fields of immunology, virology, molecular biology, and infectious disease diagnostics. In 2004 she developed a test for detecting active Lyme disease based on the cellular immune response to Borrelia-specific recombinant antigens. She has published over 60 peer reviewed scientific articles.

47) www.MELISA.org

48) Chromium-Induced Kidney Disease – Richard P. Wedeen1 and Lifen Qian2: 1VA Medical Center, East Orange, NJ; 2 University of Medicine and Dentistry of New Jersey, the New Medical School, Newark, NJ

49) Paulose Varkis, Yahoo Contributor, Masters in English, and PhD in Alternative Medicines www.associatedcontent.com/article/2270131/ten_most_dangerous_effects_of_hair.html?cat=68

50) Paulose Varkis, Yahoo Contributor, Masters in English, and PhD in Alternative Medicines www.associatedcontent.com/article/2270131/ten_most_dangerous_effects_of_hair.html?cat=68

51) www.naturalnews.com/022575.html - Cathy Sherman, Journalist

52) USFDA Hair Dye Products www.fda.gov/Cosmetics/ProductandIngredientSafety/ProductInformation/ucm143066.htm

53. www.naturalnews.com/022575.html - Cathy Sherman, Journalist

54) www.wikepedia.com/Chromium

55) Chronic Inflammation, Joint Replacement and Malignant Lymphoma- L. Lidgren, MD, PhD, Honorary FRCS, Professor, Department of Orthopaedics and Clinical Sciences, Lund University Hospital, SE-221 85 Lund, Sweden

56) Not real name.

57) Not real name.

58. "Specific Pharmacology of Calcium in Myocardium, Cardiac Pacemaker, and Vascular Smooth Muscle," www.hyper.ahajournals.org/egi/content/full/48/443.

59) Not real name.

60) Johnson & Johnson Depuy Hip Recall - August 2010

61) Not real name.

62) Not real name.

63) "Trish the Dish" a.k.a. Patricia Williamon Davis Harton

64) Chronic Inflammation, Joint Replacement and Malignant Lymphoma- L. Lidgren, MD, PhD, Honorary FRCS, Professor, Department of Orthopaedics and Clinical Sciences, Lund University Hospital, SE-221 85 Lund, Sweden

SOUL RESOURCES ~ END NOTES

65) Confusion Reigns in MoM Hip Implant Debacle, By, John Gever, Senior Editor, MedPage, Today, February 10. 2012

66.) Associated Press - "Nearly 1 in every 20 US Adults Over 50 Have Fake Knees," By Lindsey Tanner, 02-10-2012

67) Huffington Post, June 2010, "Joint Replacements for Baby Boomers"

68) Journal of the American College of Cardiology, http://content.onlinejacc.org/cgi/content/full/33/6/1578 Andrea Frustaci, MD*, Nicola Magnavita, MD, Cristina Chimenti, MD*, Marina Caldarulo, MD, Enrico Sabbioni, PhD, Romano Pietra, PhD, Carlo Cellini, MD, Gian Federico Possati, MD and Attilio Maseri, MD*

* Department of Cardiology, Catholic University, Rome, Italy

Department of Occupational Medicine, Catholic University, Rome, Italy

Department of Cardiac Surgery, Catholic University, Rome, Italy

CEC Environmental Institute Joint Research Center Ispra (VA), Rome, Italy

69) "Hip Makers Told to Study More Data," Barry Meier, New York Times, 05-11-11, www.nytimes.com

70) Not real name.

71) "Chronic Inflammation, Joint Replacement and Malignant Lymphoma"- L. Lidgren, MD, PhD, Honorary FRCS, Professor, Department of Orthopaedics and Clinical Sciences, Lund University Hospital, SE-221 85 Lund, Sweden.

72) "Allergy Test Needed before New Knee or Hip," Charles Bankhead, MedPage Today, published Feb 20, 2012. Reviewed by Robert Jasmer, MD, Associate Clinical Professor of Medicine, University of California, San Francisco. www.medpagetoday.com/article.cfm?tbid=31275

73) The Privacy Rule implements the privacy requirements of the Administrative Simplification subtitle of the Health Insurance Portability and Accountability Act of 1996. The purpose of these modifications is to maintain strong protections for the privacy of individually identifiable health information while clarifying certain of the Privacy Rule's provisions, addressing the unintended negative effects of the Privacy Rule on health care quality or access to health care, and relieving unintended administrative burdens created by the Privacy Rule. http://www.hhs.gov/ocr/privacy/hipaa/administrative/privacyrule/privruletxt.txt

74) "The Effect of Patch Testing on Surgical Practices and Outcomes in Orthopedic Patients with Metal Implants" by Natasha atanmaskova, MD, PhD; Alejandra Tellez, MD; Luciana Molina, MD; Gloria Honart, MD; Apra Sood, MD; WAel Barsoum, MD; James S. Taylor, MD Published online February 20, 2012, Archives of Dermatology.

75) "Joint Replacement Patients Benefit from Metal Allergy Testing Prior to Implant Surgery" by Travis Hill, Daily RX February 29, 2012 - Reviewed by Jospeh V. Madia, MD

76) http://www.mayoclinic.com/health/sed-rate/MY00343

77) http://www.nlm.nih.gov/medlineplus/ency/article/003503.htm

78) http://www.webmd.com/drugs/mono-9383-PREDNISONE+-+ORAL.aspx?drugid=6007&drugname=Prednisone+Oral&pagenumber=6

79) http://www.webmd.com/urinary-incontinence-oab/tc/urinary-problems-and-injuries-age-12-and-older-topic-overview

80) http://www.npr.org/blogs/health/2012/03/19/148769073/prone-to-failure-some-all-metal-hip-implants-need-to-be-removed-early#commentBlock March 19, 2012

81) http://www.huffingtonpost.com/ronna-kaplan-ma/music-therapy March 15, 2012

82) Isaiah 55:8-9 "For My thoughts are not your thoughts, Nor are your ways My ways," declares the LORD. "For as the heavens are higher than the earth, So are My ways higher than your ways And My thoughts than your thoughts.

I
can do
all things
through Him
who
strengthens me.

Philippians 4:13

The Mystery. The Journey. The Miracle.

Steel Standing
Disclaimer

The contents in *Steel Standing* are true depictions from a personal experience including actual medical events with documented results by licensed practicing physicians, surgeons, and/or their medical staff at accredited medical facilities.

The resource information is provided for educational purposes only. Any information contained herein is not intended to diagnose, treat, cure, or prevent any diseases or; medical problems anyone may be experiencing. The information is not intended to replace your doctor's recommendations.

Identities have been changed for privacy. Specific references to locations and medical facilities or organizations, unless otherwise named, have been modified/deleted in *Steel Standing* to neither attract positive or negative attention.

If for any reason the contents of *Steel Standing* need clarification, please seek advice from a qualified individual, in the medical field, and/or by an affiliate in the religious sectors.

+ + +